THE MOONLIGHT WAR

Terence O'Brien was born in Maitland, Australia and was working on a Solomon Islands plantation when war broke out. He paid his own passage to the UK to join the RAF, and completed two tours of operations before Japan entered the war. After leading a bomber flight to Singapore, he escaped finally to India where he later joined the Wingate Force. For some years he had a small hotel in the Canary Islands, and has worked as a freelance journalist, a schoolteacher and, lastly, as a director of a tile-importing company. He is married with two sons, and lives in Sussex near Chichester.

G000229571

Also in Arrow by Terence O'Brien

Out of the Blue

Terence O'Brien

THE
MOONLIGHT WAR

*The Story of
Clandestine Operations
in South-east Asia
1944–5*

ARROW BOOKS

Arrow Books Limited
62–65 Chandos Place, London WC2N 4NW

An imprint of Century Hutchinson Limited

London Melbourne Sydney Auckland
Johannesburg and agencies throughout
the world

First published by William Collins Sons & Co. Limited 1987

Arrow edition 1989

Printed and bound in Great Britain by
Anchor Press Ltd, Tiptree, Essex

ISBN 0 09 961050 7

To
Colin Hercules Mackenzie
Scholar, soldier, industrialist, aesthete
and friend

Preface

During the eighteen months I was based at Jessore as flight commander, I filled four exercise books with notes. As pointed out in the foreword to *Out of the Blue*, the complete memoir which I wrote up in 1946 from those wartime notebooks contains much personal material about myself at that time – thoughts, ideas and dreams never intended for publication – and *The Moonlight War* derives from a similar editing of that old private record.

It does not set out to be an account of clandestine operations in the Far East, nor even of our squadron's involvement with them; indeed, as will be clear from a reading of chapter 19, it is not even a complete record of my own part in those operations. The scenes and incidents which are recorded here are simply those which I happened to note down at that time. Many have nothing to do with the war at all. This is a personal memoir of a time spent in Bengal, not a historical study.

However, politics contorted so many of our operations that the historical setting is essential for an understanding of them, so I have had to turn to the archives, to historians and to the senior staff who have survived for help in completing those necessary background sets. And, because we in the air often knew only part of the action, I have also had to turn to many of the agents whom we actually dropped for details of operations which were not known to me when I wrote my original account just over forty years ago.

There are some readers who would wish to have immediate verification of these sources, but I do not like little numbers dog-tailed on to words, nor footnotes in tiny print at the bottom of a page. I find them an irritating distraction which spoil the look of the page, and I do not intend to impose them on the general reader. So those who wish to know the chapter and verse for a particular quotation, or the authority for a stated fact, will have to search for the guiding clue in the References (page 355). They might not always be lucky in the search.

Among the sources which have contributed to the additions and alterations made in my old manuscript are the following:

1 Personal interviews and correspondence with old wartime friends and colleagues.

From the RAF, RCAF and RAAF: Air Chief Marshal Sir Lewis (Bob) Hodges, Air Vice Marshal P. G. (Peter) Farr. And those who left the service – P. Arkell, F. G. Barlogie, P. A. Black, J. Churchill, A. B. Coy, R. Fretwell, B. G. Hewson, J. A. King, M. Langer, T. H. Lee, R. F. Stothers, J. Tubbs, Prince Varanand.

From the British clandestine groups: above all, I am deeply indebted to C. H. (Colin) Mackenzie who was in command of Force 136 throughout the war. Colonel J. R. Gardiner who headed the Burma section also gave me some help, as did these of the men we dropped – A. F. Bennett, C. G. Blathwayt, D. K. Broadhurst, R. Critchley, J. H. Davis, A. Denning, T. Foulkes, E. Grinham, D. Guthrie, D. Headley, D. C. Herring, W. Howe, R. Jayne, P. Kemp, D. G. Kino, P. V. Lewes, W. S. Moss, D. Romyn, R. A. Rubenstein, J. Smallwood, D. Smiley, A. S. (Bob) Thornton, C. R. Tice, A. A. Trofimov, P. E. Turnbull, I. R. Warren.

From (and about) the OSS: J. R. Allan, S. L. Falk, M. (Bob) Flaherty, C. L. Gray, N. R. Larum, T. B. (Tom) Leonard, O. M. B. (Oscar) Milton.

2 From others outside the clandestine forces: Louis Allen, Brigadier M. Calvert, F. W. Wilson, R. G. Young, Major T. Knott, Brigadier Shelford Bidwell, Richard Ollard.

3 Unpublished records.
I have been able to read those written by A. F. Bennett, A. B. Coy, C. H. Mackenzie, R. A. Rubenstein, Saw Shwin, and three others who wish to remain anonymous.

4 SOE archives.
These are not open to the public. Some people did keep copies of their reports, the originals of which are now sealed away in the files, and those copies that I have seen leave me mystified why such stale old stuff is still being kept hidden from public view. M. R. D. Foot has suggested that the most likely reason is that no one in the Foreign Office has had time to go through it all, file by file, and discover if in fact there does remain any item still too sensitive for release, but I have no doubt myself that there are also sins they wish to hide (cf page 218).

However, the custodian of these SOE papers, Christopher Woods, is empowered to provide information from the archive, and he has been helpful in supplying me with field details on several operations which I flew, and with particulars from some of the Force 136 reports.

5 Public Record Office (PRO) at Kew.
The squadron, station, and group records are filed under AIR 27, 28 and 25 respectively. The Operational Record Books (the ORBs) have been used largely to help me identify those operations which I had described in detail in my notes without identifying them by code name or date that time. The ORBs

for 357 Squadron are not complete; some operations, such as my original attempt to land Colonel Peacock, have escaped record, and none of the Dakota operations flown incidentally from Jessore, when the flight was actually on detachment at Rangoon, has been recorded – the fault for this last omission probably lies with me for not arranging such cover at that time.

The staff and political files were a revelation to me. There is an astonishing amount of treasure scattered about within these WO and FO files, particularly if you happen to have part of a lead yourself – a code name in your log book, an incident recorded in your old wartime notebooks, a man's name mentioned in a colleague's letter. Any one of these can give a sudden, sharp relevance to a signal or report or memo contained within one of the tatty old file covers kept at Kew. More than one mystery in my own wartime notes was solved by discoveries among the WO papers in the Public Record Office there.

6 Other sources.

I have been given access to the Mountbatten archives at Broadlands and there again found a solution to one or two wartime mysteries, but this material also has been vetted by the SIS, and again they have withheld many documents from the researcher's view. Whether this decision is always taken in the interest of state security, rather than merely to cover up some discreditable action by a Foreign Office official, is a question that might occur to some people – particularly those who recall the note to page 184 in the References (page 356), dealing with the missing letter written by Mountbatten.

One or two quoted comments, and an occasional passage in the text, have not been given attribution in the reference section. This is because the informant has asked me not to disclose the source.

I am grateful to all those mentioned here, and also to the anonymous contributors, for the help they have given me.

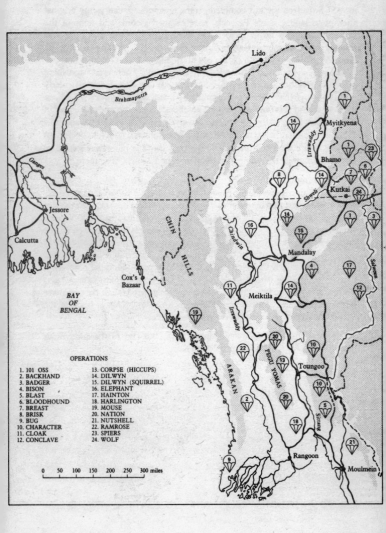

OPERATIONS

1. 101 OSS
2. BACKHAND
3. BADGER
4. BISON
5. BLAST
6. BLOODHOUND
7. BREAST
8. BRISK
9. BUG
10. CHARACTER
11. CLOAK
12. CONCLAVE
13. CORPSE (HICCUPS)
14. DILWYN
15. DILWYN (SQUIRREL)
16. ELEPHANT
17. HAINTON
18. HARLINGTON
19. MOUSE
20. NATION
21. NUTSHELL
22. RAMROSE
23. SPIERS
24. WOLF

0   50   100   150   200   250   300 miles

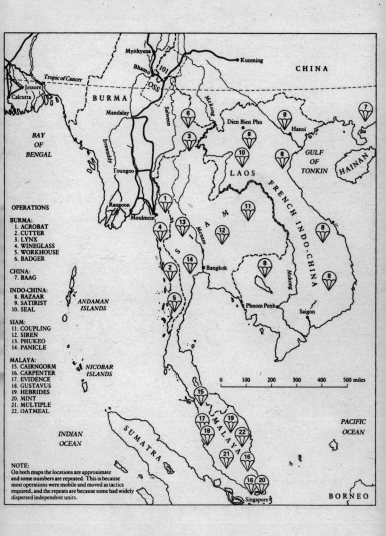

OPERATIONS

BURMA:
1. ACROBAT
2. CUTTER
3. LYNX
4. WINEGLASS
5. WORKHOUSE
6. BADGER

CHINA:
7. BAAG

INDO-CHINA:
8. BAZAAR
9. SATIRIST
10. SEAL

SIAM:
11. COUPLING
12. SIREN
13. PHUKEO
14. PANICLE

MALAYA:
15. CAIRNGORM
16. CARPENTER
17. EVIDENCE
18. GUSTAVUS
19. HEBRIDES
20. MINT
21. MULTIPLE
22. OATMEAL

NOTE:
On both maps the locations are approximate and some numbers are repeated. This is because most operations were mobile and moved as tactics required, and the repeats are because some had widely dispersed independent units.

1

I seemed to have blundered into a meeting of conspirators. In the clear autumn light of the Bengal sun the railing shadows were like strips of tar across the grey concrete veranda, and as I approached the open doorway in crepe-soled stealth I heard a soft North American voice finish with what sounded like the words 'deliver the uniforms'. The reply, though low, was memorably clear:

'There will be no uniforms on this seal. But you'll . . .'

He gave a startled cry at my appearance in the doorway. He was standing with a Canadian navigator by a trestle table, the leather case of a field telephone in his hand, and he thrust this behind him as if to conceal it from me. From the three stripes on his bush shirt I guessed, correctly, that he was the commanding officer of the squadron described by headquarters as the 'secret lot' – and, moreover, that he guarded that secrecy as a precious charge. He hid the leather telephone away behind him on the table and waved his hands to blur sight of it as he urged me and the Canadian out of the room, all the time firing a reprimand of questions. What was I doing there? How long had I been listening? Where had I come from? Who was I?

Finally, with the three of us out on the veranda, the wing commander gave me pause enough to squeeze in the explanation that I had been sent to command the flight of C–47 Dakotas shortly to join his squadron. He still remained suspicious.

'Show me your identity card.'

You carried it with you, of course, but rarely did anyone actually ask to see it. That day, however, Wing Commander Moore not only examined it closely but studied my face to check it against the photograph; the Canadian, Bolingbroke, gave a

11

surreptitious nod of greeting as we waited to see if the document was acceptable. A hoopoe passed the end of the veranda in undulating flight, like an aircraft with faltering engine, and finished with such a swoop into a cassia bush that the delicate pastel-pink flowers were set all aquiver from the impact. We waited in silence. At last the wing commander gave grudging acceptance of the identity card, saying it 'seemed' all right.

'We have to be very careful about security here, you understand,' he said. 'Didn't they warn you in Delhi about that?'

They had not. They had been far too anxious to sell me the job. Six months earlier, just before taking off with Jackie Coogan's glider party to land behind the lines, an air marshal had spoken to six of us RAF officers going in with the Wingate Chindit columns and promised that we could refer to him personally if we were unhappy with the posts offered to us on return from the expedition. I had kept threatening personnel staff at Delhi with this promise when they tried to push me off into various office jobs, so they had finally produced this vacancy in the Special Duty squadron.

What they had divulged in trying to sell it to me, for I had become something of a nuisance by then, seemed to shock the wing commander. He was so obsessed about security that even the outright mention of such titles as ISLD, Force 136 and the OSS made him noticeably jumpy. He paddled his hand at me for silence, looked hurriedly about the veranda and then abruptly changed the subject.

Yes, yes, yes, enough of that, we could discuss the Dakota flight later. Had I been assigned a room? Where was my kit?

The tonga which had brought me from Jessore station was standing in the paltry shade of a toddy palm outside the basha hut. Moore's final words at that first meeting reverted once again to security.

'You must bear in mind our work here is secret. Very secret. So watch your words all the time. Understand?'

I agreed to be mute, he withdrew to his hideout, and we escaped to collect my gear and settle with the driver of the tonga. Bolingbroke latched up the back of the Chevrolet three-tonner once I had tossed up my sleeping bag then, as we started off down the aircraft taxi-track towards the officers' mess some three miles away, he began to tell me about the set-up.

RAF 357 Special Duty squadron had been formed a few months earlier and had only started operations from Jessore a fortnight before I arrived. The airfield had been constructed on a jute plantation, and as we drove towards the perimeter we passed a patch of the jute plants, self-seeded perhaps, growing close beside a dispersal pen in which a B–24 Liberator was trembling in thunderous uproar of an engine test. The plants jutted just above the grass mound of the pen and I could see the seed pods flailing about in the prop blast like seaweed in the turmoil of an undertow: a gaudy bee-eater that had come like a dart over the plants was hit by the slipstream and gave a flash of iridescent greens when it was swept away on the flow.

'That's our kite for the *Seal* op,' Bolingbroke said. 'Hope it's not such a sweat as last time.'

The comments overheard on the veranda began to make sense. *Seal* was the code name for an operation dealing with the underground in Indo-China, and in explaining the reference to uniforms Bolingbroke introduced me to the political complications inherent in so much of the clandestine work in our area. In this instance, as contact had to be made both with de Gaulle sympathizers and with Vichy officials, two separate groups of three agents had to be dropped, and because of the differences between these French factions the two groups of parachutists had to be kept not merely separate but altogether ignorant of each other's existence. This was not difficult at Jessore but the operation had been staged through Kunming in China, an airfield controlled by the USAAF. This introduced the second complication and explained the uniform business.

The hostility between Roosevelt and de Gaulle naturally had an effect on American attitudes, and in our area this was particularly noticeable in the China theatre where American objection to the French was officially implemented and uncompromising. The two Liberators could not therefore land at the American-controlled airfield of Kunming with French parachutists and expect the usual US cooperation; their presence had to be concealed. So they were fitted out with the uniforms of RAF sergeants for the staging flight, and each aircraft carried a parcel containing their French uniforms into which they would change just before the drop.

The aircraft had gone to Kunming separately. There the first three were settled into a billet on the airfield and the second lot in town, ready for the operation the following night. Unfortunately this had to be postponed because of bad weather, so they had to spend several days on the ground. Bolingbroke's crew, and the Australians on the other Liberator – about half our aircrew were Canadians (RCAF) and Australians (RAAF) – had to stay close to their separate charges all the time, their planned movements for the day being secretly passed to one another so as to avoid contact.

It was not possible, however, to avoid the USAAF personnel who ran the aerodrome and they, as opposed to staff officers pursuing official policy, were just as openly friendly to visiting aircrew as they were in the rest of the South-East Asia Command (SEAC) area. So personal contact was inevitable and questions were asked.

What part of Canada, Australia, Britain, do you come from? Have a Lucky. What are you doing here? Do you know about Smoky Joe's place?

'They were a real friendly bunch over there,' Bolingbroke said. 'That was our problem.'

It was one of communication. Not one of the six Frenchmen spoke English. So the sociable Americans found themselves faced with uniformed RAF aircrew who apparently refused to talk to them. An explanation had to be produced: it was that the men were French airmen who had joined the RAF, had just arrived in India, and were being trained as future despatchers. It was an implausible story but apparently it sufficed, for there was no intervention from senior officials at the base.

When presently the weather cleared over Indo-China the Liberators went off into the night and dropped the two parties into their separate sites. Immediately the agents had gone down the chute, Bolingbroke said, the aircrew were fighting about the distribution of the smart new RAF uniforms they had left behind them.

14

The *Seal* operation going off that night, he said, was being flown direct to Indo-China. There would therefore, as I had overheard Moore say, be no uniform problem on this occasion.

Leaving the airstrip we drove through a scattering of bullock carts on the outskirts of Jessore town, and along an avenue of margosa trees with light graceful foliage that splashed the road in sprays of grey shadow. Outside the last mud hut we passed a woman in a pale lilac sari showing a strip of bare midriff that looked like a polished leather belt; she was standing by a cauldron perched on a smoking fire and the acrid smell of the burning dung stayed with us in the truck as we sped on through the flitting shadows of the tree trunks.

In this low-lying delta area of Bengal, with the water table so close to the surface, the roadside was littered with pools and tanks of dark still water. Many of these were covered with a glossy layer of water lilies flecked with blossom-pink flowers; ducks and egrets were dabbing about the edges, and buffalo were occasionally visible only as snouts snuffling above the surface. On the banks the saris laid out to dry looked like tiny tulip beds in a springtime city park garden.

The officers' mess, which had once been a girls' school, was an attractive white Palladian block with stone arches running the full length of the façade on both floors. On the right of the gravelled approach there was a smaller building, white stucco flaking, stone balustrades to a front veranda, and I had been allocated a room on the top floor. Between this house and the imposing mess building there were three new long blocks, thatch-covered, with wide concrete verandas running along their full length. There were about a dozen rooms in each, mostly with their doors now open, and in the late afternoon the aircrew were sunning themselves in cane chairs, feet up on the wooden railings, with dhoti-clad bearers drifting about in the shadows of the rooms. Across the drive and close by a thinly leaved acacia tree was a shower block from which a towel-wrapped figure was walking back towards the huts. It was all so comfortably enticing after months sleeping out in the hills of northern Burma under the pelting monsoon rain.

It was a month before the Dakotas arrived, plenty of time to prise out some information about the various spy organizations and to accustom myself once more to Air Force ways. I had been with Wingate's force for eighteen months, living first in the Indian jungle then finishing hundreds of miles behind the lines up in the frontier range between northern Burma and Yunnan; for those last four months we had been dependent on aircraft for food and supplies, so I had a unique understanding among the pilots about the work and conditions of the men whom they dropped, and then afterwards serviced each moon period, in those dark green hills running along the Chinese border.

The squadron at that time, apart from the four Hudson pilots, was composed entirely of Liberator crews, and as the clandestine organizations were only just beginning to build up their strength in the field the squadron was not yet working anywhere near to capacity. I suggested to Moore that it might be useful experience for me to go on a few operations with a Liberator crew, but he turned me down. Nor would he allow me to take on one of the few Hudson operations that were still being mounted.

'Don't want anything to happen to you before your aircraft even arrive,' he said.

He had reason for such pessimism. I did take one up locally, the first I had flown since those final days in Java back in 1942 when we lost the last of the fifteen we had flown out so urgently from England, but it was such a rattle-trap old machine – impossible to synchronize the engines because one of them had surging revs, and there was also a flickering oil-pressure gauge – that I was content to stay grounded until the Dakotas arrived.

It was a good time to wait. October is one of the loveliest months in Bengal, a time when the rains have definitely finished and the sun shines clear over the monsoon-rinsed countryside – crisp-cool mornings with the ground mist tingling fresh on your face, days of balmy warmth under a limpid sky, brief delicious twilights with a golden haze enveloping the margosa trees along the roadside, and night skies glittering clear with a thousand galaxies of stars. We paid attention to the night sky, and particularly to the phases of the moon, for all the operational flights were conducted during the twelve nights or so ranged about the full moon.

It was not easy to discover exactly what operations were being carried out during that October moon, for there was as yet no operations room where one could attend briefings; these seemed to be carried out surreptitiously by the wing commander in his room, with no one present but himself and the relevant crew. Secrecy was his preoccupation. It was of course enjoined by all the clandestine organizations, none with such Masonic fervour as the ISLD (Inter-Services Liaison Department). ISLD was the Indian title for MI6 or SIS (Secret Intelligence Service) – a particularly deceptive title for an organization renowned for its lack of liaison with anyone or anybody, let alone just the services. They had an officer, a namesake of mine, Charles O'Brien, stationed more or less permanently at Jessore, but such was the shuttered security of ISLD that he himself often did not know the location until after us. The chief in Calcutta, Colin Tooke, was reluctant to put anything on paper, kept all his agents separated from one another, and even his second-in-command was ignorant of many of the operations Tooke arranged. It was he who requested we use the word 'Joe', as in England, instead of agent, which he thought was compromising; the meaningless synonym was favoured by Moore and used widely at Jessore, even in the official Operations Record Book (ORBs).

Nearly all the ISLD Joes were indigenous people and we had little contact with them. But those who did speak English were still reluctant to discuss their operations, even with the pilot who was flying them: I tried once to make helpful conversation with one who looked nervous about a practice jump, and stopped in the fuselage to ask him where his operational jump was being made. He looked quite shocked, as if I had mouthed some appalling blasphemy:

'You know I can't tell you that!' he whispered.

I was the person who was going to brief the pilot exactly where the DZ was located and the timing of the drop, but even when I told him this he still refused to discuss the matter.

The records of MI6 in war or peace are never made available

to the public. However, the flight commander of a Special Duty squadron, involved in nearly all their operations, and curious about the organization, could inevitably learn much about their activities.

Force 136, the title given to SOE (Special Operations Executive) in South-East Asia, was not quite so obsessed with security. It was easy enough to visit their Calcutta headquarters, their operatives were all trained together in the same jungle-warfare school, and their operations were planned and detailed in documents that were not so difficult for a participating pilot to discover. The occasional minor officer would try to exalt his routine task with a blaze of spydom, but most agents would chat freely with you about their operations. And when I asked a senior officer one day just how wide their activities ranged, he said:

'Well, we did have a plan to assassinate Ba Maw, for example.' Ba Maw was the leader of the Burmese puppet government.

'What happened?'

'We couldn't at the time find a suitable Burmese – he had to be Burmese – for the job. Of course, when the Burmese army changed over to our side it would have been easy, but there was no point to it then.'

Ba Maw was, in fact, the subject of an assassination attempt, but it was a group of Japanese officers who tried to kill him. They botched the job, so he survived two threats to his life.

We also had a representative of the American OSS (Office of Strategic Services) on the station a little later. Though this organization was also strict on security, they did already have in progress in northern Burma a major operation that was common knowledge to anyone who had fought in that area. This was 101 Detachment, and in *Out of the Blue* I have told something about this OSS unit and the help they had given us in the Wingate campaign. We had nothing to do with them officially in 357 Squadron – they were serviced by the US 10th Air Force – but I did manage a few unofficial contacts with old friends later on when landing in their area. Our official contacts with OSS were with 404 Detachment; we were responsible for

18

servicing this unit which operated in the southern area and was much more secretive about its activities. But again, you could learn much if you were curious.

Of all the clandestine organizations it was D Division that provided the most diverting sorties. Although they were almost as secretive as ISLD, and just as averse to written records, I did have contact several times with Peter Fleming who commanded the unit and he was quite happy to chat about their operations. The 'D' stood for Deception and D Division was particularly practised in radio deception – mainly through a number of double agents, enemy-planted spies who had defected. The best of these was a German-paid Hindu but his control was unfortunately in Afghanistan, a slow channel of communication useful only for strategic purposes. For tactical intelligence the Japanese-planted agents had to be used, but their channels of communication were so involved that D Division was constantly devising schemes to establish better contacts with the enemy.

A typical oddity was an operation called *Backhand*. The purpose of the drop was to persuade the Japanese that they had gained a valuable deserter, a man who not only had a trusted radio link with Allied HQ but was eager to cooperate with them in a deception scheme. It was assumed this would be acted out like a normal double-agent play: the Japanese would start transmitting messages that might be useful to us and we could send back messages that would lead them astray. The Germans had used this sort of imposter contact to capture some fifty SOE agents on landing in Holland. The volunteer decoy had to be an Indian army officer, as such a defection was far more credible than that of a European officer – indeed the Indian National Army (INA) was a Japanese-sponsored unit fighting with them at that time. A call was put out among selected Indian regiments and presently a Punjabi captain was chosen from among the volunteers. He was given a new identity, then officially cashiered for insubordination, so that the disgrace of his alter ego was put on record. He was then supposed to have volunteered for the mission so as to avoid actual imprisonment for his fictional offence.

Next he spent a month with D Division, with his new identity, learning his cover story and all the usual double-agent drill – how to play his role once the enemy accepted the story, the kind of information to extract from the enemy, and how to pass it back through Japanese scrutiny. They gave him only a short course in the use of radio – technical instruction was not necessary because the Japanese would ensure the set was expertly maintained – and then they brought him to us for the drop.

So we took him off on the night of the full moon and dropped him safely over open paddy fields in lower Burma. This was a studied choice; had he landed amongst the hill tribes, the Kachins or the Karens, they would have hidden him away at once and protected him fiercely from ever achieving his prime purpose of being captured. The Burmese plainsmen, however, were as cooperative as anticipated and took him straight to a Japanese sergeant at a nearby stores dump. There the Indian told his story; that he had been parachuted into Burma to spy on them but that he really hated the British, and wanted to help the Japanese crush his colonial oppressors.

The Japanese sergeant, however, did not play the role assigned to him by D Division. The stupid man beat up the Indian with an ebony ruler. He had no interest in his story about defection. He thrust the radio aside as unimportant, beat him again and again until he stopped talking about it, then tied him up against a coconut palm and sent off a report to his superiors. Presently a sergeant in the Kempei-tai, the Japanese secret police, arrived and after that his position improved and events began to move more or less according to Fleming's script.

He was taken to a Kempei officer, together with his radio now properly treasured, thence escorted to Rangoon. There he was able finally to transmit one or two messages which proved that he was indeed a genuine spy. The Kempei-tai now had open to India a channel of great deceptive potentiality. And D Division back in India, having received those opening messages, congratulated themselves on hooking their fish and sat back to play the catch.

Unfortunately the Kempei people in Burma were not very bright. As happened so often out there, the scheme was too subtle for them. The Indian's complicated story explaining how he came to get the job – the court martial and the volunteering business – and all the falsified documents and circumstantial detail so painstakingly prepared for him, were too profound for the local Kempei officials. They lacked the sophisticated background of European spydom, and simply discarded the suitcase radio as a useless piece of equipment once it had proved his authenticity. Why should they wish to make contact with the enemy?

More infuriating still, they then used the Indian for their own selfish purposes. He struck them as a useful addition to the INA, which they were nurturing to fight against the British, and they put him in charge of propaganda on the puppet force down in Rangoon headquarters; so D Division not only had no profit from their efforts but had on the contrary provided the enemy with a useful addition to their anti-allied propaganda team.

For weeks D Division kept up their vain appeals on the radio for a response from their expensive double agent, but no one in Burma was listening, and only when the army finally reached Rangoon months later did Fleming discover why his calls had never been answered.

At Jessore his passage had passed unnoticed. To the aircrew he was just another Joe going out on another operation. For all the efforts of the wing commander in stressing security at the base, it was impossible to hide the evidence that we were not just an ordinary bomber squadron. It must have been clear to anyone who passed only a few days on the station, provided he had normal eyesight and hearing, that the set-up was unusual. In England, I am told, the local tradesmen could pick out SOE agents by the standard suits they wore and the standard suitcases they carried as they wandered about Baker Street talking phrase-book English; you could also tell them in Jessore by their incongruity in that situation.

Why were little groups of Americans, French, Burmese, Chinese, Malays, Gurkhas or Annamese wandering about an

RAF station in Bengal? Why so many British and Indian army officers, all of different regiments? And what were those long black cylinders they stowed in the Liberator bomb-bays or attached under the wings of the Dakotas? Why did we keep taking these strange visitors up in our aircraft and dropping them in little groups in a nearby field, day after day? A most unusual squadron, surely?

Any visitor who displayed such curiosity, however, would soon find himself in a tense personal interview with the wing commander. Overt discussion of our activities brought swift rebuke. He would not even accept newcomers into the fold until confident of their discretion; when the Dakota crews arrived presently he insisted they be kept away from the flight hut until he was assured they were properly reticent. After a week under scrutiny he instructed me one morning to bring them to this office where, after a warning to a pilot who had innocently wandered by the basha huts where the agents were billeted, he told them they had passed their test and would be accepted under his command.

My own clearance was not so simple. He reproved me in the mess one day for asking Shave, Bolingbroke's Australian pilot, about a sortie he had done the previous night, then he went on to wonder accusingly why I asked so many questions, not only of aircrew but also of the Joes when they visited the mess. I think he had remained a little uneasy about me from that first day. The identity card might prove I was an RAF officer, but when asked about my previous squadron I had avoided the easy checks on my answer by claiming to have been with the army. Walking about in the jungle, so I said.

A pilot in the jungle? A residue of suspicion must have remained, because that morning in his office, after he had finally cleared all the new Dakota crews, he asked me to wait a moment. When they were all out on the veranda he said:

'You took up a Hudson on test last month, didn't you?'

I agreed – and wondered how he knew about this.

'You should enter it in your log book. I've signed all the others. Enter that flight and bring me your log book, will you?'

My log book would have given him some answers, of course.

But then, in response to that very simple request, I had another unlikely story that frustrated this attempt to check my RAF background.

It was on 6 March 1944 that the USAAF Air Commando landed me in the glider two hundred miles behind the lines, there to spend the next three appalling months in the Kachin hills with an isolated group of Wingate's Chindits. Our packs contained only the most ruthlessly checked essentials; all the rest of my kit I had stored down at Bombay where, just prior to this, I had been in command of RAF Station Juhu; Grindley's Bank in Bombay had a godown in the dock area at the service of its customers, and I deposited there the black tin trunk with all the books and papers and clothing accumulated since the escape from Java.

A month later, when we were clambering about the mountainous border ridges between northern Burma and Yunnan, a ship called the *Fort Stikine* came in to Bombay carrying seven tonnes of gold and thousands of tons of explosives. On top of this main cargo from America was a small load of cotton that had been taken aboard at Karachi, and, instead of being kept miles out in the harbour at the ammunition discharge point, the ship was allowed in to the dockside to unload the cotton. There, when the hatches were removed, a fire was discovered in the hold. It was too late by then to get the ship away, and although the fire brigades poured into her so much water that she almost foundered the fire eventually reached the explosives.

The *Fort Stikine* disintegrated in a shattering roar that was heard two hundred miles away, wiping out all the dock installations, destroying or seriously damaging sixteen other ships and hurling one completely out of the water. The explosion, said to be the greatest in the war until Hiroshima, killed four hundred people, injured thousands, and showered the city with debris and dismembered bodies and gold bullion . . . part of a lifeboat on a tram . . . a man's leg in a convent garden . . . a £50,000 gold bar at the foot of a marble throne on a movie set. A trivial item among the losses in that devastating explosion was one black tin trunk – with my flying log book inside it.

So I now had no proof of my flying record in the RAF,

nothing to back up the story that I had done a tour of operations in Blenheims and started a second in Hudsons back in 1940–1 in Europe; that I had then flown out to Singapore and operated there until the final collapse, subsequently had a command down in Bombay, and finally had landed behind the enemy lines in a glider earlier that year. Just my word for it all. And when I told the wing commander that the log book had been lost in that catastrophic disaster, his earlier doubts revived. What disaster? He had heard nothing about a great explosion in Bombay.

I should have guessed this. The *Fort Stikine* explosion was one of those wartime disasters, similar to what happened to that troopship out of St Nazaire in 1940 when over a thousand lives were lost, that the authorities decided would be better not proclaimed. The ban in India had been even more successful than in England. Blackout on the news had been complete, no newspaper in any language, no radio station, no publication of any kind had been permitted to mention the disaster; all I had received was a duplicated letter from the bank telling me that an explosion had destroyed my luggage – my main informant had been a naval friend who had been in Bombay that shattering day. When I told Moore the story that morning he listened watchfully, and at the end just studied me in dubious silence for a moment.

'I see,' he said at last, clearly not seeing at all.

One couldn't blame him. A pilot might conceivably have his log book burned in a plane crash, even have it stolen from his room, but to have it in a godown at Bombay dock, there to be destroyed by a cataclysmic explosion which had been kept a secret from all the outside world, was excessively fanciful.

I have no certain knowledge that Moore ran a check on me after our session that morning but would be surprised to learn he had not. His obsession with secrecy extended even to the very code names that were specifically designed to cover reference to the various operations. Not only were these not allowed to be mentioned in letters, but they were even forbidden to be written down in the aircrews' log books, the only permitted description for a sortie being the single word 'operation'. I understand ISLD had inspired this nonsense, though their code names usually referred to the actual agent and not the operation, as was the case with Force 136. On two occasions in the flight hut Moore found me writing in my notebook, and the second time he could not suppress his anxiety.

'You're not writing anything about our work in those books of yours, are you?'

It was a tricky moment. What I was actually writing just then was a note about his leather field telephone, and I could see his name blaring out from the top line of the open page, within a foot or so of his vigilant eyes. I put my hand out to gesticulate reassurance – and cover the page – as I lied about the contents. I was only writing a note about a buffalo seen that morning, I said, about the slovenly way it was slouching along the road chewing the cud, head raised in supercilious indifference to our passage. Hadn't he noticed it?

This trivia about buffalo mystified him out of suspicion. But he did go on to reprove me again for being so inquisitive about the work of the squadron; he had discovered I had been in the operations room reading the ORBs and said I should concentrate on my Dakota flight, not go around checking on past or present operations of the Hudsons and Liberators. They were not my concern.

There was nothing to gain by argument so I did not bother. But when presently we started operations in the Dakotas, I told the crews to use the code names in their log books; he had not given a specific order about this, and the ban did not make any sense to me. Why give a code name for security reasons, and then use the compromising word 'operation' when logging it? An organization in Delhi was devoted to providing code names for all operations in the services, the object being to ensure there was no confusion and that the names were meaningless. We used them in the log books, and discussed them openly, and I am convinced our work was the better for it.

When a plane crashed it was impossible to repress questions and discussion about the fate of the aircrew; even the wing commander accepted that. One Hudson crash that year excited such interest that the authorities finally issued a press release about it – without, of course, mentioning the squadron or giving any clue as to what the aircraft had been doing at the time.

It had happened before my arrival when a Hudson had been out on a drop to the *Spiers* group; this was a Force 136 operation to train guerrillas in support of the ruler of Kokang (the Akond?) against Chinese bandits in the border area. The accident was not unusual, the Hudson had engine trouble during the drop, and, if you are flying at slow speed well below ridge level in a valley at night and an engine falters, then the odds are heavily against your survival.

In this instance the pilot did manage a slight measure of control in the descent, so although he and three others were killed when they hit the hillside, two of the crew did manage to survive the impact and ensuing fire. An American patrol group which happened to be nearby in China heard the news, and reached the site by next morning. Major Leitch, the leader, gave immediate help, signalling his base who sent off a doctor on the five-day mule ride over the mountains to the crash.

Meanwhile, action had been taken at Jessore. When Graham, our squadron doctor, heard about the crash he at once volunteered to go. He had never jumped before but, as he told me later, that did not seem an important qualification for the task.

'I've been on mountain rescue in Wales and that seemed of more practical value in the circumstances. Anyway, they were men from our squadron, so of course I had to go.'

He did not mention that he had been decorated for one particular rescue effort in the Welsh mountain. I discovered that much later.

One of the parachute instructors volunteered to go with him and on the night following the crash they took off for the site. They arrived over the DZ at daybreak to find the 6000-foot ridge covered with that patchy dawn mist I knew so well – in fact I was down there on that very mountain range the same morning, about a hundred miles to the west, and probably looking across such a deep valley at the trees, also packed in cotton wool, as I listened to the gibbons hallooing their joyous greeting to the new day.

'The sergeant went down the slide before me,' Graham said, 'and he was sort of waiting in the air for me when I came out. He kept giving me instructions as we floated down, shouting how to stop swaying – by yanking at the cords and spilling the air.'

They landed safely and were met by Major Leitch, who told them that one of the survivors had died, but the other, the Canadian navigator Prosser, was still hanging on to life – his major injuries were a fractured skull and a badly smashed leg. Graham tended Prosser in the hut for several days, guarded by the small American patrol, but when the US medical team under Captain Hookman arrived the Japanese were closing in on them and Leitch decided they must move. So Prosser was put on a stretcher and they started off on the long haul through the mountains and the Japanese patrols, heading for an emergency strip used by the USAAF in China.

The journey over those cramped mountain ranges that straddle the border of northern Burma and Yunnan took them a month, mostly through Japanese-held territory, with the wounded Canadian being carried on a litter all the way. Finally they reached the emergency airstrip and there a USAAF aircraft landed and flew the party back to India. Prosser spent many weeks in hospital but in the end made a complete recovery.

It had been a near thing though. In the first few days, with the will to survive crushed by the extent of his injuries and the apparent hopelessness of his plight, he had come closest to death. When, in a lucid moment, he spoke of his weariness with the struggle, Graham answered him with the common squadron ridicule of solemnity.

'What makes the grass grow in Texas!'

'Maybe there won't be a crop this year,' Prosser whispered.

But he managed a grin, and after that he fought steadily, and in the end successfully, for his life.

2

Unlike the Americans, who had only the OSS, the British had a confusion of clandestines in South-East Asia. Force 136, ISLD and D Division were the most important, but E Group (MI9 and MI19), PWD (Psychological Warfare Division) and BAAG (a group in contact with Hong Kong) were others for whom we worked. Although the separate groups were jealous of their identities and there was rivalry, even friction, between them at times, they did meet on common ground at Jessore. All of them, including 404 OSS, came to us for final parachute training, and for delivery and servicing of their agents behind the lines in South-East Asia.

Ours were the only aircraft in the command that were adapted for their purposes. Both the Hudsons and the Liberators had been fitted with slides and when our Dakotas arrived in November they had also been modified for their role – some had been fitted with long-range tanks, some with external racks for dropping containers, and all had cables for the parachutists' static lines. They were ready for immediate operations and even those like myself who had never flown one before could have gone off that same night had a job been available, for a gentler aircraft than the DC3 has never been made. It is as reliable as a steamship, responds to the slightest pressure on the control column, and even without using the automatic pilot it can be trimmed to such steadiness you can relax almost to sleep.

The aircraft were a delight to enter. They were in saleroom condition. When you climbed up on to the unmarked aluminium floor of the fuselage you could detect the tang of the lubricant on the static line, the fibre straps holding up the benches were still uncreased and freshly rough to the touch,

28

and the cockpit door was such a close tight seal that it fluffed open at the release of the catch. Inside the cabin there was the smell of new car, of leather and paint and fresh rubber, the floor was covered with seaweed-green carpet, the pilots' seats were impeccably unwrinkled mounds of soft green leather, the instrument panel glistened clear with the phosphorescent figures still purely defined, and the throttle knobs were so polished smooth you felt compelled to stroke the cool surface.

Our flight headquarters was set up close by the northern end of the strip, in a small brick hut with a thatch roof that gave out a sound like distantly galloping horses every time the pert little palm squirrels went chasing over it to jump on to the drooping foliage of the jalpitri tree behind – whose hard seeds the villagers collected so as to make necklaces. There were just three rooms, a double-sized one for the crew room, a room for the flight sergeant and his men, and my office. There we started to learn about work with the clandestines, and about the activities of Force 136 Parachute Training Section commanded by Major Thornton, with the first actual drop being a practice run I carried out early one morning that November.

I rose at dawn that day and went out on to the veranda in pyjamas to check the wind. The sun had not yet risen, the listless palms along the road were black silhouettes against the rich orange glow in the eastern horizon, the sky overhead was a limpid blue, and the air was absolutely still. In the mango trees at the end of the drive the crows were beginning to stir; at dawn they give a rattling noise, rather like frogs croaking, and then gradually work up to their normal melancholy cawing. From the back of the mess building a trail of cigarette blue smoke was climbing straight as a palm trunk up to merge into the blue of the zenith.

Conditions were perfect, Thornton told me on the phone. He would meet us at the aircraft.

He always ran his practice jumps at dawn or at dusk: the wind was usually then at its gentlest, and on this first Dakota drop he was particularly anxious for perfect conditions. The group was composed of six Gurkhas who were due off on their operation two nights later. Although a truck was going to the practice ground, which was about five tortuous miles away and across two swing bridges, Thornton as usual preferred to drop in from the air. This pleased me, for his fall would provide a practical guide to wind condition.

He drove up with the six Gurkhas just as we five aircrew reached the aircraft – we had one experienced despatcher, the extra two were there to watch and learn. The Gurkhas, stubby little figures in their jungle green uniforms, and clutching parachutes that seemed disproportionately big, smiled in response to my greeting – just three months after leaving the battalion my Gurkhali was still roughly serviceable. The door panel had already been removed and when I climbed up into the fuselage Thornton was inside testing the roof cable with savage jerks. It must retain the parachutist's static line when he jumps. If not he is dead.

He came up forward to join me when we taxied out of dispersal, passing a Liberator slumbering in its pen and sending a coven of crows scattering from some mysterious meeting in the long grass near the end of the runway. In the still morning air the Dakota lifted off smoothly and flew itself on trim up to 600 feet, then I eased it gently into a turn so that when we straightened out the practice DZ was visible directly ahead. It was distinctively darker than the other open spaces of lakes and paddy and pasture, for it was ploughed frequently so as to make a soft landing for the parachutists. In the centre a small fire was sending up a thin line of blue-grey smoke that was swaying very slightly like a filament of cobweb when a door is closed. The field was rectangular, the long run being over four hundred yards, and with a scattering of trees at both ends.

Once he had seen the truck was waiting below, Thornton, his legs splayed by the parachute harness, waddled back into the fuselage. I flew on directly over the DZ, looking down through the open window to note the position of the smoking fire relative to a group of coconut palms away to our port side. This was my checkpoint. We continued a watchful circuit, sensing air currents and drift, right hand caressing the throttles back to dropping speed, and stretching the downwind leg so that there was plenty of time to get alignment exactly right on the final run-in. Approaching the DZ all was steady, airspeed 90 knots, altimeter at 600 feet, control column loose in my hands.

I called 'Stand by red' to the navigator. He was standing beside me, hand up on the switch above the window, waiting for the order.

In the fuselage behind me Thornton would by then have clipped on his static line and again checked its hold with a vigorous tug. When the red light flashed he would move to stand at the open doorway, the white static line from his parachute stretching like an umbilical cord up to the roof cable. In his case the despatcher would be standing idly by – Thornton had done a thousand jumps and had no need of a despatcher's expertise. When the port engine nacelle just began to block out my coconut-palms check I called for the drop.

'Green – go,' the navigator repeated, flicking the switch.

In the seconds that followed I was tingling for the faintest difference in control or sound, but still could not tell when Thornton actually left the aircraft. I called 'Red – stop' as we neared the trees, and the moment the navigator hit the switch I banked steeply in turn so as to see where Thornton landed.

Looking back down beyond the wing tip I could see the white circle of his developed parachute sliding across the dark furrows of the field. He was oscillating slightly but then he suddenly jerked his body sideways, hands high on the shroud lines, and the swaying motion stopped. I could not be sure when he actually hit the ground, but the canopy abruptly lost rigidity and shivered down into flaccid collapse behind him standing upright. He thumped the parachute release, then there was a flash from his upturned face and he held his two arms high in approval.

The navigator went back to check the Gurkhas as we circled wide over the placid lake where two ducks ripped a series of little white holes in the blue surface as they took off in startled flight. Because the stand-by period can be tense for many people, I made a shorter run-in the second time, only a few seconds on red before calling 'Green – go'. Whether because there were six men going out, or because I had become more sensitive to the action, this time I knew when they jumped;

there was a definite shiver in our transit, as though we had hit a little eddy of air, and this was followed by a faintly perceptible backward pressure on the stick as, subconsciously, I compensated for the sudden loss of weight aft.

Again, instantly on the stop light, I dropped the port wing steeply in turn to see how the six fell. To my surprise there were only four parachutes sliding across the DZ. The string was landing each side of Thornton in the centre near the fire so there had been plenty of time for the other two to jump. Assuming there had been some problem with despatch, I asked the navigator to go back and check.

When he had gone I looked down at the field and saw the four Gurkhas land; the canopies gave that spasmodic wriggle as they settled on the ground, the men tumbling out clear of the flutter of white. For some disturbing reason the truck was suddenly bounding over the dark ploughed surface towards the trees at the far end. Then the navigator was back beside me, shouting, his eyes wide.

'They all went out.'

And two were dead. I knew it with cold certainty on the instant. We banked steeply and straightened out to fly low over the field where the truck was still bouncing towards the trees. Thornton too, now the others were down, was also running in that direction. I could see no sign of parachutes in the trees but felt sure they must be there. And they were, but not developed enough to be visible.

The despatcher came up forward, and even before landing we guessed what had happened. The normal practice, which he had carried out, was to shout 'Go!' as he thrust each man through the doorway; in a group he strikes a rhythm, 'Go . . . and . . . Go . . . and . . . Go' as he thumps them on the back and out, but the fifth Gurkha that day had broken the rhythm. He had suddenly grabbed the side of the doorway with a grip of terror which, with most of his body outside, was impossible to retain against the force of the slipstream, but did however delay his full clearance for perhaps a second. The next man, following in correct tempo, had gone out almost on top of him.

The two parachutes had become entangled, Thornton told us

back at base. They never developed. The men had shot across the end of the DZ trailing cloth behind them and smashed into the trees.

It was a type of accident he had known before on one occasion when instructing in England. Experienced parachutists were aware of this possibility in a string; for this reason they preferred to jump first or last when with novices. In that position they could ensure a safe gap between themselves and any dangerous hesitator. There were over a thousand jumps down on the practice DZ at Jessore during the next twelve months and we never had another fatality.

It was just a few days after the Gurkhas' deaths that I carried out the first Dakota operation. This was on the night of the November full moon and it provoked the sharpest rebuke the wing commander ever delivered to me.

It was an ISLD operation. Their organization had splintered in the fall of Burma and they were now gradually rebuilding the network, several agents having been dropped over the previous few months. Their job was not to fight, but to gather long-term intelligence, political, economic and military. They were there as secret agents, not guerrillas. They had to avoid notice, just quietly observe and discreetly report. We had two packages to drop that night to one of these ISLD agents, a Burmese who was code named *Brisk*.

The wing commander instructed me to take a Hudson pilot called Dodwell with me. He had done about a dozen drops, he told me. He would be able to advise me if any problems arose.

It was an extravagant operation. When I climbed up the steps with parachute in hand that night the fuselage made me think of the aisle of a cathedral. Planks of brilliant moonlight were slanting in from the windows and there was nothing immediately visible in the whole of the long vaulted space; only when I moved up the metal floor, footfalls echoing in the emptiness, did I at last see two lonely packages at the far end, like forms hunched in reverential prayer. Just two packages for a fifteen-hundred mile journey! This was early days: ISLD had still to be challenged on such wasteful flights.

With Dodwell in the second-pilot's seat I started the engines and ran them up briefly, flashed the lights for the chocks to be removed, then taxied out of the pen towards the strip. The landing lights were not necessary to taxi, the moon was almost full in a brilliant night sky, so bright that we were borne on the barge of our shadow out to the flare path. A few minutes later we were airborne and climbing away over the flat delta land of lower Bengal.

Flying over the delta area in the moonlight you see how close the water table is to the surface. That night, in the rivers and lakes and paddy fields and tanks, the silvered moonlit reflections were strewn over the whole landscape as if an immense mirror had been shattered on the dark velvety earth; above us the brilliant night sky looked like a moth-eaten blackout curtain against silver-bright outer space, with the luminous star dust of the milky way a threadbare swathe where the light almost broke through completely. We climbed smoothly up to twelve thousand feet to give a carefree margin over the Chin Hills, I turned the rheostat down so that the instrument panel reflected only a gentle glow-worm light, switched to automatic pilot, and then sat there thrilling to the glory of the night.

It was not like setting off for a bombing raid in the old days in Europe, when the comparative security of the sea crossing on the outward journey could not be enjoyed because of the hell that awaited you on the other side. Flak was so rarely met in Burma that at debriefing you reported it as an event, and the chance of an enemy night fighter being in the air was so remote that even the glimpse of a black shape blotting out the stars would only make me wonder whether it was an RAF or USAAF aircraft. Our real enemy, the weather, was in benign mood, the monsoon was months away and we had an aircraft that compelled confidence, so my only concern that night as we slanted down over the Chin Hills towards the Burma plain was whether we would find the triangular site of the DZ and the agents waiting for us there.

The Irrawaddy drifted into view as a massive scar in the moonlit plain, and beyond it we could just discern the Shweli as a neat tree-lined ribbon of water that flashed silver when caught in line against the moon. The sight was vivid in my memory;

only a few miles beyond that river junction, nine months earlier, I had gone hurtling down in a glider, so I knew exactly where we were. And I was certain that the pallid triangular clearing below us, only a few miles short of the river junction, was indeed the site we had seen that morning in the photograph at briefing.

But there was no reception. Not a glimmer of life was visible from two thousand feet as we swung into a circuit . . . not from a thousand feet when we banked steeply over the centre of the site . . . not from a hundred feet when we swooped across with our faint moonlit shadow flittering over the dove-grey clearing amid the dark trees.

'No one there,' Dodwell said. 'Let's get away.'

He had never been down there in the jungle awaiting a drop. I had. There were plenty of explanations for the lack of a reception. It was criminal to fly seven hundred miles with a precious cargo for someone, and then not wait a moment or two while he was searching for matches, or waiting for a blacked-out Japanese truck to pass on the road nearby, or trying to sneak a way past a herd of elephants to get to the site. To give them time, and despite the confident identification of the site by me and Dodwell and the navigator, I said we would check position by a timed run from the pinpoint of the Shweli river junction.

Dodwell argued but was overruled. I was determined to make the check, though not entirely for the reason given to him. What I had to do, having come so close, was to see again the pear-shaped clearing of the *Chowringhee* site where we had landed that exciting night in the glider earlier that year.

To my surprise, and thrill too at the sight, my own mark was visible on the Burmese landscape. A thousand feet below us, down there in the pale cleared area of the dark forest, you could see clearly the line of the strip that I had started cutting with the six Gurkhas that first disastrous night; the glider carrying the caterpillar tractor had crashed into trees and killed all aboard, so we had been left with only five spades and our kukries to build an airstrip. Working right through that first night, while the others hauled the remaining gliders under the teak trees, we had cleared six hundred yards of a landing strip before a bulldozer was landed the next night to complete the job.

But I had started it all. Coogan had laid out a quick rough line for the other gliders but it was I who had afterwards stepped out through the tall kaing grass a line that avoided the buffalo wallows, I who had directed and worked with the Gurkhas cutting and levelling the airstrip on the site we called *Chowringhee*. And there it was still, a grey ribbon stretched taut and clear down the centre of that pallid clearing below us. You could see it out of the cockpit window and I wanted the others to share the excitement. Look, I did that!

I tried to impart my excitement to Dodwell but his interest was elsewhere. This dawdling over enemy territory distressed him. We must go straight back to base, he kept saying. On operations over Burma you did not hang about; you got in and out as quickly as possible.

The pride at seeing my old achievement was dampened by his persistence on this theme. So finally, with a nostalgic pang for the lost me down there, I turned the aircraft away from the past and flew the carefully timed course from the junction of the rivers. We arrived, almost exactly to the second of the navigator's ETA, over the same triangular clearing. It was certainly the briefed DZ. But it was still without a glimmer of life. In spite of Dodwell urging retreat I did two more low circuits before finally abandoning hope, and then we climbed away over the patterned plain towards the high moon and the dark mountain range of the border with India.

I had assumed Dodwell's desire to leave at once when we found no reception was because he did not like roaming about over enemy territory. On the return journey, however, he told me that his objection sprang from concern for the agents down below, whose security must not be compromised; in fact, in those early days of exaggerated caution the Liberators would also carry a bomb to drop on a nearby target so as to give the impression that that had been the purpose of the sortie. Wing Commander Moore would not be pleased about the action I had taken, Dodwell declared.

The wing commander was not at the debriefing when we landed back at Jessore just before dawn. However, he read the record later that morning and Dodwell's prediction turned out to be correct. A call came to report to his office immediately.

'When I read the ops report on *Brisk* I could not believe it,' he said. 'But I've spoken to Pilot Officer Dodwell. He says he did tell you to leave the DZ at once when you found no reception. But you ignored his advice and went on circling the site for half an hour.' I disputed this. The run to the river junction took some time but we had only done a few circuits over the actual DZ.

'Five in all. Five. By which time the whole countryside knew the location of the DZ.'

This was nonsense – I did not say so, of course, but just told him that in my opinion an aircraft circling at night covers far too wide and vague an area to give a precise guide to a DZ. It would have been much wiser not to argue at all, there was no profit in it anyway, and to try and quote my own experience at the receiving end of a drop was pure disaster. He snapped quick and hard at the first mention of that:

'I don't care what *you* did behind the lines. I'm telling you that if you are briefed to expect a reception, and you do not find it on arrival, then you leave at once. Do I make myself clear?'

He did. And it was apparent, quickly and sharply, that this order was not susceptible to further argument. So I stopped talking. Next time there would be no supervisor with me; I could do whatever seemed right at the time without necessarily telling the full story to ops room on return. So I just nodded when he said I had behaved stupidly.

I left his office still unimpressed. I could not believe the manoeuvres we had made would have put any ground party at risk. Even had we circled for half an hour, and then at last roused the agents down below, the Japanese were still unlikely to locate the site before the parachutes had been dropped, the containers all collected, and the ground party were away to their hideout. The Japanese did occasionally attack a DZ but this was always a consequence of treachery or accident, never by obtaining a fix from circling aircraft.

We had one such chance encounter on the Chindit campaign when one of our groups working with 101 OSS was caught in the middle of a supply drop on the Chinese border at Nahpaw. This was an old hill fort like those you see in Westerns – wooden palisades, interior parapet, and great wooden gates. The actual DZ was the open slope immediately below the fort and in the clear moonlit night the Dakota landed everything perfectly down the slope. Unfortunately a Japanese unit had halted for the night on the wooded ridge overlooking the site. They had watched in surprise as the signal fires were lit on the slope below, then when the plane arrived and the parachutes started to fall they realized they had a bonanza.

Although they could actually see a drop in progress, it still took them about half an hour down the hill track to reach the site. By then the drop was finished and the men were in the fort breaking down the containers. Fortunately the hungry Japanese, having rushed in through the broken gates, were so bewitched by the food treasures they began tearing open K ration packages instead of getting on with the killing business, so our little group was able to escape.

The commander of this unit was 'Fish' Herring, who had been working with a teak company at the outbreak of the war. He later joined Force 136, after handing over his unit to 101 OSS, when the Kachins to their delight went on to US rations and rates of pay. Then I finished with the army, came to Jessore, and soon Herring also turned up there for despatch on an operation – he was not the only old acquaintance who switched to the clandestine organizations when the Chindits were disbanded.

Herring went in to join *Hainton*, down in the mountainous border states far to the east of Mandalay. This was an operation designed to raise a guerrilla force in that remote area in the unlikely event it should ever become relevant to the Burma campaign, but it was we on the squadron who bore the only casualties suffered on that operation. It was on a sortie to them that Shave and his nine crew, including the Canadian Boling-broke, were all killed about a week after that meeting the day of my arrival at Jessore.

On a supply drop presently to *Hainton* I made the first test of carrying external containers. Three of our Dakotas had been fitted with 'para-racks', enabling six of the big containers to be slung beneath the fuselage; we carried four only on that first test, for we had six ordinary packages to be thrust out of the door as usual.

The effect of the bulky external containers was noticeable right from the start that night. It took an extra hundred yards to get into the air and there followed a sluggish rate of climb once we were airborne. Settled on course at 8000 feet, however, there was little discernible difference in handling, and presently I forgot about our appendages and relaxed.

On a still night, settled high above the earth and with the aircraft steady on course, there is no sense of forward motion. You sit there in the cockpit in air-conditioned tranquillity, the engines with a steady ringing tone of perfect synchrony, control column trembling in automatic precision, the phosphorescent figures, dials and switches a soft-glowing pattern of symmetry that hovers steadily on the periphery of vision as you look out at the night. All is calm. Just a faintly perceptible gentle swaying motion – you can believe your craft is suspended by a wire from the heavens, and little currents of air keep it faintly stirring. Far down below, the landscape passes moisture-slow under the wings of the aircraft; patterned fields of paddy, black blocks of forest, and the silver strips of rivers that lie between the shadowed ridges barring the way to Burma.

Without needing to adjust our course we picked out the Mandalay bend that gave a check, then we flew on over the Shan Hills until at last the Salween river gave us the final checkpoint. A few moments later, when we began the descent on course for the site, the T of fires suddenly appeared ahead like five tangerines in precise position down there on the dark slope; they looked like solid fixtures from a distance, like marker buoys on a shipping channel, but as the swirls of smoke indicated, they were in reality raging, twisting bonfires. We slanted down, down and down until the dark mass of the jungle had separated into individual trees, then we levelled out and flew through fleeting wraiths of smoke on the check run over the site. A pleasant scent of burning wood pervaded the aircraft.

I gave a flick of the navigation lights. From near the top central fire a torch flashed back at us. LONG . . . SHORT . . . LONG. The letter K. We were on target.

The DZ was in a valley. On the test run, when I was lining up the dark yew-green slope of the mountain on the port side to find a checkpoint, I could see the stars go flickering through the palisade of trees lining the ridge. A check on the radio altimeter tallied roughly with both the aneroid ASL reading and visual estimate of 600 feet above the lively fires. I stroked back the trim wheel so that slight forward pressure on the control column was needed to keep us level, then when the fire at the head of the T had passed underneath the wing I eased back the pressure so as to clear the trees on the ridge, and started the 180-degree turn.

By this time the despatcher had taken out the inset door. Only one package was to go out on the first run, a marker, and it would by then be set up near the open doorway, with the despatcher himself clipped on to his safety line. The navigator returned to confirm all was set to go, then switched on the stand-by light at my call. The faint red haze of its reflection appeared in the cockpit window.

I edged the throttles back and the aircraft sank smoothly down into the valley. Shadow-gashed hills began to rise up each side of us, the airspeed indicator died away to 90 knots. Down below there were figures waving, witches worshipping amid the sacrificial fires, again that scent of wood smoke. Then, just when the centre-top fire was blurred by the port propeller, I called for the drop.

'Green – go,' the navigator repeated.

I saw the movement of his arm, for at that moment I had to glance to the right to pick up a ridge feature as a checkpoint for the next run. There was an easy one – directly over the shimmering prop blade was a tree with a flattened crown that slanted almost parallel with the Milky Way. It was caught in a snapshot, processed and fixed in mind in the time it takes to flick a glance aside, then I flicked another glance down at the instrument panel before darting back to the danger of the ridge ahead.

'Red – stop. Red – stop,' I called.

He repeated the order as his arm jerked. I pushed the throttles forward and again eased pressure on the stick to allow the aircraft to clear the trees, but this time not so smoothly, for at such slow speed she juddered slightly at the beginning of the climb. Once the airspeed had reached 130 knots in steady climb I tightened the turn, and then quickly straightened out, so low over the ridge that you could pick out individual trees, one of them pallid in blossom. We managed to see the landing and collapse of the marker parachute.

Wide to the right, slight overshoot.

After that it was simple. The next run-in adjusted for width, green light switched on just a little before the prop blade reached the tree with the flattened top, and the system worked. All five parachutes landed within the DZ. The containers could have gone out also but I wanted to get the feel of their departure, so kept them for a separate last run.

That was a satisfying performance. When the navigator flipped the switch you could not only feel a definite jerk-lift of the aircraft, but there was also a dull 'chunk' sound accompanying it. We noted only three parachutes falling, and assumed one had candled; the failure rate for supply-parachutes was one in twenty, and most of the contents could be salvaged anyway, so this was mainly a matter for record and not undue distress. So, fairly content with our night's work, we climbed away on course westwards across the Burmese plain for India.

We were flying left-wing low – lateral balance must have altered slightly with the departure of the containers – so I leaned down to adjust the little aileron trim-wheel until she was flying hands-off again. Once that was settled the aircraft moved through the calm night as smoothly as a boat on a flat, smooth lake. There was suddenly a strong aroma of coffee, and in the reflection of the perspex I saw Cooper, the Canadian co-pilot, moving up towards me with cup in hand; he was one of the extra crew brought along for experience and though, as with the others, it was his first flight over enemy territory, he was relaxed, sitting in the second's seat and chatting about life in Canada until I finished the thermos-tainted coffee.

The flight navigator, however, was far from relaxed. Even in perfect times Carter worried about navigating, and that night on his first operational flight he remained tense throughout. To distract him, for he liked making calculations, I expressed a keen interest in discovering what effect the external containers had had on our performance, and he went back happily to his compartment to compare the figures between the outward and return journeys. But the therapy was a failure, because when finally he came up to say the figures were the same I reacted with surprise, and he took this for distrust of his calculations. This put him back into a dither of anxiety.

He said he would check everything again, muttered something about airspeed and started back for his table.

I called him back, told him not to worry. We could look into it next day back at Jessore. But the damage had already been done. He had to check everything again, he said. There was no calming him so I let him go, shrugged off concern, and then as peace settled gently once more I began to hum my homecoming song.

I had created the tune four years earlier in England when the relief of escape through the flak-storms over the battleships at Brest was always so overwhelming, and the exhilaration of a blissfully safe night flight back over the Atlantic so beguiling – the Blenheim engines singing sweetly in accord, and soft blackness all about – that the urge to express the ecstasy of spirit could not be contained. It was the well-known Longfellow lines from 'The Day is Done' I used to sing to a tune of my own creation:

> And the night shall be filled with music
> And the cares that infest the day
> Shall fold their tents like the Arabs
> And as silently steal away.

In the Blenheim nights I would sing it aloud; my navigator, John Gilmore, a Canadian Mountie, would usually be snoozing over his table in the nose of the aircraft on return, but such was the racket in a Blenheim that he would never have heard me even if back in the seat beside me. But the Dakota had carpets and padded seats and sound-proofing and I could hear Cooper chatting with the radio-operator behind me. A raised voice would certainly be heard and amused glances exchanged. Not daring to disclose to them, or to anyone in the world perhaps, how wondrous it felt to be alive and untroubled in the glory of the star-filled night, I sang the song softly, swaying to the tune, and happy for the journey to go on and on to the end of time.

Poor Carter knew no such bliss that night. He finally came up to admit he had been unable to engineer any material difference in his original figures, and I told him again not to worry. Maybe, I said, the gauge was faulty, or an engine was running too rich, or the external para-racks were just as much a drag alone as with the containers. But he was not satisfied. Despite all I could say he went on worrying about it right back to base.

In truth, I did suspect he must have made some miscalculation; there must surely have been some drag from those bulky external containers. But I did him an unspoken injustice. It was when we were actually landing in the dank pre-dawn mist back at base that we discovered the true explanation for the unchanged figures.

The airfield at Jessore was particularly susceptible to ground mist in the winter. It was a devilish phenomenon, for the mist would settle fifteen to twenty feet above the ground, perfectly flat pearly sheets of it, so that you could stand on the balcony of the control tower and see a glittering display of stars, then go downstairs and find yourself in clammy greyness. When a patch of ground mist was directly over the runway, you had to be extremely watchful not to be deceived into accepting it as the concrete surface and stall-land on to it – nearly twenty feet above the ground. You could break the wheel strut doing that. The trick was to look over towards the control tower and gauge your height from that, instead of the false surface in front of the aircraft.

There was mist that night on our return from *Hainton*. A sheet of it was set above the runway, just about touchdown point, so I was looking left towards the tower as we slanted through it, easing back the control column as I felt towards the stall.

43

We hit with a thump. She had dropped in the stall instead of levelling out, even though we still had airspeed in hand. The reason for this became apparent on the instant. There was a loud bang, a shimmering flash lit up the mist, and the control column jerked in my hands as if from a nearby shell-burst. A metallic clatter was briefly audible through the popping of the exhaust stubs and I thought at first there had been an explosion in the port engine, that something had been blown off, cowlings or some chunks of the actual engine. But there was no damage visible as we ran clear of the mist between the orange lights of the flare path. It was only when we came to a stop and turned to taxi back down the strip that we saw the explanation of the clatter, and of that mysteriously unaltered petrol consumption.

A black container was lying on the moonlit runway amid a tangle of parachute shroud lines and canopy. There had been a hang-up. That explained the wing-dip that had necessitated the unusual adjustment of lateral trim. It was also the reason for the early stall on landing, the crunching consequence of which had been to jolt the hang-up free and send the 250-lb container crashing into the concrete runway. It gave off a shower of sparks, bounced heavily and hit the tailplane so that the control column had jerked in my hands, then hurtled forward to finish up wrapped in a confused tangle with the lines and canopy of its parachute.

I think it was the very next day that a notice came to the flight office from group headquarters to say that our para-racks were not suited to the type of containers used for the clandestine forces. The four Dakotas of 357 Squadron so equipped were to be fitted instead with 'universal carriers'. A date in the dim future was intimated but I arranged to have it done the following week by the simple expedient of banning the carriage of external containers until the new racks were fitted. We never had a hang-up in the squadron again.

3

Clandestine flying operations in the Far East had a slow build-up. The first sortie was in June 1942 and during the next eighteen months only ten more were flown with borrowed Hudsons. It was not until late 1944 when 357 Squadron was established with ten Liberators and ten Dakotas that the dramatic increase occurred; in the December moon period that year we flew more sorties for clandestines than had been flown in the whole twelve months prior to the arrival of the Dakotas.

The increased work came almost entirely from Force 136. They had, by their nature, taken longer than ISLD to develop operations. ISLD could drop a national with a radio into any Asian country and be in business at once, but you could not expect a 136 operative to form a guerrilla organization immediately he disentangled himself from his parachute on the DZ. He had to contact local people and discover their loyalties before he could even decide if a partisan force might be established in the area; only then could he start arranging for arms to be dropped and training to begin. You dropped arms and explosives to 136 guerrillas, to the spies of ISLD you dropped a radio and bribing silver to keep their sources sweetly flowing.

One could therefore expect, two years after the Japanese occupation started, ISLD to have secret agents once more reporting from all occupied countries – as they were. And expect that Force 136 would by now have prepared the ground for action – as they had. And that the US dual-role OSS would be at about an intermediate stage between the two distinct British groups – as they were. This, roughly, was the state of the game at the end of 1944:

BURMA Force 136 had established contact with the two

nationalist groups (AFO and BNA) and was striving against the resistance of the Burma Office for permission to arm them. They had good contacts with the hill tribes but as yet only one guerrilla force in the field. ISLD had several Burmese agents, perhaps as many as a dozen, located about the country quietly observing and reporting. The major active guerrilla group in the country was 101 OSS in the north, but our squadron did not service them; we were responsible only for 404 OSS which covered the south, but it had yet to start operations.

SIAM Force 136 had for months been working with the Finance Minister, Luang Pridi, in Bangkok, and having difficulty obtaining permission from London to arm his resistance groups. Meanwhile ISLD had established at least four agents in the country. The OSS had no one there yet, but had asked 136 to suggest a suitable drop site.

FRENCH INDO-CHINA Force 136 had the collaboration of the governor general, the plan for resistance had been settled, and we were already dropping arms and agents there. Again, ISLD also had several agents, four at least, carrying on their normal spying tasks. The OSS interests in FIC were run from China by the USAAF, had nothing to do with us, and were characterized by bitter conflict between the US and French.

CHINA This was almost entirely an American show. Our only contact was with BAAG (British Army Aid Group), a unit run by the Australian doctor Lindsay Ride, which helped escapees from Hong Kong. We lost two Dakotas with 12 aircrew in the occasional sorties we did for them from Kunming. Force 136 had political contacts there, and ISLD had numerous Chinese agents but we did not supply them.

MALAYA Force 136 had an agent with the communist MPAJA, and they had also left some men behind after the surrender, but they had no radio contact yet with anyone in the field. ISLD had also landed several parties by submarine and had been in radio contact with them for some time. That month we did the first drop in Malaya and it was an OSS team.

Until then the use of aircraft had been uneconomical, ISLD being particularly insistent that no other organization was to share an aircraft carrying any of its agents in case they were compromised. This was a ridiculous waste of space and under pressure of the increased work we kept arguing with ISLD about the restriction, and occasionally defying it. We were able to add oddments to Force 136 aircraft without any fuss. A few canisters of PWD (Psychological Warfare Department) leaflets could be safely added to even a fully loaded aircraft and as E Group operations were often just an individual effort – an agent dropping in to help fallen airmen or escaping prisoners of war – these too were easy to accommodate.

Even D Division, which could call on very large inter-service resources for its major operations, still had frequent little capers which could easily be included in a serious operation. That December of 1944 we fitted in one of their frivolities on an ISLD sortie – unknown to the sponsors who would certainly have objected.

I was told of it late one afternoon when sitting with the doctor on the white-pillared veranda of the mess, all serene as we relaxed in the soft light of the setting sun, glasses tinkling with ice – I had a lime juice because I was on operations that night. It was pleasantly cool on the shaded veranda. A gentle intermittent breeze kept wafting delicious tendrils of perfume from the heliotrope bush by the path, and from within it came the rich melodious whistle of a mynah calling every now and then for his evening crumbs – he used to whistle something very close to the first four notes of Brahms' Lullaby, for this generally brought a response. At the far end of the drive the dark cloud-shaped bulges of the mango trees were set against a transparent organdie sky, with just the single fleck of a late homing vulture sliding slowly down the cloudless horizon to its nocturnal roost beyond the village.

Then into this peaceful scene a jeep came noisily into sight below the trees, raising a filmy screen of pallid dust against the dark green background. It continued bounding over the rough gravel drive to finish with a harsh skriek of gravel in front of us. D Division had arrived.

The head of D Division was Peter Fleming, the travel writer, and I think I only saw him once at Jessore. Usually, as in this case, a junior officer would turn up with his mystery gift. This time it was an army lieutenant, with him our group captain who introduced us, but I missed the name, being so distracted by the curious leather object he was carrying. This proved to be a combined map case and overnight satchel, designed by a real brigadier. The talc covering the map was suggestively marked to indicate places of operational significance, and the pouch sewn on the back was covered with a buttoned flap. When I approached the jeep – the group captain had called me down to join them – he opened the pouch to extract a brigadier's rather dirty red-banded cap which he seemed to think called for admiration; there were also pyjamas, shaving kit, and one or two other personal items. Then he told me the story.

The markings on the map were meant to be movements of army units, battalions and brigades, and tucked into the flap beside it were two or three memoranda identifying the brigadier and giving helpful interpretations of the map markings. He showed me the items with some pride, drawing attention to the worn state of the map case, to the hair-oil stains around the inner rim of the hat band, to the old crease markings on the map. All went to prove that these were genuine used articles, he said; they had thought of everything, right down to the rumpled squeezes of the toothpaste tube.

'Good, isn't it?' he kept saying enthusiastically.

Our job was simply to deliver the map case complete to the Japanese. They were supposed to assume it must have been dropped accidentally by a clumsy or drunken brigadier during an observation flight, pass the map immediately to their intelligence and the Japanese would then take misguided action as a consequence – perhaps.

The DZ was on a road near a village south of Bhamo where a large number of Japanese were billeted, and the details were quickly settled. I promised to do the job on our sortie that night, and in parting he slipped me a bottle of Scotch – unfortunately the group captain saw this, and so I had to share it with him.

We made the drop that night from about twenty feet on a treeless stretch between paddy fields; we could see the map case

48

clearly as a black blot on the narrow pallid strip just outside the village. That was the end of it as far as we were concerned, for as with nearly all D Division jobs we never discovered if there was any profit in the exercise. I did ask Fleming about it some months later and he said he had marked the job down in his game book as only a remote possibility. And he added:

'But then it only cost about half a dozen bottles of Scotch.'

I pounced on this, of course, but it appeared that the captain had been honest. Half a dozen bottles of Scotch had been paid to a real live brigadier for his cap and map case; the maps and documents and overnight articles were all D Division props, but Fleming had seen the curious map case with its owner at a meeting. It had actually inspired the drop, so he had to have it. The brigadier, persuaded by the attention his story would command in select company, and sweetened by the six bottles of Scotch, had finally obliged.

The aircraft on which D Division had stolen a tiny space for its map case was on an ISLD operation, dropping a single agent near the Salween River, where his main duty was to report on the river traffic in the border area with Siam. A tally of passing boats and trains and trucks was a basic ingredient of all ISLD reports, it was a preoccupation that had its origins right from the birth of the organization.

It was Mansfield Cumming, a junior officer in the navy, who founded MI6; the first foreign agent was appointed when the Foreign Office asked Cumming for information about goods traffic in western Germany, and Cumming decided to pay a man to count the trains that went through his local station. The first agents were not full-time spies, nor had they any special training. They were men who had some job in the vicinity and were paid a small fee for counting the number and size of trains that passed their viewpoint. This information, extended later to include lorries and boats, became of close interest to the military during the First World War, by the end of which Cumming had become employed full time in a room of the Foreign Office gathering a wide range of information.

In the ensuing peace the main customer for Cumming's information, the War Office, lost interest in his wares and it seemed as if the unit was about to be axed in the postwar cutback of the armed services. But the British government had become involved in the Russian revolution and so Cumming appointed a few agents in that country, and these men presently were sending in such valuable information that Churchill was among those who argued that the section could be useful in peace as well as it had been in war. So it was reprieved. And under its title of ISLD in our India command MI6 still maintained, as did the organization in the rest of the world, that original affection for tallies of passing traffic by rail, road and river.

The delivery of the Dakotas and the extra Liberators, and the sharp increase in our commitments to the clandestines, were not the only dramatic changes in the squadron that December. We also acquired a new commanding officer, Bob Hodges. He was my age, in his late twenties, and had also done a tour of operations on bombers in England, but he had been shot down and had then spent six months in a jail in Marseille before escaping and making his way home again; he had subsequently completed a second tour of operations in command of a Special Duty squadron servicing the clandestines in Europe, so he knew how the job should be done.

Things changed quickly on his arrival. He was impatient with the mystique created locally about our task and with the whole fusty set-up at Jessore, and he quickly swept away the dramatic trappings of spydom. The leather field telephone was discarded, a telex was installed that dealt direct with RAF group headquarters, briefing took place openly in a normal operations room, instead of through secret session in private quarters, and he dragged the squadron out into the clear as a normal RAF unit organized within a normal RAF station and under a normal RAF group headquarters like any other squadron. I found his fresh approach exhilarating, his experience reassuring, and his company relaxing and enjoyable.

I could not share his total lack of interest in making direct contact with the clandestine organizations, however. Bob was a regular officer, a professional, and he stuck to air force channels; during the whole time of his command he never once visited 136 headquarters in Calcutta. Such cool detachment from the delicious FANYs (First Aid Nursing Yeomanry) was beyond me; I was constantly devising reasons to query minor details of operations which our RAF group had passed to us – trivial matters which I could best resolve by a personal visit to 136 headquarters. Bob allowed me complete freedom to run the Dakota flight and never questioned this quixotic concern about minor details which he would have himself left to the RAF group headquarters to resolve.

The increase in our squadron activity at the end of 1944 was not all productive. A great deal of clandestine work is wasted effort. Some projects, such as the assassination of the Burmese head of state, are stillborn because of practical problems in mounting them, some develop into operations which then atrophy because, as with many D Division efforts, the enemy ignores the invitation to participate, and some are merely contingency plans to deal with a possible enemy action which never eventuates. Such a contingency operation was *Hainton*, on which I had the parachute hang-up that December.

Hainton never did develop its original intent. The main purpose had been to raise a guerrilla force to obstruct Japanese reinforcements which might try to move through those mountains on the Siamese border, and an incidental object was to gather intelligence. Herring discovered on arrival that the majority of the population were Siamese and not at all aggressive, so they were suited only to the non-violent aspect of the operation. This worked out well enough. There was actually a Japanese garrison in the area but if they knew Herring was amongst them and training Siamese guerrillas – or, in the gratified view of the Siamese, feeding and clothing them – the enemy took no action; and as Herring's instructions were to lie low until ordered to strike he did remain quietly at ease in those pleasant hills as he waited for the bugle call that was never to come.

One can see the wisdom of this *laissez-faire* attitude from 136 headquarters. A guerrilla group could not dislodge the Japanese garrison, and to attack it irrelevantly – if the peaceable villagers could have been persuaded into such aggression –

51

would result in purposeless casualties not only to the assault party but also to the local people subsequently. For the Japanese were merciless killers in their savage reprisals against the hill tribesmen; they killed indiscriminately just on suspicion that a village might have given even a polite greeting to their enemy. It was a stupid policy that provoked the bitter enmity particularly of Kachins and Karens, and resulted in the deaths of thousands of Japanese when they were finally put on the defensive.

There were a number of other contacts with groups and places I had known in my army servitude, one of the earliest being *Dilwyn*. By December, when I visited *Dilwyn*, it had become a small-scale operation, having been stifled by Stilwell; just a few Kachins joined by the occasional British officer we dropped in for a brief period. I had first heard of them nine months earlier when wandering about those so-called 'hills' that rise to seven thousand feet away east of Bhamo.

That contact had been a felicitous one. It had happened on 5 April 1944, and the note in my diary says simply:

'Garden of Eden – a Yawyin village.' It was all I needed to set the memory of that day.

We had climbed a hill, not one of the cruellest, only about four thousand feet, but it had been a steady continuous climb that most of the time had us fully exposed to the mountain-clear rays of the early afternoon sun; by the time your sweaty body had reached the top that day you had cursed practically every exposed item of your equipment – the grenades in your belt that hit your right elbow every now and then, the revolver that thumped against your groin, the kukri sheath that grated against your thigh, the binoculars that kept beating against your chest, the doubled Gurkha hat that kept slithering forward on your sweaty forehead, and that sharp projection in the appalling burden on your back which kept chiselling into the same skinned patch just above the hip bone, however much you tried to wriggle it away to a fresh position. There was always a sharp projection in your pack, and always on the inner side against that raw spot, however carefully you filled it and arranged the waterproof cape and blanket to avoid it.

So we came finally to the top, a plateau with a village just a little ahead, and there suddenly was grass, a bank of emerald green with a tall ailanthus giving shreds of tattered shade into which we collapsed in exhausted silence. With recovery from the climb the senses began to take note. There was a freesia-like scent from the tiny coral-pink flowers of a cassia bush behind us, a hoopoe could be heard faintly hoopooing in the distance, and the bees were humming like a giant dynamo in the ailanthus branches above our heads. Reclining on the grass we looked directly along a track of creamy gravel that passed straight through the centre of the village – about half a dozen bamboo houses, all with the same honey-coloured thatched roofs and plaited walls, raised on stilts a few feet above the ground and with little platforms at the front. A separate house was directly across the track from us, and as we lay there quietly resting a man and a woman came out on to the platform and stood for a moment just looking at us in untroubled curiosity.

They were beautiful. The Kachins we had seen up to this time had all been dressed in scrubby lungyis and blouses so we were totally unprepared for the impact of these two. The woman, a delicate little thing, was wearing a loose turban of royal blue with crimson stripes, a blouse of peacock blue and over it a fawn jacket that rippled like silk, and her tubular full-length skirt was the same material as her turban. The man was almost as stunning; ankle-length navy lungyi, saffron-yellow smock loose to the waist and fawn shirt below, tight turban the same colour as his wife's. Suddenly everyone was smiling.

They were Yawyins, a peaceful people who have therefore suffered more than most tribes from the depredations of the Chinese marauding through those hills since time began. Of course the circumstances under which we met the Yawyins that afternoon must have lent much to their enchantment; the climb was over, ahead was a gentle stroll along the upland valley, there were no enemy forces anywhere in the nearby hills, so the appearance of this brilliantly clad gentle couple was perfectly timed for delight. The man, who was carrying a wooden digging tool, smiled as he talked to our Kachin guide, and gave us all the help we wanted: he told us about water, supplied us

53

with a new guide to take us onward, and was happy to sell us enough rice to provide everyone with a rare meal of it that night. They made you feel conscious of your personal squalor, ashamed too perhaps at the invidious comparison between his decent little wooden hoe and the murderous weapons that we flaunted all over our bodies.

The guide took us on a couple of miles along the ridge track to a taungya, a patch of hill jungle cleared for rice planting, and there we set up bivouac for the night. It was early next morning when we were loading the mules that the two Kachin *Dilwyn* men arrived on the scene in their jungle-green uniforms. They had been in a village twelve miles away on the Chinese border, sound asleep about midnight, when two young men from the Yawyin village arrived to tell them we were in the vicinity. The Yawyin chief, who knew they were somewhere in the area, had sent four separate groups out into the night to enquire in the Kachin villages of their whereabouts, simply because he thought we might like to meet them.

This was the first time we knew for certain that Force 136 had agents already established in the area of our Chindit operation. The discovery made even more forceful the criticism I had previously voiced about Wingate's plan for our glider landing in Burma. It was, I felt, an error to launch the glider advance party on a blind landing. I had a personal interest in this blunder because I was in one of those gliders and I knew it was mere chance that I had not been among the casualties suffered in landing.

'Why didn't he use the clandestines?' I kept asking the Wingate fans – which amounted to nearly the whole battalion, in fact.

Not to have called in Force 136 for discussion was bad enough, but when I discovered that a *Dilwyn* team was actually in the area at that time the failure to utilize them seemed almost criminal.

They found out about the expedition by accident a few weeks before it was launched. An officer of the Gurkhas one night on leave thought it safe to mention his work to a friend in Force 136. It turned out that the Wingate operation was not only news to his friend but news also to everyone else in Force 136, right through to the top. To Colin Mackenzie, the head of Force 136, it seemed absurd that such an operation was being mounted without use being made of his men already in the area. He was all the more incensed because General Slim, the army commander and Wingate's immediate boss, was starting to voice criticism of Force 136 for carrying out private guerrilla operations, which had no particular relevance to his campaign, instead of assisting the army with intelligence.

'It is difficult to assist people who take pains to avoid your help,' Mackenzie said, when he learned accidentally of Wingate's plan. He insisted that a further effort must be made to offer their services and instructed his assistant, Brigadier Guinness, to contact Ritchie Gardiner, who headed the Burma section, and go with him to show Wingate where the *Dilwyn* men were, and how they could help. Gardiner at first refused. He had already met Wingate and found him so abusive as to make it impossible to discuss cooperation. Only when Guinness said that he would go with him did Gardiner finally agree.

'But you will do all the talking,' he said. 'I'll just explain locations with my maps.'

The insoluble difficulty about offering their help, however, was that Wingate did not like the clandestines – not Force 136, anyway. Maybe he had crossed swords with SOE in the past, which is plausible because his own clandestine activities in the Middle East as well as Burma would surely have impinged upon the official secret agencies at some time or another. Nevertheless the meeting that night in the tent was a clashing failure. Wingate gave them a torrid hour of criticism. He refused to accept any 'interference' in his plan of entry, and only when Guinness bravely went on pressing to be used did he finally throw him a crumb. He would allow *Dilwyn* to arrange reception for the small scout unit commanded by Herring, which was to operate with our particular group far over on the Chinese border. Having said this Wingate indicated the doorway of the tent. They were glad to escape, but once they were well clear of the tent Gardiner made a sudden chilling discovery. He had left his maps behind.

'Then you go back alone,' Guinness said firmly.

Gardiner had no alternative; the marked maps had to be retrieved. The scene on his return was his most vivid memory of that whole episode. Wingate was standing in the middle of the tent, in his bare feet, arms folded, maps spread out all about him on the floor: 'Just standing there,' Gardiner said, 'with a sardonic grin on his face. As much as to say "Well, I showed those two out all right." I'll always remember that look on his face – that sardonic grin of satisfaction.'

Inevitably, against such an inimical background, there was a misunderstanding even about this concessionary plan. The *Dilwyn* party did send the agreed signal that all was safe and then went to the landing site, but Wingate expected confirmation of their arrival there and when this did not come he reached his desired conclusion. SOE had botched the job. Just as he had expected. He would not therefore risk sending his scout force anywhere near them; instead he ordered them to land at a site nearly a hundred miles away.

There had been another association between the clandestines and the Chindits, this involving D Division in its early days. The most successful of Wingate's commanders in the field was the brilliant Mike Calvert; he went in by glider on the opening night and if he knew that Force 136 had a party already in the area he may have felt, with some justification, that they had little new to offer him; he had probably taught them their trade, for he had commanded the 136 Jungle Training School eighteen months previously. After this was abandoned on the collapse of Burma, Calvert had fought a private delaying action northwards, accompanied most of the time by Peter Fleming who was conceiving D Division games even then. Calvert, an engineer as well as an explosives expert, was an ideal companion for the imaginative Fleming.

One of their stunts, inevitably, concerned the presentation of false documents to the enemy forces, a plan that Fleming and Wavell, who was Commander-in-Chief, had concocted between them. The documents were planned to be found in a crashed car ostensibly carrying Wavell's ADC. Calvert tried to crash it by driving at speed then slamming on the brakes as he spun the wheel sharply. Fortunately for him, for he might well have killed himself, the car simply skidded sideways. Eventually, after two perilous attempts, they managed by muscle power to topple it over the edge of the road.

The artistic details followed. They smashed the windscreen and the car body, and Calvert cut his arm then splashed blood about the wheel and the driving seat. On the floor below the wheel they left their prize – the bloodstained brief case containing amongst personal papers the misleading information devised for the Japanese expected along the road within the hour.

By then of course the two plotters were well away, so as usual never discovered if the Japanese had fallen for the trick. Nor did they discover what casualties they probably caused by a box of grenades that they left beside a bridge a little further north. Calvert had carefully removed all the ten-second fuses and then just as carefully replaced the spring-clips, so that anyone pulling out the pin would have the thing explode in his face as it left his hand. I never asked Fleming about it but feel sure he would have wiped off all fingerprints, resealed the box to its pristine delivery condition, and probably added a forged guarantee from the grenade manufacturers.

This was only one of the many contacts with the Chindit experience. Lazum Tang, a Kachin friend, also surfaced again that winter. I had spent a week with him on a reconnaissance in the Kachin hills during the time he was with Herring's group. He and most of his unit had now merged into 101 OSS, which had developed extensive operations in that area – Stilwell relied on them not only for intelligence but also to cover his left flank on the advance southwards to open the road into China. When I met Lazum Tang accidentally one afternoon at the airstrip north of Bhamo, he told me about a recent contact with a Japanese patrol; it was a typical track ambush, as practised by both Force 136 and the OSS throughout the campaign in Burma.

Lazum Tang and his men had been waiting several days for their trap to be sprung. There was a track that ran along the edge of a patch of the indaign, that tall, thin deciduous jungle which is a good source of teak and where the floor is comparatively clear of growth. He had set up a machine gun covering the track where it crossed a dry chaung. The gun was nearly a quarter of a mile away from the crossing, much too far for accuracy, but the purpose was not to kill. It was to entice the enemy to use the dry gully as a route to outflank the gun position. The real killing ground was in the chaung itself, about halfway towards the gun position.

The Japanese patrol reacted exactly as planned. They came crackling through the great dry leaves on the forest floor, raising pink dust from the laterite surface, and chattering noisily as they slanted down out of sight into the chaung crossing. When the leading two men reappeared up out of the dip on the far side the distant gun opened fire. A moment later, with the echoes of the machine gun still reverberating through the trees, the two leading Japanese had hurled themselves back into the gully, apparently unharmed, to join the others. The gun then stopped firing.

The twelve Japanese took the predictable course. They started along the winding chaung almost at once, whether to outflank the gun or simply to escape is impossible to say; but they came in file, their figures concealed within the deep gully, side-stepping one after another through a narrow gap between the bank and the tangled roots of a fallen tree. On the far side of this obstacle the chaung opened out again, and a flat patch of sand about fifty yards in length stretched between the steep banks right up to the next bend; there, concealed up on the bank, the ambush party were waiting, guns pointing towards that perfect killing ground of the sand patch.

When the last man had eased through the tree gap the ambush party opened fire. On and on and on. Even after the twelve men were lying in the torn sand the bullets kept ripping into the bodies so that they went on jerking as if in life. And when the Kachins finally stopped firing the red stains were already visible on the ruffled white sands of the chaung. None of the ambushed men had been able to fire a shot before they died.

Lazum Tang carried out the usual procedure; he took note of

the ranks and other information from the uniforms, and he searched the bodies for documents. The leader wore a captain's insignia. Among his documents was one that Lazum Tang showed me later and which I can still see clearly every time I think about this incident.

It was a small notebook in a cover made of bamboo strips. The pages were thin tissue and between them were pressed a variety of flowers, mostly the common flowers of the Burmese plain – marine blue and creamy primula, the azure cone of a cherita, golden begonia together with its sea green lopsided leaf, the dark violet flower of torenia. Spidery Japanese script accompanied each specimen, probably giving name and location of find. And in the back of the book was a colour-tinted photograph of a little bonzai tree, covered in coral pink blossom, and a woman leaning over it so that her right cheek was brushing against the soft blossom, almond eyes and smiling lips. She looked ravishing.

I had to remind myself of another Japanese army captain. He was the one who one day went into the village of Sinthe where we had stopped for half an hour; he ordered his men to seize the headman and all his family, together with four other complete families – twenty-one people in all, men and women and children – and he took them back down to Bhamo. And there, in the public square, he cut off their heads.

No flowers for them.

4

It was just a week or two before Bob Hodges took over
command that the two army majors decided to coerce me into
making a parachute jump. They made their move early one
evening when Moore, who would have blocked the project at
once, was away for the night.

There were only about a dozen of us in the mess at that
moment. I had come over early to meet two new pilots who had
just arrived; they were both Australians from Sydney, and we
were chatting nostalgically about the pines along Manly beach,
about Circular Quay at morning rush hour, and spring days
when the harbour hillsides are misty blue with jacarandas in
flower. Four other officers were still censoring letters at the end
table and a few more were lounging in the cane chairs just
outside the door on the veranda. The army majors had arrived
early also; Thornton, his dog at heel, was leaning on the bar in
close private conversation with Warren.

In this quiet time before the crowd assembled for dinner any
loud comment would arouse the attention of all present, so
conditions were ideal for the plan. However, I happened to
glance in their direction when they turned to come towards me
and was instantly on guard. Their attitude reeked of compli-
city. They approached, not with the usual jovial greeting but in
improbable solemnity – Thornton, solid and square, the brown
and white retriever waddling behind him, and Warren, slight in
build with clipped moustache and khaki neatly pressed. I spoke
before he could even begin his spiel.

'I don't believe you,' I told him.

'No, it's serious, Pat,' Thornton said, after a slight pause at
this setback. And he went on in loud stage voice, reaching for

the back of the theatre: 'We wondered when you want to do your jump?'

The two new pilots both looked at me in surprise. What sort of squadron was this? The censors stopped work, chairs creaked outside as bodies turned towards the doorway. I said nothing, just waited for the plan to unfold.

'It's the tradition,' Warren explained. 'New flight commanders always do a jump.'

The squadron had only had one other flight commander, that of the Liberators, since its inception earlier that year and I happened to know he had never used a parachute. I told them to go back to the bar, have another drink, and do some more work on the plan. Warren gave up at once when some of the watchers began to grin but Thornton did make a final attempt, asking me to consider the poor impression my craven refusal would have on the new pilots, but by then there was noisy derision all around so he too abandoned the play.

But there was little satisfaction in the victory, for I had actually been thinking about asking Thornton if he could wangle a drop for me. Moore would never have allowed it, of course, it would have to be done surreptitiously, but I could have devised some scheme to circumvent the ban. Had I played along with them that night it would have been easy, but reaction against being set up as an easy mark overwhelmed common sense and so I lost out on the deal. After that it was not until months later that I managed to get my drop.

They tried it out on Bob Hodges shortly after he arrived, by design when he was alone. That night I was out near the China border where we spent an hour searching for the DZ because the agents' idea of reception fires was to point a torch directly upwards only when we were running across the actual drop-site. It was just before dawn when I returned to my room and I was deep in sleep when he went off for his drop. So I never had a chance to interfere.

It would have served no purpose anyway. Even if Bob had learned that he was being hoodwinked he still would have jumped. He was an enthusiast for experiences, and he accepted the gift without concern for its spirit. A month later when 358

Squadron joined us on Special Duties he joined the majors in inveigling Peter Farr, their commander, into making a jump also.

Ours was the only theatre of the war in which four-engined aircraft did more parachute-dropping than bombing. It was a novelty to have parachutes as a major topic of conversation on a squadron. At debriefing in the operations room of a bomber squadron we used to talk about flak and searchlights and bomb bursts; in fighter squadrons you heard chat of bandits and angels ten and deflection shots. But at Jessore you talked about parachutes when you returned to the ops room for debriefing . . . how many seen to develop . . . where they landed . . . hang-ups . . . candles . . . faulty static lines.

You would come back in the early hours, the moon now set and the airfield swaddled in dank dawn mist, and in the big gloomy room, with the sharp smell of strong tea intermittently cutting through the stink of cigarettes, there might be fifty or more aircrew being debriefed – soft weary voices, drooping figures, dulled eyes. It was not only aircrew who would be slumped on the wooden forms under the smoke-dimmed lights; there would often be officers from the clandestine groups also, for both ISLD and the OSS sent conducting officers with their Joes so that they too would give their stories at debriefing. And parachutes always entered into the talk at those sessions.

Force 136 controlled all parachute matters. They had by far the largest permanent staff at Jessore, split into three sections: stores, despatch, and parachute training. Both ISLD and the OSS had smaller depots with resident officers who arranged the despatch of their operatives and materials, but they and all other groups relied entirely upon Thornton for the parachute practice of their men – and the occasional woman. He had nothing to do with stores parachutes – the failure rate of five per cent appalled him – but he was the final, and very experienced, authority on agents' parachutes and the techniques of their use.

He was a frequent visitor to our squadron mess but often on Sundays the luckiest of us would drive over to his place beyond the eastern perimeter of the airfield and join him there for one of his curry lunches. His cook made the best curry I had ever tasted, medium strength with meat ruthlessly stripped of fat, lots of coconut, lime, sliced banana and tiny cubes of orange, and among the dozen or so side dishes a homemade mango chutney with huge rich chunks of the outer fibre-free flesh; with it he served a delicious dahl so thick you could stand a knife in it.

It was like a holiday over there. You were beyond sight and sound of the airstrip, and you could walk over open paddy fields and pasture interspersed with little palmy groves and their scattering of clay-brown huts; there was a crumbled greystone shrine which in springtime was enveloped in fragrance from the roseate blossom of two small mohur trees, and where one afternoon I heard an old man playing on a pipe a poignant air that reminded me of the cries of a dugong heard one still night off shore in the Solomon Islands. There was always birdsong along the track, kingfishers glowed on the railings of a little bridge over the roadside stream, and at the end of the path was a placid lake where teal and widgeon came flighting down in the evening to huddle in the shoreline reeds.

Much of Thornton's business was conducted on the airfield, in a training hangar full of his specialist equipment. Here was a slide such as that in the Liberator, and a platform with an opening like the Dakota doorway, both of them good replicas of the real thing; they included static lines which the men were trained to hand to the despatcher for clipping to the strong point and then to check the anchorage themselves by a sharp tug on the line. The Joes would go shooting down the slide or jump from the platform on to wide thick mats when being taught how to land, and how to roll onwards so as to break the fall.

The landing speed of a parachutist is the equivalent of a jump from a wall about eighteen feet high, but can be reduced by judicious use of the shroud lines. For practising such a manoeuvre there was a cradle suspended from the high roof by a cone of ropes, like the shroud lines of a parachute; in this a man could be set twisting or swinging, and so learn how to manipulate the shroud lines to bring his descent under control, and to pull himself up for a softer landing. There was a dry spicy smell about the practice hangar, hessian ropes and sacking and leather, always a pleasant incongruity when your nose was all prepared for the usual hangar stink of petrol.

The agents always seemed to like the hangar training. In the shadowy interior you would often see chunky British majors as well as delicate girl-figured Annamese tumbling about on the mats in free enjoyment, long after their training session was ended. It was rare, however, to find someone who felt the same enthusiasm for the actual practice jumps. One or two cut their training schedule down to a single jump, and it seemed to me that those who fought against anything more than this obligatory minimum did have a point. They argued that the timing of their whole operation would be jeopardized if a man twisted his ankle or suffered some other minor injury. This did happen: Alan Cross, for example, so keen to go in on the OSS operation *Pilot*, then broke an arm on a practice jump and was never able to make the drop.

The slide exit for parachutists was standard modification in all Hudsons used on clandestine work in Europe but it was unusual for the Liberators; in the Middle East they used the camera hatch as an exit, the Joes just plopping out one after another like piglets from a farrowing sow. But in India the RAF liaison officer at Force 136 decided that if Asiatics went through the camera hatch, the direct impact of the slipstream on their small light bodies would turn them upside down and entangle them with their parachutes. No one challenged this decision, nor noticed that tiny Thais went out of Dakota doorways without ever getting into a flutter; it was accepted as specialist gospel and a slide was duly fitted into the Liberators. It projected well below the fuselage, so could not be in position all the time.

This was a serious disadvantage. The slide was clumsy to fit into position during flight, the job took about quarter of an hour, and it reduced the space available for packages – not containers, they were carried in the bomb-bay. But the slide did land men close together. Six could fit into the slide, packed close together, as if in a bobsleigh, the leader with his feet outside it against retaining pegs. When the green light flashed he pulled his legs together and then the six men shot down in a clump, as if forcibly ejected by a powerful spring, leaving their static lines clattering about against the slide. Curiously enough there was never a case of parachutes becoming entangled in a Liberator drop.

The dropping techniques of pilots varied. I did check out the performance of all the Dakota flight but did not impose any particular system on the crews; if they were able to land their Joes and packages consistently on the lighted area down in the jungle, then their method was as good as any. The Canadian Ben Hewson, deputy flight commander later on, always left the drop commands to his navigator. Ben would fly on the course directed by the navigator, who stood beside him with hand on the switch and gave him directions like a bomb-aimer; the navigator decided when to give the green and when to shut it off, Ben just concentrated on steadily flying the set course and height. Several pilots followed this procedure. Some controlled the drop themselves and made their first run on calculated wind, while others relied on the smoke from the signal fires as their guide.

My own method was always the same. I dropped a single package first as a sighter, using smoke for wind direction guide where available – agents who used only torches often had a way to go, and trees to climb, in the dark deep wood before they slept that night. Our resident ISLD representative, Charles O'Brien, was always grumbling about dropping only a single package on a run. He said we should try and get everything out on the least possible number of runs, that we put the site in jeopardy otherwise. This was claptrap. The man on the ground wants accuracy above all else; if he gets that from the aircraft then he can collect and get away all the quicker if threatened. I told the pilots to ignore Charles.

The ability of pilots to land parachutes accurately varied, of course, but the difference in performance was more usually associated with the type of aircraft than with the standard of flying. This led many agents to draw invidious distinctions between Liberator pilots and those of the Dakota flight. You would hear men who had spent months behind the lines asserting that we in the Dakotas were the superior pilots, and you could be sure they had their DZ tucked into a narrow valley, or had a high ridge within a mile or so of the site, so Liberators could never get down close to the ground. Others would say the Liberator pilots could drop a far more compact group than the Dakotas; these were the people who had a flat DZ without any nearby hazards, so allowing the big aircraft to lumber in low as the Dakotas and drop their slide-load of agents and a bomb-load of containers in just two runs. There were skilful and indifferent pilots in both flights, but it was not safe to determine them by simple assessment of parachute spread on the DZ. You had to be there in the cockpit on the night, and be a pilot yourself, to make any such judgement.

Once on their operational flight most of the Joes were anxious to get the drop over and behind them. I cannot recall anyone ever refusing to jump. The only difficulties I ever heard of were the few cases where a man had hesitated, particularly at the doorway of the Dakota, and had to be moved – Duncan Guthrie, whom I dropped later on *Character*, had a word for this process when he told me about a Karen in front of him who clung to the side of the doorway:

'I just winkled him out,' he said.

This hesitation in a string could not occur on a Liberator slide, and I only ever heard of one determined anchorite on their missions. This was a Chinese who had been keen all the way to the DZ but grew quieter towards the end and then finally refused to get into the slide; the conducting officer was a huge Frenchman, and he did not waste time trying to persuade the man. He simply clipped on the static line, picked him up and threw him down the slide and out into the night. The agent landed all right and reported on schedule next night that the drop had gone 'all very good as in plan'.

Such reluctance was extremely rare. The majority were only too anxious to finish the waiting. This was particularly so in bad weather when the plunge down into the menacing hills, and subsequent weaving about in the shadowed valleys as you hunted for the site, would have the aircraft thrashing about like a wounded beast. Then the Joes would be pleading with you to drop them whatever reservations you might have – the lack of briefed reception, wrong recognition signal from the ground or doubts about the location – all were trivia to them; their sole objective was to get out of the aeroplane and end the fearful wait as well as the fearful journey. However, I never heard of any aircrew who would have swopped jobs with them.

Respect was often mutual. Airmen, sitting there safe above the ground in their familiar machine, would look down at the dark writhing mass of jungle and shiver at its menace; the agent, bouncing about in a whirling lump of metal which must surely at any moment smash into the trees that were almost touching the wing tip, would pray for escape to the safety of the ground. Pilots would come back filled with respect for the Joes who had calmly jumped out to a tiny clearing down amid the dark menacing trees; Jimmy King would speak with awe of Nimmo's final word of thanks, and cheerful wave, before he went down on the blind drop that led to his death a few weeks later. And the attitude of some agents towards aircrew was expressed by John Bowen, whom we dropped one night to *Walrus* in the Karen Hills:

> I drank a cup of tea with the navigator and the wireless operator. I remember thinking what lucky devils they were to be up there in that nice cosy cabin while I, in a few moments, would be going out of the Dakota doorway into space and down into that sinister green countryside below. Then I thought that after all I should in an hour's time have my feet on the ground and that afterwards my feet would remain on the earth for ever and ever, but that these poor devils were doomed to continue on these dreadful journeys through the clouds over dark green countryside. And I pitied them more than I pitied myself.

As one who had spent four months fighting and fumbling about in those cruel hills along the border to China, my own feelings were ambiguous. Nearly always I was grateful to be in the air and would call for the green light with fearful admiration for the men in the fuselage behind me who were hurling themselves out into the night; and afterwards I would feel vaguely guilty about the comfortable leather seat and soft lights of our little cabin as we came throbbing back home to the safety of Jessore.

But on wild monsoon nights, when you had a five-hour flight out through the turbulent cloud masses before having to plunge down within the wild dark hills and start groping through storm-lit clouds in search of the signal fires, to be swirled about by the turbulence as you dropped them their supplies, and you had insufficient fuel to do anything but take the direct route through the maelstrom over the high Chin Hills on return, then you thought back to the good times you had known down on the ground and you wished you were down there in a friendly house again, drinking sapa, the peppery Kachin beer, beside the fire, listening to the thunder reverberating in the hills and the rain thrashing through the trees as you lounged on the bamboo floor in warm security with your Karen friends.

The statistics are interesting. We aircrew at Jessore suffered forty times greater loss of life than did the men whom we landed safely down there in the jungle; only five parachutists were subsequently killed in action in Burma and none at all in Siam and Malaya, but we lost over two hundred aircrew – the French soldiers who parachuted and landed to join their army in Indo-China are not included in these figures. Parachuted agents were in greatest peril not down in the jungle on their operation but while they were sharing our danger in the air; eight of them were killed with aircrew in planes which were shot down or crashed.

What is equally surprising is that there are only three recorded fatalities in the actual drops. One had a faulty parachute, and a Karen whom I dropped into one of the trees scattered about a *Character* site was probably a victim of fouled static line. The third fatality was a sergeant on the *Funnel* operation in Malaya; the despatcher reported on return that all the team had landed in the DZ but we heard from the field next day that the sergeant had actually fallen into an old tin-mining pit and drowned. The surface was carpeted with water lilies and he probably thought it was a patch of luscious grass, for he did not release himself just before impact as trained to do when entering water; the outcome was that he became entangled under the water with the shroud lines of the collapsed chute and so drowned under the canopy.

Another casualty, according to some people, was a Shan who was never heard of again after being dropped blind – at a map-chosen site with no one waiting on the ground. He was thought to have landed fatally in a tall tree, for his parachute was seen floating down perfectly all right into a valley along the Chinese border. But it seems to me more likely that once he was safely back in his own country he may have simply decided to go home to his village and have nothing more to do with our dangerous wars. Several of the Chinese dropped early into Siam took that very sensible course.

There were quite a few injuries in addition, of course, and not all were suffered by men falling outside the planned site. Old rice clearings could be hazardous drop zones, because jagged tree stumps were often hidden by the returning jungle, and isolated trees within a DZ were often dangerous because they left the pilot with no perfectly safe line for the drop. One man was lucky to escape serious injury when he plunged through the roof and floor of one of the huts the Kachins set up when guarding their hill rice crop.

Even a landing on a good clear DZ could be a hazard. A Karen landed on a container that had just been dropped by another aircraft and broke a leg. A man in ISLD fractured his skull in an uncontrolled swing on landing but he survived. Of those who landed on the actual signal fires one fell flat when the wood pile collapsed and he was badly burned about the face. A Siamese broke an ankle when he landed on a tiny cairn marking a grave, another dislocated a shoulder when he came down on a buffalo cart waiting to haul off the supplies, and a Karen suffered no harm himself when he missed an elephant by inches but the frightened creature let out a squeal and wheeled away so quickly it knocked a waiting collector unconscious.

Trees were a worry to nearly all agents. Landing in a tree was a real possibility, particularly on a blind drop, because almost all our sites were in jungle clearings, and mostly in mountainous country where a DZ might often be only a hundred yards in length. In later years, I understand, parachutists developed techniques and equipment to cope with tree landings, and, once safely in their tree, abseil down on 'tapes' of rope they carry. But at that time, the only landing resource was to bunch the body into a tight ball, with hands over face and knees tucked tight up to chin; that drill, and rubber pads tucked into clothing, might enable a man to survive the actual crash into the branches. Then, however, particularly on a blind drop, he faced the greatest peril. He had to get down to the ground.

Some of the big dipterocarps in Burma such as the kanyin have trunks up to more than a hundred feet before the first branch, so that even if a man had managed to survive the tree landing in good shape he faced a formidable problem. Later on, one or two of the Joes who went in to Malaya were taking ropes with them, buying them privately for fear of such an occurrence, but most of them, and certainly all of those we dropped in Burma, went out without such resource – ordinary fibre ropes of full safety length would have been far too bulky anyway. For them there was no safe way down from the big trees. An OSS friend, who was stationed in the northern hills specifically to track down airmen who had to bale out, said to me once:

'All you find sometimes up in the tree is just bones mixed up in the harness.'

Such was the fate of many USAAF aircrew who had had to bale out from aircraft foundering in the violent weather encountered over the dreaded 'hump' – the mountain range between India and China. One man from Force 136 told me that if he were trapped in such a predicament he would use his cyanide pill. The dubious rationale for the issue of this pill was that if you were caught, and interrogation became unbearable, you would manage to get it from where it had been secreted – and somehow not found by the Japanese in their body-search – then slip it into your mouth to end torture forever. This ultimate resort was not available to USAAF men on the hump run, nor did we in the RAF carry the suicide pills.

Some agents had parachute problems before ever clearing the aircraft. A Force 136 man was trapped in a terrible predicament one night over Siam when, as fourth man on a Liberator slide, his static line caught up in the webbing on his shoulder. He was flailing about below the aircraft in the 150 m.p.h. slipstream with no idea why he was still attached to the static line, and unable to free himself even if he did. It would have been easy for the despatcher to cut through the static line of course, but then the parachute would not be pulled open; the odds were heavily against a man being able to get at the sealed pack on his back and somehow tear it open before he hit the ground.

His life was saved by his proximity to the aircraft. His shoulders were just within reaching distance of the despatcher when he stretched himself down to the end of the slide; in this position he managed to cut through the man's shoulder webbing and free the static line, which then jerked out taut as usual to snap open the parachute. He fell some distance from the others but luckily landed on open ground and was able to meet up with his companions at the rendezvous early next morning.

Rogue parachutes could be a danger to the aircraft itself – and the lives of all those in it. A Liberator out over Laos one night had a faulty container-parachute which opened instantly, as soon as the bomb doors were opened, and became caught up on the tail skid. The container at the end of it, a metal cylinder six feet long and weighing 250 pounds, was swinging up and down like a deadly pendulum, smashing into the fuselage as it was bandied between the force of gravity and the fury of the slipstream. The aircraft reeled from the thunderous clouts, the sounds re-echoing in the fuselage like clangs of doom. In this instance there was no static line inside the aircraft, its connection was down in the bomb-bay; and the parachute shroud lines beating up and down below the fuselage were out of reach from the end of the slide, even when at the top of their upbeat.

The despatcher had an awful solution: the two wireless operators would hold his legs and let him down beyond the bottom of the slide, out into the tornadic force of the slipstream, when perhaps he could reach the shroud lines on each upward fling and bit by bit cut the container free. I would not have thought it possible to hold a human body against the wind pressure outside a multi-engined aircraft like the Liberator, but they managed it. Moreover the sergeant succeeded in the task of cutting through all the shroud lines, and so ridding the aircraft of its demon attachment. He deserved a medal for his daring exploit, but as far as I know he never got one.

The force of the slipstream is fully apparent if you try to put your hand out of an open car window at speed – the pressure hits like hosed water and the flesh on your fingers is drawn taut against bone – so when a man jumps he expects to be hit violently by the air. The subsequent force exerted by the opening parachute, however, is not so apparent; your harness absorbs the shock evenly about your thighs and chest and shoulders, and so you scarcely feel it. But the sudden deceleration from terminal velocity down to about 18 m.p.h. is in fact a severe jolt, fatally severe for one crew member of a Liberator in trouble one night.

The aircraft suffered multi-engine failure ten minutes or so after leaving Jessore and the crew were ordered to bale out. McClusky, one of the wireless operators, could not find his parachute – the Liberator has all sorts of nooks and crannies in its bulky fuselage – and so Collins, the Australian who was flying as second pilot, offered to share his parachute.

With the plane floundering down towards destruction there was no time for rational thought in those wild last seconds, and McClusky accepted, rather than continue his search. Collins's parachute was the usual aircrew type – it clipped on to the front of the harness – so McClusky climbed on to his back and clung tightly. They went out as a unit, and managed to stay together against the anticipated smashing impact of the slipstream. It must have seemed the worst was over then, but McClusky had not reckoned on that force of the developing parachute. When the savage jerk suddenly came it caught him unprepared, or impotent against its force, for it burst his desperate grip away from the shoulders of the Australian and he went hurtling down to his death. The aircraft crashed near a village and killed two more people.

The Liberators, with their bomb-bay containers and slides for packages, never had parachutes open within the aircraft as we did at times in the Dakotas. When dealing with ten or more packages on the slippery floor of a Dakota as it was bounding about in a valley DZ at night, trying to rush them through the open doorway in the brief space of the green light, or kicking out free-fall bags of rice as you tried to ignore the trees so close that you set the flying foxes flaring, it was inevitable that accidental stress would sometimes be put on a connected static line and a parachute burst open in the aircraft. The usual procedure then was to wrap the parachute roughly about the package and push the complete thing out of the door. I never heard of such a bundled parachute not developing normally, and sometimes wondered if all the static line paraphernalia was really necessary.

It was wise to wrap the opened parachute about the package however, not just let it be dragged out. One despatcher who did this nearly caused a fatal crash. The parachute opened instantly in the slipstream and was swept back to finish above the tailplane with the 100-lb package slung below, so the shroud lines were wrapped over the tailplane. And standing helpless at the doorway the horrified despatcher could see that the heavy package was being drawn up slowly and would finish smashing against the elevator, so plunging the aircraft out of control.

Again, luck was with the crew that night. The parachute began to swing violently from left to right, the plane was uncontrollable for a few moments, then suddenly the shroud lines shot off the edge of the tailplane and the parachuted load floated down normally to the ground. It had torn the de-icing strip completely from the Dakota tailplane but otherwise caused no damage, and the pilot was able to finish the drop normally. Thereafter the despatcher treated prematurely opened parachutes with the same caution as did his fellow aircrew; he wrapped them close about the load before thrusting the whole bundle out the doorway. No lesson is more surely remembered than the one you learn from a lucky escape.

5

I liked Charles O'Brien all right as a person but as an ISLD officer he could be infuriating. I had known him back in England as an elderly intelligence officer – he had flown in the First World War – and had had a sharp difference with him one night at debriefing. We had bombed a German escort vessel off the Dutch coast and he said I should have turned back to check the results of our low-level attack, despite the ship's venomous flak, and my short reply to this nonsense had earned a rebuke from the wing commander in operations control that night – not so much for the rejection of Charles's criticism as for the word used in doing so.

It was no surprise to find that someone with such a sense of priority about intelligence should have been subsequently posted to MI6, nor to discover that, like most of his fellows in that service, he considered his work far more important than the fighting war, and far too secret to be shared. A typical instance of this provocative conceit occurred on a practice drop near the end of the moon period that December.

There were eighteen men to be dropped that evening, and the first irritant ISLD managed in this simple exercise was to persuade Thornton's deputy that the drop should not be shared equally between two Dakotas; Charles, who was a squadron leader, thrust his rank at the lieutenant in asserting that his two men must go out alone, as they would on their operation, so they had an aircraft to themselves and the sixteen from Force 136 went in the other plane. I was reluctant to change arrangements already made by the parachute school, but made it clear I thought it was a stupid way to run a drop.

This had been on the phone, earlier that day. When we met

74

that evening at the flight hut the men of 136, Kachins and Gurkhas, were all talking noisily on the veranda but the two ISLD Burmese were waiting apart in a jeep with Charles and a major who had come out from Calcutta to watch the drop. After I discovered from the flight sergeant what aircraft had been prepared I suggested we all pile into the three-tonner and go together to the dispersal pens; the major was startled by this suggestion of friendly coexistence and looked quickly at Charles who was already vigorously fanning the palm of his hand at me in rejecting such an association.

'No, no. We'll make our own way.'

What possible harm could come of the contact? I was tempted to declare one of the aircraft unserviceable, and so force him into him sharing a single flight. Instead, I did a compass swing after the drop, and so kept Charles and his friend in the air for half an hour. This so often happened with ISLD: you suddenly found yourself in obstructive mood, wanting to frustrate or fiddle them in some way. In the end something did happen one day that made me so furious I filed an official complaint against the organization.

I went to dispersal one afternoon to do a flight test for a sortie that night on their operation *Bug*. The aircraft was parked in the furthest dispersal bay, one I particularly favoured, and I left the pick-up on the grass verge and walked the last fifty yards to the pen. The sun was low in the sky, glistening the grassy mound of the dispersal bay, and there was a delicious scent of citrus blossom from the squat little tree beside the mound. This was the reason that pen was favoured. I never saw any fruit; I think it may have been one of those four-season lime trees because there always seemed to be blossom on the tree, and its fragrance trailing about the pen, particularly in the evenings.

As I looked towards the globe of its glossy green foliage that afternoon a blue magpie burst clear with a noisy flap of wings and then went streaming away, with its long tail wavering about behind as if it were too loosely attached to the body. The flight sergeant, waiting by the little aluminium steps that clipped on to the Dakota doorway, watched it too, then turned to me and shook his head:

75

'Quite a load you've got tonight, sir. Are you sure the weight is okay?'

He looked far too solemn to be serious. I was standing by the ladder and could see no sign of any packages on the flat metal floor immediately inside the doorway, but he was watching for my reaction so I felt impelled to play along. Climbing up a step I leaned across the sill and looked up the fuselage. Through the starboard window the rays of the afternoon sun slanted bright as new-sawn planks across the dark interior, and it took a moment or two before I could see through the bright illusion and at last discern a single package huddled up in the corner near the cockpit door.

A single package? There must be more to come. Hadn't they said anything about loading the rest?

That was the lot, so they had told flight. I was certain there had been some mistake and after a quick test flight I drove over to the ISLD hut to see Charles, who was coming with us on the mission. I told him there had been some muddle with stores, they had loaded only one package.

'That's right, Pat. Just the one,' he said. No explanation, just an autocratic wave of dismissal.

That finished my bright afternoon. One 85-pound package! What made me all the more incensed was that he seemed to be affronted by my protest. His attitude was that as this was an ISLD operation it was therefore beyond question.

But it was scandalous. The DZ for *Bug* was down near Rangoon. As far as Charles knew the package contained some silver rupees and other 'odd bits and pieces'. This may have been a guess – he was rarely well informed on his sorties – and I discovered forty years later there was certainly a radio in it. Six of us, including him, were going to fly twelve hundred miles just to drop a single package, on the same night that seven Liberators and two other Dakotas were flying out to Burma and Laos and Siam, all with room for an extra package, and all with plenty of fuel to divert for the ISLD drop. The sortie was an outrageous waste of our time, of fuel, and of precious flying hours.

I thought seriously about refusing to carry out the operation, but concluded that that would achieve nothing; I would be put under arrest, a deputy would assume command, and the sortie would go ahead as ISLD planned. But some move had to be made and as Bob Hodges was not available – he was away sick and I was acting CO at the time – I dragged Charles down to station headquarters to see if the group captain could do anything about it.

Group Captain Wightman was an elderly bald-headed regular officer with whom I had an amicable relationship; he flew with me occasionally as observer on operational sorties, and I felt sure he would share my objection. He did, but not to the extent of rebellion. That was unthinkable for a regular officer plodding steadily towards a pension. The proper course, he said, was to go ahead and do the job. File an official complaint afterwards. That was the way to deal with it, Pat. Through the proper channels.

So I had to settle for that. But not happily. Charles lectured me about making such a tempestuous fuss, saying the Hudsons had often carried just one or two packages without a murmur. Who was I to question the decisions of the Secret Service? I did not know exactly what the package contained, nor how vital the contents might be.

But this argument was irrelevant. It was no more secure to send it alone in a Dakota than to include it as a trivial addition to a Liberator load – indeed, as many of their pilots had far more Special Duty experience than I had at the time, that should have been the preferred course. His reaction, and the whole operation, struck me as a prime example of the arrogant attitude of ISLD. He was saying: We are MI6, the Secret Intelligence Service, and you ordinary people cannot comprehend the importance of our work. Just shut up, and carry out exactly the instructions we have given you.

Down at my level of squadron leader, and with no contacts in air command, there was little I could do within the next four hours to arrange an additional drop somewhere. The best I could do was to get from PWD the biggest load of 'nickels' they could raise. Nickels were propaganda leaflets which we carried in packages that were opened by a static line, or in bomb-flare cases with a small charge that blew them open in mid-air – or, as happened once, and without damage fortunately, inside the aircraft.

The PWD people did pretty well. They managed to collect eight packs and to target the same number of villages, but I was still conscious when we came to dispersal for take-off that night that the Dakota was carrying less than five per cent of its capacity load. When I strode up the spacious echoing fuselage and saw the single hessian package standing at the end I felt like kicking the thing. Twelve hundred miles for that!

That was not the end of ISLD arrogance that night.

Under the soothing splendour of the silver moon, and in tranquil passage over the glinting immensity of the Bay of Bengal, I began to feel ashamed. The radio operator and Cooper, the Canadian co-pilot with us that night, were chatting behind me and I heard a surge of sound when the cockpit door opened, then when it was cut off again Charles's voice had joined the others. Normally he would have come up to take the co-pilot seat for a while, chat about our time together on the airfield in Norfolk and about his own experiences over the trenches in the pre-parachute days of the First World War, but after our little difference he was reluctant to come forward that night. So I turned and called to him. He came up quickly, settled into the seat, and then with tactless mastery he complained:

'I don't know about all these leaflets on one of our ops.'

But this time he failed to sting. By then the spell of the great full moon, the glittering stars on the deep blue backdrop of sky, and the sweet singing of the engines, had worked their charm, and my only reaction to this monstrous conceit was to burst out laughing. Then he was reminded of a night flight over the Somme and began to talk about Sopwith Pups and life in the RFC mess close behind the trenches, and a clash with Goering's squadron one day on a dawn patrol. I knew most of his stories already, so attention lapsed. Presently I scarcely heard what he was saying as the Dakota engines went on throbbing in that same dreamy rhythmical humming that a child makes when engrossed in the world of a toy. Above the cockpit the moon was

78

so seductively bright you wanted to keep turning your cheeks towards it so as to enjoy to the full its soft caress. Then too there was the matter of flying an aeroplane.

It was about ten o'clock when we finally turned towards the coast of Burma. For half an hour before that the black sharpness of the Arakan Yomas had been lined along the port-side horizon like a torn and jagged edge to the canopy of stars, but after our turn the mountains began to drift imperceptibly towards us over the flat moonlit sea. There followed a period of intense map-reading when we presently came to the low-lying land of the delta; the Irrawaddy starts to disintegrate about a hundred miles in from the coast and by the time it reaches the Bassein area, where our DZ lay, the great river is a snarl of a thousand separate strands, which are so swirled about by the ebb and flow of the monsoon rains that the cartographer has no permanent state to chart.

They defeated us after a few minutes, so I gave up the attempt. Ignoring the enticing pattern of silvered streams we searched instead for the unnaturally straight line of the railway track that somewhere sliced through those scattered dark shapes of solid land. I wanted to avoid the Japanese airfield at Bassein so we kept well north of the town and presently, without having roused any opposition, we did pick up the faint line of railway that was our pointer to the DZ. A few minutes later, now down to about a thousand feet, we found our DZ. To my surprise, however, I noticed a small fire glowing at the edge of the trees.

We banked steeply about it and I asked Charles if the fire meant anything to him.

It did not. Maybe he had instructions to avoid any sign of life for he asked me to circle widely. I did so, sliding down first to fifty feet or so for a close look, but the fire seemed to be unattended – by that time anyway. We ranged about for a time, low over the flat marshy land, then Charles suddenly pointed to a long thin band of trees away towards the railway track.

'That will do,' he said.

It was the actual words he used that made it so preposterous. Not 'That's the spot,' or 'How far are we from the DZ?', something that would indicate a prearranged setting, but his words suggested a decision based purely on impulse. Moreover he wanted me to drop the package in the actual trees. When I told him that that would be stupid, you could see a glint of water in there, he would not admit his mistake and insisted that that was where the *Bug* package had to go.

This could not possibly be right, whatever his orders; even D Division, whose sorties could be full of mystery, would be unlikely to drop a package into water where it would disappear (though we did do a deliberate lost-drop into water for them later on). But Charles insisted he wanted the parachute to finish within the trees.

It did not. I dropped it close beside the trees from five hundred feet, low enough to ensure it could not drift into the water, and he had no reason to be dissatisfied, for I did not bank steeply enough to allow him sight of the parachute on the ground. Then we went up a few thousand feet to a comfortable height and started north up the delta lands on the zigzag course over the villages to be served with our leaflets.

We arrived back at Jessore in the clammy hour before dawn, had a short session at debriefing, the crew went off to bed, and I sat down at the back of the room and began to write away my fury about the whole stupid sortie of *Bug*. It would have been wiser to wait a day, to consider argument and subdue passion, but I was in no mood for counsel of wisdom that night. Protest had to be made, at once and vehemently.

We worked on a payload of 9000 lbs and I highlighted this to stress the insignificance of the 85-lb package. I pointed out that our track passed close by three separate Force 136 teams, any of whom could have benefited from our wasted capacity. I listed the nine other aircraft on operations that night, any of which could have taken the *Bug* item. And I stressed the fuel figures, slightly exaggerated of course, to give legal precision to the charge of waste. I think I also gave our casualty figures to show a risk to lives but am not sure of this; there were other arguments too which I have forgotten, for the letter was long – far too long for its purpose.

When Bob Hodges returned to duty and read the report he

agreed a protest had been necessary but was amused rather than complimentary; he said he might have put it rather more briefly, and not quite so high-pitched in tone. Afterwards, when we received only a perfunctory reply from headquarters, I was sorry I had not waited for him to return to duty and write the complaint. Bob was a staff college graduate, he knew the language and the method for such matters, as I realized when reading through some of his letters later; he would have produced a far more damning indictment than mine, and one, I felt sure, that would have commanded attention. Mine disappeared without trace. ISLD remained serenely untouched.

But then came a splendid opportunity to profit from their smugness.

Just a few days later, I had a chance meeting with Gavin Stewart, the head of Force 136 in Calcutta. I had been to a meeting at air headquarters, and with time to wait had dropped in to the Grand Hotel for a long cool drink. It was midday, the palm court was crowded, an Indian duo of pianist and violinist were playing 'Smoke gets in your Eyes', and as I stood for a moment looking about for a vacant table there was a local pause in chatter and a turning of heads when an Indian woman of serene beauty, wearing a midnight blue sari with a border of gold, went gliding between the tables and past me towards the foyer. On recovery from this intoxicating sight I saw a hand waving, and recognized a face.

It was Bill Reynolds, a major in intelligence whom I had met in Delhi when reporting on possible airstrips sighted during our Wingate trek. He was sitting with a civilian whom he introduced with a name lost under the screech of cane chair as I sat down. But then, when I told Reynolds my present job, he pointed to Stewart and said:

'Well, he's your boss then, isn't he?'

Not the exact truth, but close to it. I had been to the 136 place a couple of times, had heard Stewart's name frequently, but had never seen him before. He was a big man, with a damaged left arm that he seemed unable to straighten – he swung his whole shoulder around when he picked up his glass. Both he and Reynolds were interested in the Wingate operation, they asked

81

about various aspects and personalities, and then when Stewart enquired about our reception of supply drops on the campaign I had a flash of inspiration.

So I told them, Stewart particularly, what had happened at the village of Sinthe.

It was earlier that year, about a fortnight after we had landed behind the lines, that I first saw Sinthe. It was early morning and I was with a Gurkha platoon led by Peter Wilmott; we had climbed two thousand feet and were taking a halt on the ridge, looking out on the plain where a sinuous ribbon of pearly mist still lingered over the Shweli river, just the crown of an occasional kanyin or other tall dipterocarp showing through like a barge on a ghostly stream. Once his pack was off Peter strode ahead to a clump of bamboo to check the track, then he turned and beckoned to me. When I came up to him he practically pushed me around the edge of the clump, saying:

'You must see this!'

It was a scene from another world. There were a dozen or so bamboo huts in a scattered line up the slope, all a golden brown in the crystal morning light, with grey-blue smoke wavering up through the thatched roofs to merge into the azure blue of the zenith. I could see a woman, with two huge bamboo culms dangling from her shoulders, moving in swaying gait towards the nearest house. Beyond her, two children chasing a chicken had to diverge around a man squatting on the ground with head lowered, intent on some handiwork, and a pig was waddling past him towards the shade of a small densely leaved tree. Immediately ahead of us, about ten yards away, there was a little nat shrine in the grass at the side of the track, set up on a short bamboo pole like a nesting box fashioned with loving care.

And as we stood there a young kachin boy in a grubby lungyi suddenly stood upright out of the grass, his head bowed over his cupped hands held close to his naked chest. He was turning to go back up to the village when he saw us, and for an instant he was stilled.

Two men . . . wearing jungle green battle dress . . . carrying guns.

Before we could make any gesture of reassurance, however, his brown face flashed a delighted smile. Then he brought up his hand to the forehead in an open-palm army salute, releasing a sulphur-yellow butterfly which wobbled away in unsteady flight down the slope. Clearly he had had happy contact with our sister Gurkha column on its passage through the area two days previously, for he then ran towards us and raised his hand to be shaken. We responded, and called up our Kachin-speaking Gurkha to complete the introductions.

Once we had learned that there were no Japanese in the area we accepted his eager invitation to enter the village. Just as we started up the track after him, a young girl came running down, equally fearless, to join our procession. She was his older sister, as we discovered presently, ten years old and with her black hair tied by a bamboo thong into a pony tail. The two of them kept glancing back at us with excited giggles as they led us up the track.

As we approached the first hut the headman advanced to meet us. He looked not much older than us, in his late twenties perhaps, and wearing a copper-coloured lungyi with a big Kachin dah sheathed in a wooden scabbard at his waist. When the children continued to giggle between themselves during our introduction, he spoke to them sharply; they seemed untroubled by the reprimand however, kept looking up at us and making surreptitious little salutes, then suddenly they burst out laughing again and broke away to go running hand in hand ahead of us, presumably to share the story with their friends.

The headman told us that the platoon from our sister column had passed through two days previously, and taken a supply drop that same night in a clearing four miles away along the ridge. We learned from him that although the Japanese used the foothill road frequently, none of them had ever come up to the village. Nonetheless, I thought it unwise to use the same DZ as the other column for our drop; he told us of a clearing a few miles to the east and I decided to check on that as a possibility.

He led us up the track between the bamboo houses, answering our questions freely through the interpreter. We passed a woman who was weaving a drab-looking cloth on a clattery wooden loom, and behind her on a little flattened area a girl in a brick-red lungyi was winnowing rice from a broad shallow basket, spraying a golden flutter of husks at the peak of each sweep. The crouching figure we had seen from the bamboo clump turned out to be an old man with a flimsy grey beard who was carving a pipe bowl with the extreme tip of a rusty dagger; he peered at us short-sightedly for a moment, before nodding amiably and returning to his work. Beyond him a small citrus tree was trembling as a sow with big wobbly belly rubbed its side in grunting contentment against the pallid trunk. The whole scene belonged to the long past, a village out of time, like one of those golden visions of rural serenity recorded by Constable.

The roof of the chief's house jutted out like the curving bow of a schooner, and you climbed up two steps to the platform before the doorway. We followed him into the smoky interior where festoons of soot dangled down in the gloom like Spanish moss in a Louisiana swamp, and there we squatted on the springy bamboo floor around one of the two hearths and enjoyed our first taste of sapa. The headman's tiny, very pregnant wife insisted on pouring it for us herself from a huge length of bamboo culm, one of several that were stacked beside a crossbow against the screen wall.

Our two young guides, their only children, watched and listened with rapt attention, entranced by our strange sounds and appearance, and when I asked about a monkey skin hanging on the wall they both raced to see who could bring it back first. About fifteen minutes later when we left, they both came with their father, running and jumping along the track beside us until we reached the edge of the jungle. We gave them each a Hershey bar and they bowed their thanks. We started down the steep track and when we looked back presently from the corner they were still there, not waving, just standing on the ridge against the clear blue sky.

The very next day a Japanese platoon came marching up past the little nat shrine and into the village. It seems that the passage of our sister column had been reported to them, and their reaction was devastating, as I have already related. They seized the courteous headman, his pregnant wife, and the two children who had followed us on our way, together with four other complete families – twenty-one people in all, men and women and children – and took them back down to Bhamo. There, immediately on arrival, they were publicly executed. Beheaded. Their crime had been to offer hospitality to strangers, as their custom obliged them, and as they had done in the past to all who passed their way. Including Japanese.

That was the story I told Stewart that day in the Grand Hotel. It was aimed at him, for he was in a position to grant a small favour to the survivors in Sinthe. And in case it did not occur to him I asked him outright.

What about dropping them a few bags of rice?

He was not unsympathetic, but he said that unless they had a group operating in that vicinity it would be difficult to deliver anything to the village. All operations were planned, listed, and approved at Mountbatten's HQ in Ceylon. He could not order one of our aircraft off on a private stunt. Force 136 had a ration of flights, and had to work within that limit – through our RAF command group.

That was when I had an even brighter flash of inspiration. ISLD could provide the flight.

I did not tell Stewart that. I did not know the man at all. He might well have refused to have anything to do with such a piece of skulduggery; he might even have had a close relationship with ISLD and told them about the suggested deceit. I just said that he could leave delivery to me, that we did occasional RAF ferry trips to Myitkyena and I could easily fit in an extra thousand pounds or so. He just nodded at that, then dismissed the subject with a wave of his good hand. And that was how we left it.

I never met Gavin Stewart again; he did come out to Jessore once or twice and I visited his headquarters occasionally – on matters of spurious importance, designed purely to make FANY contact – but I never did discover how he actually arranged the release of the supplies for Sinthe. But he did. The problem would not be one of justification, for the clandestines were not governed by precise supply scales and regulations like the regular forces, but there must have been some forms to fill and that might have been difficult for him. In large formations it is not so easy for commanders to get at the stores; it is the sergeant in the actual shed who can best arrange such fiddles.

Anyway Rex Jayne, who was in charge of 136 stores at Jessore, presently contacted me to ask what exactly I wanted for 'this Sinthe job of yours', and it was with him that I worked out the list. We settled on ten sacks of rice and five packages, which meant that Sinthe had five parachutes for a starter. Three of these were standard non-food items from the stores – knives, dahs, axes, cloth, cooking utensils, simple medical packs with instructions in Burmese, packets of seeds, and a variety of household oddments such as needles and cotton, string, candles, matches and so on. The fourth parachute contained packs of the three types of rations dropped to men in the field, the US K type, Indian army, and Australian army; the other package contained fifty pounds of precious salt.

I cannot remember exactly how long we had to wait for the drop, but it could only have been a matter of days before ISLD, as expected, provided the aircraft. They made it easy too. Their operation *Breast* called for only four men and five packages, little more than a thousand pounds, and there would not be a conducting officer on the flight – ISLD had another sortie off that night. So I marked myself down to take *Breast*, and this time, rather to the surprise of Charles O'Brien, the paucity of the load did not excite even a murmur of complaint from me.

Although Charles was not travelling with us that night he did come to dispersal to deliver his group and see them off. He did not get a look inside the fuselage however; I met him outside, told him we were having trouble with our radio, and asked him to go over to the control tower to check if they were receiving us. Once he drove off down the taxi-track we went aboard, started the engines, and were away before he returned.

Out of the fifty or so operational flights I carried out on the squadron five were unsuccessful, and of these failures *Breast* was the only one when I landed back at base completely happy with the night's work. *Breast* was marked down as unsuccessful because we failed to deliver the four Kachins and their packages to their site. A reception T of fires together with recognition letter was supposed to greet us, but we found only dense jungle in the area of the pinpoint, and not a glimmer of light from within the dark mass. For half an hour we went skimming about the nearby ridges and swooping through the valleys, but without any response from the tree-clad slopes. So we abandoned *Breast*. Back over the plain we map-read for about a hundred miles north up the Irrawaddy, and then turned into the hills to Sinthe.

There in the shadow-sharp moonlight, making four circuits in all, with the freefall rice going down safely clear of the huts on to the open slope near the nat shrine, we delivered the present from Force 136 – by unwitting courtesy of ISLD.

It had been a close-run thing. That was the very last night that ISLD ever sent out such small loads; from that time onward they began to fill their aircraft on every trip, sometimes detailing as many as three of their sites so as to ensure the sortie was fully utilized. Never again would it have been possible to fit in such an illicit drop. I had caught them just in time – by pure luck, as I thought back in 1945.

There is a postwar footnote to the story, however. It concerns the complaint filed that night after the one-package *Bug* sortie, which I thought had disappeared without trace. It had not. On the contrary, it had gone to our supreme masters. It had reached P Division itself.

I have no idea how they organized these things in Europe but the law lords of clandestines in South-East Asia were P Division. This group came into being in 1944 when Mountbatten decided that order had to be established throughout the length and breadth of his spydom. He called a meeting of the commanders of the major clandestines – the OSS, Force 136, ISLD and D Division – and stressed the necessity for a coordinating body to check and approve all planned operations. Even ISLD, reluctantly perhaps, had to agree to such control.

The risk was not only that one organization might in ignorance jeopardize the security and lives of another – this did happen several times – but that they might precipitate an action by the enemy which the army was actually striving to avoid. D Division schemes were particularly susceptible to such a disaster. As Fleming himself put it so neatly on one occasion:

'It is impossible, or at at any rate highly dangerous, to tell a lie until you know what the truth is going to be.'

Several times D Division had worked on deceptions which later became actual objectives of the army. One near blunder was when they set out to convince the Japanese that we were planning to land on the coast and launch a drive towards Prome; it was only at a very late stage that the army heard about this and sent a frantic signal to stop all action, for it was a factual objective they had in mind.

P Division was created to prevent such confusions, and to supervise the priority of resources – most particularly the use of our aircraft, as Gavin Stewart had pointed out to me that day in the Grand Hotel. It was a powerful organization which ultimately controlled the activities of all the clandestine forces, ensuring that a properly orchestrated work emerged from the individual virtuoso performances of the several instrument leaders.

The Division was commanded by Captain Garnons-Williams RN and his OSS American deputy, Commander Taylor. I do not know why two naval officers were appointed to command this powerful unit, for apart from a few submarine landings in the early days the navy had no part at all in servicing the clandestines, but perhaps it was thought that they could be impartial in their decisions for precisely this reason. Anyway, they were the lords of us all on clandestine work in South-East Asia; when they gave an order the whole chain of command in OSS, SOE and ISLD would start to clank in response. And down there in their Ceylon HQ one day Garnons-Williams himself chanced to see a complaint by a pilot called O'Brien about an ISLD operation called *Bug*.

His reaction was sharp. A signal was despatched at once to the heads of all clandestine forces instructing them that they must get their operations officers to collaborate so as to avoid waste. He cited the appalling example of a 357 Squadron Dakota having flown an enormous distance over enemy territory carrying 'only one wireless set', and he made it clear that he would not tolerate such ridiculous waste.

So that was the real reason, not just pressure of activity, why ISLD suddenly began to fill its allotted aircraft. I only discovered this signal in the archives forty years after the event – and discovered too how lucky we had been to take the Sinthe gifts on the underloaded *Breast* sortie. For it was just a few hours after I landed at dawn on 1 March 1945 that P Division issued their peremptory signal to the heads of all the clandestine forces. Even ISLD had to come to heel then.

6

The Americans arranged their clandestine affairs more efficiently than the British. Instead of a dozen different organizations, of which the major two even had different masters right back at government level – Force 136 (as SOE) came under the Ministry of Economic Warfare, and ISLD (as MI6 or SIS) came under the Foreign Office – the Americans had a single worldwide agency, the OSS. It had one master, the remarkable General Donovan, and he dealt directly with the supreme commander of the US forces, General Marshal. All very simple.

The activities which the British divided between the worldwide groups of SOE, MI6, MI9 and MI19 (E Group) and D Division, and the local minnows like Z Force, V Force, D Force and so on, were for the Americans the undivided responsibility of the OSS. The OSS carried out military and political espionage, guerrilla warfare, sabotage, psychological warfare, escapes, deception, and any other activity Donovan's fertile brain could conceive as being beneficial to the allied war effort. They operated as separate detachments, and usually in independent roles; but occasionally a group would work in direct association with the regular army. 101 OSS Detachment was such a group.

You did not hear much about 101 in wartime India. The OSS was almost as secretive as ISLD about its activities; even when a unit did become engaged in overt warfare they still preferred to keep quiet about it, so the published reports of the fighting in northern Burma did not mention them. Stilwell was an astute publicist who obtained wide coverage in press and films for his campaign to open up the land route to China, but the contemporary reports rarely mentioned the OSS guerrillas associated with his army; yet, like the *Character* operation of Force 136 down south later, the men of 101 OSS played a vital role on the flank of his army's advance. The final link of the China road, the stretch through to Lashio, would have taken months longer, and cost thousands more lives, but for the men of the OSS who raised the Kachin guerrilla force, and fought with them, in the northern hills.

Our squadron contact with 101 OSS was only peripheral. They were supplied by the US air force, but I personally had been with them in the hills the previous year and was able to keep in touch with old friends because Force 136 had an operation in the northern area which we serviced. This *Dilwyn* party had no right to survival; when Stilwell discovered that this group, under control of his hated 'pig-fuckers' (the British), was supplying information to his headquarters, he at once sent a signal to Mountbatten requesting it be withdrawn.

'We would not put one of our units in the southern area,' he declared, as though there were separate wars being fought in South-East Asia.

He was wrong anyway; we in 357 Squadron were responsible for dropping and supplying the agents of 404 OSS which operated most successfully in the southern area. We dropped OSS men in Siam. We dropped them in Malaya.

I have no idea how it came about, but somehow or other *Dilwyn* survived his rabid attack. Although he killed it off officially, and most of its Kachin fighters were happily transferred to 101 OSS, a small unit did somehow remain within the fold of Force 136 – though often working with the OSS; this unit was in constant radio contact with Calcutta and was serviced by us in the Dakotas.

I had contact with 101 OSS again that January of 1945, when we landed at Myitkyina late one morning to pick up a Burmese botanist who was to be prepared for a drop down south of Mandalay. I think this was a D Division project, but I never discovered what the particular scheme was because it was never put into action – once we got the plump little botanist back to India he took a job offered by the Maharajah of Kashmir and so was lost to the clandestines. Anyway when we arrived at

Myitkyena airstrip to pick him up that morning we had a message to say he was delayed over the other side of the river and would not arrive for another three hours. The crew went over to the canteen, but I wanted to have a look round the place and was strolling over to the edge of the field where there was a small dalbergia tree, the one with pale mauve flowers they use for shade on tea plantations, and was trying to reach a twig of the leaflets when a passing jeep squealed to a swivelling dust-raising stop.

'Pat!' someone shouted.

It was Marty Sigheim (I have made a guess at the spelling of his surname since I never saw it written). Marty had been with the American group known as Merril's Marauders; he and I had met when the Marauders had been part of the Wingate force. We had been together in an Anson aircraft which belly-landed on a cornfield near Indore, and we had spent three pleasant days in a hotel there before meandering back together to our training area. He was now on temporary attachment to 101 OSS, and took me over to a huge green tent where there were two other men of 101 sitting outside on a bamboo bench drinking cold beer. So were we a few moments later. We chatted about this and that, tracking down mutual friends, and then Marty suddenly cried:

'The banyan tree! By the river! Remember?'

I did. As soon as he mentioned it.

The evening after our plane crashed we had been sitting on the veranda of the hotel in Indore when an English civilian in wide baggy shorts joined us. He was a man in his fifties, an engineer who had spent most of his life in Burma and was in convivial mood. He continued drinking pink gins as he told us about his escape from Burma the previous year when it had been overrun by the Japanese.

He had been working with the Burma Corporation, which carried on some sort of mining – I took no note of the unimportant details; the essential part of the story was that in the refining process they realized silver as a by-product. There had been difficulty getting this away during the year before the Japanese invasion and when the manager decided that they would have to sabotage the plant and make their way north they had almost seven tons of silver on their hands. It was packed in bags, 158 of them, each weighing 100 lbs. His figures were precise, as was my note about the meeting, and Marty's memory.

They got away in four trucks, complete with their silver, crossed the bridge at Mandalay the day before it was blown, and managed to get through safely to Myitkyena where the trucks had to be abandoned. By this time the exodus from Burma was in full flood; the competition for places in the few aircraft leaving Myitkyena was such that the vast majority of refugees had no chance of a flight and were forced to start off on the murderous trek over the mountains towards India. There was no possibility of taking seven tons of silver. The manager was lucky enough to get four places in an aircraft for his men, so he had to cache the hoard.

The night before they flew out from Myitkyena they loaded the 158 bags into the biggest truck and he drove off with only one other man. They were back well before dawn at the airfield and there the manager gave each of the other three men a sealed envelope to be handed over to their headquarters in Calcutta, in case they did not all get through alive. However, they did get there safely, whereupon he collected their envelopes, and that was the end of the matter.

Not quite the end of the story from our pink-gin friend though. When I asked him how his letter had been sealed, if it had been possible to get at the contents at any time without it being noticed, he grinned and shook his head. Marty persisted on this line, asking if he had no clue whatsoever about the location of the cache.

'A sort of a clue,' he told us. 'When we took off that morning the pilot banked over the river. The manager was sitting beside me in the bucket seats and he pulled me close by the window to point out a tree. He said: "There towards the river – that's the banyan tree. See it? That's the one in the letter." He didn't say any more.'

I remembered the discussion clearly because I wrote it up in my notebook afterwards, not for avaricious reasons but because it was an interesting item among all the horror stories of those who tried to escape on the collapse of Burma. Marty had a slightly different version to mine; he was sure that the tree was actually beside the river, and that it was south of the town. What was more he had taken trouble to search along the banks of the Irrawaddy and had actually discovered a banyan tree which he thought could be the one that was marking the cache. We set off in his jeep a few minutes after the memory had been roused – Marty having given some other story to his friends.

It is about five miles from the airstrip into Myitkyena town. You drive along a dusty road bordered by clumps of eupatorium, some of which, despite it being midwinter, were in powder blue flower, and then a line of jacarandas with two large gaps where the Japanese had built machine-gun emplacements. We passed a little pagoda with its guarding Chinthe glittering painfully white in the bright clear winter sun, and in the paddy field beyond it a buffalo was walking slowly across the dusty earth, alone on some private mission, legs flopping out loosely in every step.

Near the town we turned on to the southern road down past the railway yards where a group of men were hammering away at an old steam engine that was pockmarked with shrapnel holes. Just as we passed there was a whistle from one of the trains, a high-pitched wheezing note exactly like that of the steam tram which used to run down our main street in Maitland back in Australia. For a moment I was back in bed on the veranda of our home, the fragrance of the climbing roses sweet in the still night air; then, in the frightening darkness, came that pitiful attempt at a whistle, friendly and comforting, from the approaching tram. I could sleep safely then, for the chuffing sounds and three further whistles would follow in the next five minutes or so as it halted at the nearby terminus and the engine changed ends – plenty of time for a child to escape under its protection into sleep.

We followed the ferry road towards the river. After about a mile Marty turned off the road and we went bouncing down a narrow track towards the forest reserve where the little green parrots return to roost every night in flocks of thousands from their feeding grounds in the hills. Just short of the trees we left the track and drove across the glazed spears of grass to stop by a huge clump of bamboo.

'There she is!' he said, and stopped the jeep.

We were within about twenty yards of the bank of the Irrawaddy which here divided around a huge sandbank in the middle of the stream. The river, now at winter low, was flowing slowly without a ripple; it looked a clear deep blue and as flat as glass in the still morning. There was a strong scent of hay, clean and dry, from the fallen bamboo that was lying on the rocks, and when we got out of the jeep a woodpecker was drumming a tattoo somewhere within a huge propped-up pandanus beyond the bamboo. In the sharp winter light you could pick out distinct houses in Waignmaw village over a mile away on the far bank, and to our left we could see clear up to the block of huts by the ferry.

Not quite clear. There was a tree cutting out part of the view. It was a huge banyan, on a small knoll and set back a little distance from the bank. The shape was unusual; its lower branches were spread wide but then they narrowed abruptly on both sides and the foliage went straight up to a flat crown, so that in outline the tree looked like a monstrous top hat. The trunk was bulging with a muscular display of embedded roots, and when we approached I could see that there was a small wooden platform set around the base; on it had been placed a little offering, a mound of tubular blossoms from the scarlet winter-flowering gesnera.

There was no grass on the ground about the platform. The earth was grey and so hard you jarred your spine testing it. But there were about half a dozen distinct patches of disturbance, mounded squares of darker earth, like large molehills scattered about the tree, at distances up to twenty yards. I started to move over towards one, curious, wondering what animal could have made such mounds, but then suddenly guessed the explanation. I looked at the shamefaced Marty and burst out laughing. He hunched his shoulders, held out the palms of his hands:

'I had to give it a try, after all.'

He said the issue spade 'happened' to have still been in the jeep the day he drove there – but that I could not believe; nothing removable stayed in a jeep, even the wheels were not safe in some areas. He said he had taken a few wild chances, ten and twenty paces in various compass directions but common-sense, and the rock-like resistance of the ground, had soon killed off his hopeless fancy.

I had not the slightest temptation to try my hand, even had there been a spade in the jeep. The silver could be hidden anywhere within fifty miles of Myitkyena, and not necessarily close by the river; even if this was the right banyan tree out of the dozens near the bank, it might merely have been part of a complex clue, like the one in Poe's *Gold Bug* – useless without the rest of the key. Marty admitted he had now given up the hunt; he comforted himself with a sour-grape assurance that some local would have sniffed out the treasure long ago and have it stashed away beyond reach, of The Burma Corporation as well as us. That was my bet, too.

We were both wrong. The company did recover the treasure, as I learned subsequently. A few months later, in the summer that year, the manager of The Burma Corporation discovered the treasure exactly where it had been buried two years earlier. Every single bag of it. I never did find out if Marty's banyan was the one in the clue to the cache.

*   *   *

There was another OSS contact just a few days later, this time down at Bhamo. I had to land an elderly Burmese who had some role within the Burma National Army, the group under Aung San which presently switched its support to the allied cause. I was actually handing him over on the strip to a lean scholarly looking army captain when I saw a familiar figure step out of an L5 which had taxied up to pause with engines running noisily beside us. It was Pete Joost.

Pete was a permanent member of 101, not on temporary attachment like Marty. I first met him earlier that year near a village across the border in Yunnan; we had several wounded in our column at that time, also a Japanese prisoner who was a tiresome responsibility, so I had been sent off into the hills to check out the possibility of enlarging a small poppy field strip so that twin-engined aircraft could use it. I met Pete on a track near the village one day when the air was filled with sounds of military action. We had ducked into hiding together behind a clump of rhododendron when a Japanese patrol suddenly came hurrying along the track. During the next two days we roamed about the area together, checked a line for the airstrip, and had a memorable meal with Oscar Milton, another OSS agent who had a hideout on a ridge overlooking the plain of Sima'pa. Oscar was one of the few Englishmen that Stilwell respected.

Pete was an unmistakeable figure – even though at first sight that day he was bent low under the wing of the L5, hand holding down the peak cap he always wore, and with his clothing being rippled by the blast of the propeller. He was tall and muscular, but not bulky. He had been captain of the boxing team at Yale university, could walk the hills as easily as a Kachin, and his uniform always looked as if it had just come from his tailor. When he doubled away from the little aircraft, which taxied off noisily about its business in a flurry of dust, he heard my shout, recognized me at once and came striding over to greet me with a great open grin of pleasure and a great crushing grip of his hand.

I discovered that he had been up to Myitkyena to discuss a border problem and was now going back to rejoin his guerrilla force, south of the area where we had first met. He would be driving along the road, past the very spot, where we in the column had ambushed the Japanese trucks. When I asked if he knew the place and if the culvert had been repaired, he said that if I was so interested we should go together and have a look at the site. He had a jeep, we both had time to spare – so we decided to go for a drive down memory lane.

The road climbs up quickly out of Bhamo. Less than fifteen miles away from the town the mountains, through which we had trudged in the spring of that year, rise up to seven thousand feet. The climb away from the plain was also a climb away from the typical indaign forest where there is a crackling uproar of dead leaves and puffs of dust at each footfall as you go crashing between the bare-trunked trees. In the hills the trees were greener, the shadows darker. The road weaved a passage up through little gulleys and chaungs, and lush tropical vegetation began to replace the stunted bizat bushes, willow-herb and wild rose that grew alongside the plains road.

Once into the hills the road narrowed, the trees crowded closer and greener, and we drove through colonnades of shadow with huge ferns screening the ground from view. The only trees I could recognize among the dense mass were various types of fig but even these were difficult to identify because of liana and creepers and epiphytes which engulfed the limbs; glancing back down at a turning it looked as if an aircraft had dropped a mass of garden debris on to the forest, leaving the trees all covered with alien growth. There was little colour, just the chiaroscuro of light and shade dappling a variety of greens.

We surprised clusters of jungle fowl feeding along the edge of the road; they would run scattery along in front of the jeep at our approach, only taking to flight when on the verge of being hit, then they would stream away in the air with their long tails rippling behind them. The only other bird I saw was a crimson-back woodpecker, which undulated alongside us for perhaps a hundred yards before swooping up finally over a huge fern and disappearing into the shadows.

I recognized the ambush spot at once and shouted at Pete to stop. We halted almost directly below the huge fig tree beside which I had stood with the platoon commander when the first Japanese truck came grinding up the hill into the ambush. We found two traces of our passing, some cartridge cases in the ferns beside the edge of the road, and an empty tin of the chopped egg and ham from a K ration pack. The road action was after my meeting with Pete in Yunnan, and in telling him about it I mentioned the macabre action of two Kachin guides who cut off the head of a truck driver to take back to their village; the Japanese had killed the headman and burnt his house, together with the nat shrine beside it, so the guides wanted to show the tutelary nat spirit that they had taken revenge.

Pete then disclosed how he himself was at that moment

deeply concerned with head-hunting Kachins, that this had been the reason for his visit to Myitkyena. He had command of a large operation by this time, perhaps as many as a thousand Kachins, so most of the units had to be left to their own initiative at times and it was during such an unsupervised period that trouble arose with the Chinese. Friction between the Chinese and Kachins was endemic along the border area, often caused by the mercenaries of local Chinese war lords, but the official Chinese army troops were sometimes just as troublesome and in the retreat a year earlier it was they who had laid waste the Kachin villages and left a people simmering with hatred.

In this instance it was one of the local war lords who had started it, not unusually. He had led a group of his men across the border and attacked five separate Kachin villages, grabbed all the rice they had stored, raped their women, and burnt most of the houses to the ground. For two years, without arms or a government to protect them, the Kachins had had to bear such assaults, but now they had American friends in the OSS who could, and did, supply them with arms and train them to fight. So this time the Kachins reacted in kind. A group of them, and no one would say whether they were OSS guerrillas or armed villagers, crossed into China and destroyed five villages there – I do not know whether they also retaliated for the rice and the rape. Chiang Kai-Shek decided that the men were OSS Kachins, that responsibility therefore rested with Stilwell, and he demanded a huge sum in reparations from the United States.

The American army had set up a court of enquiry, and its finding had been that there was no conclusive proof of OSS guerrillas carrying out the raid, and that anyway the provocation had been severe and rough justice done. It was decided that this finding should be diplomatically rendered to Chiang Kai-Shek, with a syrup of dollars to help it go down sweetly. On the same day as we had met at the airstrip Pete had actually been up to Myitkyena as part of the calming mission. The delicate negotiations were going well and a peaceful conclusion was close at hand – so long as no one discovered the secret he had carried so fearfully throughout that meeting. For he knew that

99

just three days earlier a group of 101 OSS Kachins had certainly killed eleven Chinese.

He did not blame them for the action. But the timing was disastrous, and he had to hide it from discovery.

It seems that the war lord had despatched a party of his own, either to take revenge or simply to carry out an irrelevant, normal raid, but his men happened to choose a village from which five of Pete's guerrillas came. Hearing rumours of the attack the five Kachins, together with a dozen friends in their troop, started off at once to check. On arrival that evening they discovered the Chinese had not only ransacked the place but had also killed two young men who had tried to resist them. The guerrillas set off at once in pursuit, tracked down the Chinese early next morning to a bivouac near the Taiping suspension bridge, then went on over it to set up ambush positions.

The carbines opened fire when the Chinese group were treading a careful way across the single log left in the middle of the damaged bridge. They had only one possibility of escape and that was to hurl themselves off the makeshift structure down into the turbulent water of the Taiping which went crashing through polished ebony boulders thirty feet below. Those who were not hit in the opening burst of fire did just that, the dead and wounded followed more slowly as they flopped on to the log and then rolled off one by one from the swaying bridge. Ten of the Kachins were waiting a hundred yards below the bridge where the river widens out into a placid pool, and there the survivors were shot as they waded towards the sandy bank and the dense cover just above it. None of them reached the bushes.

'They took back eleven heads to the village,' Pete told me.

Fortunately he was in the area that day, heard about his men going back to their village and so he hurried there himself. He arrived only an hour or so after the men had returned with their grisly booty and he persuaded them urgently not to put the heads on display as planned. He knew that if news of this latest act of revenge leaked out at that moment, during delicate negotiations with the Chinese, there would be diplomatic mayhem, and both the OSS and the Kachins would be held to blame for the first incident now just about to be buried. The Kachins appreciated his argument; they not only buried the heads but also went back to the river and disposed of the bodies. And no word about the incident passed out of the village.

I imagine the cover-up must have been successful. The US government made a small *ex gratia* payment to Chiang Kai-Shek for the first reprisal and that ended the matter. I don't know if the Chinese war lord ever learned what had actually happened to his missing men but without any bodies as evidence it seems unlikely. When I saw Pete some months later he said there had been no reaction, nor had there been any talk in the hills about a group of missing mercenaries. One assumes that the war lords were accustomed to losing a few men from time to time, and that if blame could not be laid against the Kachins – and compensation extracted, in preference to mere revenge – they would assume that the Chinese army had killed them off, and accept this quietly as part of a war lord's life.

* * *

We on 357 squadron did not service the 101 OSS unit – they were covered by the USAAF operating out of Myitkyena – but all other OSS operations south of this area were our responsibility. *Cairngorm*, the first parachute drop made into Malaya, was an OSS operation that went off in December 1944. The drop was made by one of our Liberators on a flight that lasted more than twenty hours, so the aircraft was little more than a fully loaded fuel tanker with the three passengers as trivial additions to the monstrous cargo of petrol.

They staged this flight from Cox's Bazaar down the coast but other Liberators had started from Jessore on extreme range trips, and such take-offs were a tense time for many of us apart from the crew. Our Dakota flight hut was only about thirty yards from the runway and directly opposite its northern extremity; beyond the end of the concrete strip there was a wide grassy clearing that stretched for another hundred yards or so, then a patch of tall flaxen-tufted reeds before you came to a cluster of palms at the edge of a little stream. I never saw a fully loaded Liberator take off which did not brush the grass at the end of the strip. The reeds always either shivered from the proximity of the propellers or were flailed by actual contact, and at least one aircraft clipped the palms while I watched.

There was a horrific fascination about the process, and it was impossible not to be distracted by it. I would be in the Dakota flight office with the sergeant, studying the wall on which we chalked a diagram of service schedules as we tried to settle aircraft for the night's sorties, then we would hear a throbbing roar from the far end of the strip. I would try to carry on the discussion, to shut out the fearful sound, but invariably we would abandon work and go outside to watch. And always I would be alarmed at how little distance the Liberator seemed to have travelled since we had heard the opening roar of full throttle – and how slowly it was still travelling as it approached our end of the runway.

Its passage up the strip was more like that of a boat than an aircraft, a fat overladen barge chugging stolidly up a canal. As it drew nearer to us the speed seemed scarcely to alter, then when it was directly opposite and still firmly stuck to the ground the throbbing desynchronized roar would change for an instant into a flat ratcheting clatter – I believe this was the Doppler effect, the Harvard trainer was particularly noted for it. It was impossible to make yourself heard above it, and the flight hut itself would seem to shake under the tumult of sound.

You would see the pilot, arms quivering on the controls, chin raised high as if trying to help lift the monstrous lump up into the alien air, then the hulk was past you and that deep desynchronized roar was once more ramming into your ears – a note of desperation in it as the aircraft came to the end of the runway and began to cleave through the grass. You would clench your fists, willing the thing clear of the ground, watching it thunder towards the reeds and then, miraculously every time despite its speed, its shape, its size and its weight, it would lumber into the air and miss disaster. And you would let your breath out at last, unclench your fists, and go back into the shadows of the office chilled with sweat.

I think this *Cairngorm* unit was commanded by Captain Geaney – although I cannot be sure since I have no note on him, but it was certainly an American army officer with three Malayan Chinese. Their purpose was to contact a Chinese guerrilla force thought to be operating in the area south of Penang and, if found, to help them in sabotage and espionage activities. Like most other opening drops it was blind, but the DZ site had been checked; Force 136 had agents already in Malaya – they had been landed by submarine – and during two abortive attempts to land another team our Liberators had at least brought back some photographs of possible sites.

Force 136, always cooperative, handed over the photographs, together with their reports from the field, to the OSS who were thus able to decide with confidence upon the DZ. As there was no certainty that a guerrilla force did in fact exist in the area, Geaney could not tell what his immediate move would be after landing, and for this reason there was no predetermined plan for an immediate follow-up drop of other agents or supplies; all would depend on what he found once he was on the ground. If no guerrilla force was to be found and he could discover no other useful work for the unit, his instructions were to stay in hiding until the end of the war – expected then to be a further two years away at best.

They had a good trip down to Malaya. I flew that stretch down to Penang several times and like any passage over those equatorial waters it could be a dreadful flight when you had to pass through a tropical front. But it was a delight on those days when you found only a scatter of cumulus casting filmy grey shadows on the immense blue expanse of the sea. On such a day you would stay down at fifty feet above the deck, and close below an infinite variety of marine life would go reeling past – the glitter and flash of a leaping swordfish that you only saw after the event, great bat-shaped shadows of manta rays flitting through the cobalt waters of the deep, schools of porpoise leaving a ship-like wake as they weaved exuberantly on their plunging way, flying fish slitting tiny white lines across the surface, and every now and then the clear blue surface mottled in a thousand pastel shades by huge colonies of jelly fish. Just after the sun disappeared below the horizon a wondrous purple shade would spread over the vast expanse and then deepen slowly into the profound blue of moonlit sea; but still, down below, you could glimpse starts of phosphorescent life as you went fleeting over the deep blue void.

Under the light of a brilliant full moon they found the *Cairngorm* site without any difficulty that night. The drop seemed to go well, all parachutes were seen to fall within the DZ, and a figure was seen moving across the ground afterwards. The aircraft was at the limit of endurance and could not delay, so they turned for home after that glimpse of action and reported on return that all had gone well.

All was not well on the ground, however. The area had been cleared as the photograph indicated, but what the photographic interpreter did not know was that the stumps had not been removed and that the site was littered with them. The radio operator was badly injured by one on impact, and the radio itself was smashed into useless scrap. Geaney and his men were on their own, no reception party, and without any means of contacting OSS headquarters back in India – they had not taken pigeons with them, for Malaya was far beyond the birds' range.

Back at base their subsequent silence was correctly ascribed to some such misfortune and so we made a series of attempts during the next two months to drop a new radio. None of the searching aircraft managed to find the party, however. One reason for this was that pilots had to be precisely on target on any Malayan operation; the aircraft were operating at the extreme limit of range, so only minutes could be spared on a search for a mislocated group. The *Cairngorm* party were never discovered from the air.

Contact was finally made with the unit when we dropped in for this purpose another American whose name I cannot recall. Force 136 prepared a reception for him on a big stretch of open ground, lighting fires that were visible ten miles away, and saw him down safely into their midst. They then passed him on to the AJUF, the Chinese communist guerrillas who were the mainstay of resistance to the Japanese in Malaya, and they conducted him across country to join up with the lost team. It appeared that Geaney, despite the disastrous start to his operation, had managed to devise a role for his unit; they had joined a small detached band of communist guerrillas and with them had been carrying out harassing attacks on the Japanese with considerable success.

It was not only in Malaya that OSS units worked in happy liaison with the communist forces. In Indo-China the link was even closer, and had it not been for the assistance given by the OSS to Ho Chi Minh's followers his guerrilla movement would almost certainly have been stillborn. There must be many who wish the OSS had not been so helpful in this instance – especially among the families of the 50,000 Americans who were killed as a consequence a generation later in Viet Nam.

7

Clandestine operations in South-East Asia suddenly burst into flower during January 1945. Our squadron came up to super-strength with eleven Liberators and eleven Dakotas, the new 358 Squadron of sixteen Liberators joined us on Special Duties at Jessore, and the various clandestine organizations in that month alone launched nearly fifty different operations. They had both of our squadrons working at full strength – we were out every night during the mid-February moon scattering agents like confetti over the whole of South-East Asia . . . agents to spy on shipping entering Singapore . . . to contact the communist underground in Malaya . . . to observe Japanese troop movements in western Burma . . . to arrange secret talks with the Siamese chief of staff . . . to set up a radio post on the Indo-China Pacific coast . . . to help prisoners who had escaped from Hong Kong.

The situation out there was complex enough even before the clandestines entered. There were five countries involved – China, French Indo-China, Burma, Siam and Malaya – each with native political groups and personalities pursuing diverse interests. There were our own allied governments and colonial administrations all following separate policies, and there were three generals in distinct commands each intent on his own particular campaign. It was within this turmoil that the clandestines were trying to develop their own private schemes in secret isolation. The potential for disagreement was far too great for chance to miss.

Take French Indo-China, for example. The chilly relationship between Roosevelt and de Gaulle was naturally reflected in local US policy, and one unfortunate outcome at our level was that airfields in China were effectively denied to us in helping the French resistance in Indo-China. We had to fly a thousand miles from India to do a drop when only a hundred miles from the DZ there were US airfields in China which, had we been able to use them, would have allowed us quintuple the aid we gave the French forces.

Curiously, Roosevelt himself was sympathetic about this logistics problem in our clandestine activities resulting from his anti-French policy, and he confided to the British ambassador in Washington that if we could come to some private arrangement with General Wedemeyer, the US commander, about refuelling in China he would be prepared to turn a blind eye to it. But this gesture of surreptitious support, like his suggestion that if we wanted to land French troops there we should go ahead and not ask questions, was of no practical benefit because it was off the record; it could not therefore be quoted to Wedemeyer who remained obstructive in his pursuit of the officially established, and therefore immutable, US policy: no help whatsoever must be given to the French.

It was an embargo that probably cost us thirty lives in that moon period in early 1945 when three Liberators from 358 Squadron were lost over Indo-China. All of us involved in clandestine flights believed that these aircraft were lost in bad weather, and that had the nearby China bases been available the flights might have been safely staged from there. My view hasn't changed. However, an American military historian has recently reported the discovery of documents indicating that the USAAF deliberately shot down these aircraft, and that the facts were ordered to be suppressed, so I think our Jessore interpretation of that incident needs to be presented.

The three lost were among eleven that tried that night to penetrate a massive frontal system covering most of Tonkin province. Only two succeeded in finding gaps over their particular DZ, the other surviving six brought back their loads; all reported ten-tenths cloud over most of the area, severe icing, and violent turbulence. The explanation for the losses seemed obvious at the time, and still does to me now; these were enthusiastic crews flying on their first mission, determined to

107

make a success of the operation despite the tropical cyclone that covered the area, and they were destroyed by the fury of the weather. Nothing unusual about that; we had three crash within fifteen minutes of one another in such conditions over an airfield in Sumatra one night, killing all crews. If you have to fly near the ground in tropical storms you expect such losses.

I can believe that US night fighters might have been up in the same storms that night; I am even prepared to believe that they made perfect radar contact with something, and believe also that they actually opened fire on such contact, but after that it becomes difficult. I have to believe that a fighter pilot's claim to have shot down an unseen aircraft in that black night is proven simply because he states it, that the attack in each case was so catastrophic that not one aircraft had time to send out a distress signal, and not one of the thirty experienced RAF aircrew who were killed was able to use his parachute.

The most massive strain on credulity, however, is that the two crashed wrecks which were actually found were in the Chin Hills, over four hundred miles from the nearest USAAF fighter base in China and well outside not only their range but also the area of their operational command. I would need therefore to see powerful evidence to the contrary before diverting from the one explanation which occurs at once to anyone who has ever flown across those mountains in bad weather – the same explanation as was accepted by all of us at the time, including the commanding officer, Peter Farr, who was himself out there over Indo-China that tempestuous night.

Whatever the cause of the losses however, night fighters extraordinary or simple tropical cyclone, they might well have been avoided had the local war been fought on a fully coopera-tive basis. Had there been coordination between the separate commands in India and China the fighters would have known there were Liberators operating there that night: had there been amicable collaboration between the Americans and French the aircraft would have done the job from US airfields in China, probably in safe daylight. But affairs in Indo-China were too complex for such simple solutions, so thirty of our aircrew met their deaths.

108

In Siam the main complication was that the Foreign Office in London kept insisting a state of war existed between Britain and Siam, even though the Siamese government was striving to collaborate with us. Although this cooperation was accepted gratefully by the pragmatic Mountbatten, the Foreign Office back in London, from Eden downwards, could not come to terms with the situation. They kept quibbling about the plans by Colin Mackenzie at 136 headquarters in Ceylon to liaise with the reformed government in building up resistance groups. The head of the Far-Eastern section in the Foreign Office minuted an aggrieved response in defence of delay: 'It is a very delicate matter supplying arms to a country with which we are at war.'

In China our clients, the E Group BAAG, had problems with Chiang Kai-Shek who had his own plans for the future of Hong Kong and was not therefore disposed to be helpful to an organization which, though run by an Australian doctor, was staffed largely by ex-officials of the colonial government. The BAAG people had managed to carry this handicap and continue their work of helping prisoners escape from Hong Kong, largely because they had developed such a good relationship with the Americans who were the paymasters in China.

This accord was based on the open manner in which they carried out the intelligence-gathering activities essential to their work, passing it all on to the Americans, and particularly to the help they gave to the 14th USAAF and MIS-X (the US escape organization). The recovery of pilots shot down was one of BAAG's special concerns. They rescued thirty-eight American pilots in all, so it was understandable that there should be allied harmony for a time at least in that corner of China. We actually landed at 14th USAAF bases, were refuelled there and did joint drops with them, all due probably to the goodwill generated by Doctor Ride and his BAAG operation.

It could not last, of course. ISLD presently began to expand its units in China and disruption quickly followed. As a Foreign Office department, they ordered BAAG to hand over all its intelligence-gathering activities and agents to their control, and then promptly destroyed the local harmony. The regular, and complete, intelligence reports handed on in the past to the

Americans were suddenly denied them, for ISLD reports always went for processing to their headquarters in Delhi where the staff then decided in their own good time what would be released. It was a practice that infuriated every other organization which required intelligence for its operations, and the Americans reacted sharply. Our joint operations with the 14th USAAF ceased, fuel was no longer obtainable at American bases in China, and BAAG languished without the occasional support of our aircraft.

Down in Malaya the problem for Force 136 had been to establish communication. They did have a group, with Spencer Chapman in command, which had been left behind in the peninsula when the Japanese invaded, but as they had no radio it was not known if they were still alive and so Force 136 sent in a party by submarine to search for them. They managed to meet up with Chapman on Christmas day in 1943 but because their own radio had been damaged beyond repair this was not known back in India. It was not until a year later, when our Liberators began at last to make drops into Malaya, that regular two-way contact was established, and by that time we had lost an aircraft with its nine crew in attempts to get them their radio.

These lives might also have been saved by better organization of the clandestines. For a radio link already existed at that time. There were two ISLD parties complete with radios in the northern area; they had been landed separately by submarine in early 1943, and one of them was almost within hailing distance of the spot where the Force 136 party had made contact with Spencer Chapman. It is inconceivable that this ISLD agent, and even the other agent about a hundred miles away, did not know that Chapman and a new British group were wandering about in their area; after all, these men were trained to gather intelligence, and must have known about the arrival of such conspicuous strangers in their area. But Force 136 heard nothing from ISLD. So nine men of our squadron died in the attempt to establish a contact that was already available.

Once the Malayan problem of communication was finally resolved in early 1945 the Liberators began to make regular drops every moon period. One of the very first, however, ended in disaster for the ground party. The drop was made by Jack Churchill, who had been with the squadron since the Hudson days and at the end of January that year had made the longest flight by a Liberator up to that time, being twenty-two hours in the air. The drop was to *Carpenter*, a 136 group which had been landed by submarine some months earlier. Their primary objective was to provide information about the shipping in and out of Singapore, but they also worked with the AJUF in developing a local guerrilla force largely for protective purposes – the major guerrilla groups were located much further north up the peninsula.

Churchill found the *Carpenter* DZ without difficulty. It was a wide clearing with fires already blazing when he arrived, and the moonlight so clear he could see the men running towards the parachutes as they splayed into chalky pools on landing; on nights like that you could see them, as you came in on the next run, dragging away the previous falls, parachutes trailing behind the slanted figures like pear-shaped rafts, drifting slowly across the moonlit paddy towards the breakdown point on the edge of a clearing. On this night all parachutes opened, all fell within the DZ; a perfect drop. Churchill started back on the long flight home to report a successful drop.

But there is a postscript. Down on the ground Major Martin and most of his men worked with the help of the Chinese guerrillas to collect the containers and parachutes, hauling them to the hut on the edge of the DZ for breakdown. But all the time they were working the Japanese were closing in on the site. They happened to have a unit in the area, investigating a tip-off about a guerrilla group, and learned about the drop while it was actually in progress. By dawn they had arrived at the site, over a hundred of them.

It takes quite a time to deal with a full supply drop. It is not just a matter of picking up fallen guns and rations and marching off into the jungle. It takes two men to pull a container – in Burma I once saw an elephant used for the job. You have to drag the fallen loads to an assembly point, detach the parachutes, open the container sections or packages, then break the contents into separate loads which can be transported to base camp.

To almost all units the parachutes were also an important component of the drop, and these had to be refolded so that they would also be carried with the rest of the supplies. Martin and his party were still working on the distribution of loads when the Japanese arrived on the site.

In their opening burst of fire they killed four of the guerrillas, including Martin. The remainder managed to scramble out of the back of the hut and disperse into the jungle where they separately had a few hard days before eventually being able to regroup under the second-in-command. Fortunately they still had their radio back at base camp, and so were able to arrange a further drop and continue their operations.

Before the problem of communication was finally resolved Force 136 had actually established a radio contact with one of their agents in Malaya. But it was one which they had at once handed over to D Division for its own specialized use. The contact was with a Malay army officer whom Force 136 had sent in by submarine in mid-1943 on operation *Oatmeal* – mainly to discover what cooperation might be expected from the Malay people when we finally invaded. His name was Ibrahim Bin Ismail.

Ibrahim was betrayed by an informer shortly after landing and was captured complete with radio and all his signal codes. It was a disastrous loss which put all 136 Malaya operations into jeopardy. The local Kempei, unlike the Burma unit which had rejected the Indian landed by D Division for their benefit, reacted like a conventional spy organization when they uncovered Ibrahim; they set out to infiltrate the opposition through their precious capture.

Ibrahim, however, was as quick-witted as he was courageous and he in turn proceeded to utilize his captors, confident that they would realize back in India that he was in the bag. He said he wanted to cooperate with the Japanese; he would be happy to help them deceive the British. He was fully aware, in playing this role, that a major problem would be in dealing with his security check. This was always made, by all secret forces in all commands, very early after an agent had been safely landed, and in Ibrahim's case it had been arranged that once they had his first signal to say he was safe in position they would in the next transmission period open with the question:

'Have you met Mariam?'

The correct reply was the irrelevant: 'Two Scotsmen left here two days ago.'

The Kempei men had this information. For some reason beyond explanation Ibrahim's briefing officer back in India had put this correct reply down on paper, rather than insisting it be kept by Ibrahim in memory only; so it was all there for the Japanese to see, together with the note that said any other reply whatsoever to the question would indicate he had been captured. Hence Ibrahim's problem.

With the Japanese secret police watching over him closely on that first transmission he coded the signal to say he had arrived safely, made the contact with India, and tapped out his message. To the delight of the Kempei watchers a reply came back congratulating him on the success and sending best wishes for his mission. Then, the following morning, just as he expected, the first message that base transmitted was the security check: had he met Mariam?

The Japanese seemed to have forgotten, or to have overlooked, the security note. What is this Mariam business? they asked. It would have been dangerous to lie, the document giving the truth was in front of them, so Ibrahim pointed out the paragraph. And then he began his act. Would Force 136 have *written down* the correct reply? Of course not! That was there solely to deceive the enemy in case he was captured. The correct reply had been given to him verbally and was never to be committed to paper. It was the only response which would assure Force 136 he was a free agent. The Kempei believed him, and what he sent was: 'Yes, I have met Mariam.'

So Force 136 knew he was in the bag. They handed him over to D Division, who were delighted at the gift – a perfect Malayan link to compensate for that offering the Japanese had spurned in Burma.

It requires finesse to utilize a double agent. The enemy are watching every signal despatched and at the same time probing gently themselves for information which the agent might

113

legitimately require for his work – in this case the Japanese were naturally anxious to discover any lead to our plans for recapture of the peninsula, and also any information about the landing of other agents. They may have known, and hoped to emulate, what happened in Holland when the Germans kept collecting SOE parachutists on the DZ as they landed, because the Dutch section of SOE refused, stupidly or treacherously, to accept the message faults which indicated every time that the agents had been caught. D Division made no such mistake in India.

Their purpose was to build up Japanese confidence in the link and then to feed them misleading information – particularly valuable when the time came to launch the seaborne invasion of Malaya. They sent plausible instructions to Ibrahim, ordered him to move to a different area, and asked him to try to discover what had happened to non-existent agents well away from the area where 136 had men. We even flew a special supply drop for *Oatmeal*, which of course the Japanese received exactly in the manner ordered by D Division, with a procedure slightly different from normal just in case they did not have that information already, and with the pilot giving a straight-faced performance of a normal drop. In fact, I suspect the pilot was never told it was a deceit.

The resourceful Ibrahim, aided by the imaginative Fleming back in India, managed to string the Kempei along for months without them ever growing suspicious about the lack of substance in the information they were gleaning. So the stage was prepared for the deception signals about our invasion site and plans. But instead the war ended, and so also the deceit. The enemy all went back to Japan, Ibrahim stayed at home in Malaya and in due course became a general and Chief of the Armed Forces in Malaya.

In Burma there had been problems right from the start of clandestine activities. Hugh Seagrim, left behind after the capture of Burma, had given up his life by surrendering to the Japanese in order to stop their murderous reprisals against the Karens who had been sheltering him. Two men dropped to contact him had also been killed, and it is almost certain that all three would have been safe had ISLD not blundered into the area and aroused the Japanese. Things had been quiet in Karenni for some months; the Japanese seemed to have assumed that Seagrim had departed northwards into China, they had taken their punitive parties out of the hills and apparently had not heard about the other two men that had been dropped.

It was in this quiet interim that, despite strong protests from Force 136, ISLD sent in three agents to an area right on the fringe of Karenni, where large numbers of Burmese were living. Not only was that a daft choice of location, for the Burmese were bound to run to the Japanese with the news, but one of the men landed in a huge bamboo clump and, as the others could not release him, they actually went to the village for help. The news was quickly broadcast. It did no harm to the three ISLD men, all Karens. They simply went off on their task and escaped notice, but Kempei men came in force into the hills and by their normal brutal standards soon made people divulge news of the Europeans in their midst. The two who had been dropped were both caught and killed a few weeks later.

Seagrim was still at large, whereupon the Kempei-tai issued a threat to take Karen lives unless they delivered him. An ingenious plan worthy of D Division was put forward by a Karen friend, who asked Seagrim to contact India and request they drop by parachute the body of a European who had recently died. He should be tall and thin, which was about all that the Japanese knew about Seagrim, and the villagers could then produce this body for the Kempei and so end their hunt. Seagrim never sent the message however; perhaps his strong Christian views precluded him from participating in such an act; presently he walked in to the nearest post and surrendered himself to save the people who had befriended him. The Japanese, who had promised he would not be harmed, killed him.

The interclandestine confusion in Burma had been smoothed out, temporarily, at the beginning of 1945 but then there arose a very serious difference between the commander of the XIV Army, General Slim, and the clandestines – particularly Force 136. It concerned the supply of tactical intelligence to the army.

115

Force 136 had provided intelligence to the army of course, had even been complimented for the work done by the *Camel* team in the Arakan, but Slim argued that the amount of useful information reaching his forces was simply not worth the manpower and resources being utilized by Force 136. He demanded a better system of coordination beween the clandestines, with emphasis being directed towards helping the regular army forces. If they could not provide the goods they should be disbanded.

These criticisms from the army commander could not be ignored. So General Browning was given the job of settling the various clandestines into more effective unity. After several meetings he submitted a report which, in effect, made no difference either to the number of organizations or their independence. I happened to have personal contact with him some years later and asked him one night if he had, like me, noted a duplication in the work of the clandestines out there and why Mountbatten had not reorganized the set-up.

'We tried – I had a go at it myself,' he said. 'But they were all too well dug in to move.'

Chance also helped Force 136 survive the Slim assault. A happy coincidence provided that they were just then in January planning two major operations which could conveniently – though not permanently if they could help it – concentrate on providing the sort of tactical intelligence Slim was demanding. These two operations, *Character* and *Nation*, were designed by the Burma section in Calcutta to raise guerrilla forces covering the hill jungles that flanked both sides of the XIV Army in its projected advance down the Sittang valley.

It was easy therefore for Force 136 to show a rapid and impressive response to the army call for a major effort in intelligence to assist their advance down the valley, and within a matter of days they had produced for Slim's approval the plans for *Character* and *Nation*, designed ostensibly to gather intelligence. Their presentation was effective. With the promise of such a massive intelligence coverage the army raised no further problems about resources (such as our aircraft being devoted to the clandestines) and so the planning for these major operations now went ahead rapidly. Men started to crowd into Jessore for parachute training, scout parties were dropped into Karenni, drop sites were photographed.

To end this catalogue of complaints in early 1945 there was finally the contretemps between the clandestines and ourselves at Jessore about our performance. Both ISLD and 136 filed a murmur of complaint to our air headquarters that 'during the January-February moon period almost all the blind drops were made at a considerable distance from the DZ selected'. This was a slight exaggeration; Bob Hodges and I went through the list with the staff officer at headquarters who received the complaint, and we whittled it down to six out of fifteen – one of which I had made, so I was able to bring first-hand experience to our discussion.

It had been on operation *Ramrose*, a group going in to check local sympathies down near Ramree Island where the army planned a landing. The site was in a U bend of one of the many Irrawaddy tributaries that wriggle down to the great river from those jungle-clad slopes south of Mount Kennedy, and when we studied the photograph that afternoon in the operations room at Jessore the navigator and I both felt confident we could find the place.

Whether we would be able to make the drop at first attempt, however, was another matter, for mist was the problem in that area. Often in the winter months it would start to gather in the valleys early in the night, then build up steadily until by dawn only the ridges were left standing in the clear, like long rocky reefs rising out of a pearly sea. Once it settled on a site you had to abandon the mission, for it did not clear until the sun had worked on it. I was anxious therefore to hit the DZ on our first approach that night, and for that reason decided to head for the unmistakeable junction of the Chindwin and the Irrawaddy; from there we could map-read down to the drop site about sixty miles to the south.

It was a smooth flight out over the Chin Hills. As we approached our pinpoint however, it became clear that map-reading was not going to be as easy as expected. Although it was only about ten o'clock, a faint mist was already spreading wide from the Irrawaddy, not enough to blot out land details but, as in Turner's 'Fighting Temeraire', it blurred them as if seen through tissue. It merged the huge sandbanks into the river, and smoothed out the twists and turns of many of the tributaries into a wide misty trail. Moreover, well into the dry months by now, there was no silvery water reflection to differentiate between the main tributaries and the shallow flash-flood chaungs; all were skeleton pale in the diffused moonlight.

We identified what we thought might be our particular tributary and followed it westward, glimpsing the broken line occasionally through mist holes or thin transparent patches, but found nothing like our U bend guide, nor did we have any better luck in the next tributary. By this time we were down to a few hundred feet, with clammy wraiths of mist fleeting past us as we slid down between the ridges, and, after following three valleys, we were no longer sure how far we had come from our original checkpoint at the river junction. I sent the radio operator back to tell the *Ramrose* men that we were having trouble finding the place. He returned presently with the message that whatever happened we were not to take them back.

'Put us down – we'll find our own bloody way to the DZ,' were their actual words.

This was the usual pressure from the Joes. And I could sympathize with them. The night we went off in that glider with the advance party to prepare a jungle strip, my worst fear had been that we would be unable to put down, that we would have to return to base and make a second attempt on a later night. Such a failure is unbearable to contemplate, for you have just used up all your resources against fear.

We did a quick dead-reckoning run from our checkpoint again. But to no avail. The Irrawaddy tributaries in the south wriggle about like the twisted grain in olive wood, but nowhere among the maze of convolutions could we discern a replica of that distinctive U bend seen in the photograph at Jessore. We would fly down a mist-blurred valley until the hills piled up far too steeply ahead, then on to the next valley to check there, then another – and all the time the mist increasing, and all the time sensing the urgency from the men in the fuselage to be set free into the night.

Finally we came upon one that looked just about right. No actual U bend could be seen, but a dense patch of mist hid a long stretch of the dry river bed which from its entry and exit must have contained a sharp bend. And certainly there was a clearing just emerging from a film of mist. So, after a final ground-level swoop to ensure the surface was clear, I decided to go ahead and drop.

It was done rapidly, a race against the surging growth of the mist, sighting-shot of a package, then the adjusted runs in quick succession, tight turns, minimum of run-in. At the start only about half the DZ was in the clear; we had no idea what obstacles might be hidden in the rest, so in order to land them on the safe visible sector we had to get down to six hundred feet. This was mist level. As we did the run-in it wrapped itself around the aircraft like filmy gauze and all I could discern through it was that the parachutes had developed; then in the downwind leg a gap appeared and for an instant I glimpsed the moon-flecked clearing and five pallid cones of parachutes scarring the dark surface. Then dank whiteness again.

By the time we finished the last run the mist was clotting so fast that had just one more run been necessary I would not have done it. All the men landed on clear ground and were mobile afterwards, with all their gear safe too – as we learned next day.

However, they were nearly twenty miles from the planned DZ. Twenty miles! You wonder how you could make such a blunder. Fortunately it was only a nuisance as far as they were concerned, it meant a day's trek to get to their working area. They were not too upset when I spoke to them some months later and the leader said that given the choice that night he would have accepted a misplaced drop of a hundred miles rather than go back to Jessore.

So, although on paper the criticism of Force 136 and ISLD about misplaced drops seemed justifiable, it was from officers at headquarters not from men on the ground. It was a staff complaint that their agents were not located in the spot where the pin had already been placed on the headquarters' map, essentially a matter of tidiness. Yet pinpoint location was rarely important to the Joes, they often moved away at once anyway. Moreover, the chosen sites were often dangerously covered with tree stumps, or showed a scatter of tiny fires which could signify an enemy bivouac, or surrounded by hills which prevented you going in low enough to ensure landing them on the clear area. So you rejected them on sight. The prime objective, surely, was to land a man safely; better he survive out of place than land literally dead on target.

In response to the complaint from the clandestines, the staff officer at air headquarters, after that discussion with us at Jessore, filed a report indicating how the organizations could help us achieve the type of accuracy they desired. They should submit maps giving a fifty-mile square within which the drop could be made. The RAF would then take photographs of areas within that square which were safe and identifiable, and the final decision about the site would then be made in consultation between the RAF and the organization.

When our group staff officer discussed his suggestions I urged him to add that the pilot and conducting officer, or leader of a group, could alter the DZ on arrival if they were not happy with the chosen site. However, he thought this too wide an option and would not include it in the report. I told the Dakota pilots they should do that anyway; if there was the slightest indecision in their minds about making a drop on a particular site, they should discuss the difficulty with the leader of the party before sending them out into the unknown.

If a man's life is at risk he must surely be the one to decide if and how that risk be taken – not the pilot, and certainly not a staff officer back at safe base, hundreds of miles away from the danger.

8

In the first week of February I landed at Dum-Dum again. This is the main airfield in Calcutta, built on the site of the old arsenal where dum-dum bullets were invented and produced for many years, until banned by international treaty at the turn of the century. It had been a small grass field when I last landed there some two years earlier when leading out a flight of Hudsons to doomed Singapore, but now it had a great concrete strip and was as highly administered, and as chaotic, as any other busy airfield. The crew, a Canadian trio under training, went off to the canteen when we met the driver from Force 136 with his station wagon.

With me was an army captain – I have forgotten his name – who had cadged a lift down from Jessore and spent most of the flight complaining about the staff at 136 headquarters. He had been on some operation recently in the Arakan, had lost his boots when crossing a stream, and on the next drop had found they had sent him a mismatched pair of which neither boot was even the size he had requested. When I sympathized with him he went on to list all the other grievances he had nurtured against headquarters while he was in the field, and he was still at it as we drove off into Calcutta.

You heard these tirades from the Joes at times, and having myself been dependent for three months on air-drops I had done my own share of griping about the blunders and carelessness of staff back at base. Even on the squadron there were still times when you wondered if they were at fault for a failure; the very night before that Dum-Dum visit I had been out on a seven-hour trip to the *Elephant* party in Burma and had again failed to get a reception from the ground, so had had to bring the load back to Jessore. As we were driving into Calcutta I still did not know if it was 136 headquarters or the men in the field who were responsible for this latest wasted effort. The captain however had no such doubt.

'Of course the office wallahs botched it,' he said. 'They've got it all going for them here – FANYs, restaurants, plush hotels. While we sweat it out in the jungle they've got all this for themselves.'

He waved his hand as if to indicate the luxurious surroundings enjoyed by the staff, but he was so embedded in his grudge he was unable properly to see his example of 'all this' silken delight. The car was weaving a slow horn-riven passage through a swirling mass of living creatures . . . gaunt sweat-glistened Bengalis pulling rickshaws filled to bulging with gross dhoti-clad men or enormously fat women in brilliant saris . . . coolies in loin-cloths straining their emaciated bodies as they hauled their heavily loaded carts . . . a small naked boy having a pee into the gutter between two others who were splashing in the black turbid flow . . . a man behind them spitting out crimson betel juice as he crouched beside his stock of black overripe bananas, market throw-outs now laid out on the pavement for sale.

The cramped open-fronted shops had names like International Construction Company and Consolidated Indian Steel and World Brass Corporation, and in the tiny dark interiors one or two loin-clothed figures would be banging metal with a hammer or turning it in a fire which sparked furiously from the gusts of a carcase bellows. Crowding all about us were white Brahmin cattle and buffalo and pi-dogs and pigs and crows and human beings, all nuzzling and pecking and snapping and fighting about garbage and carcases and excrement, on the road and pavements, in the gutters, and in piles against the walls. The whole scene was enveloped with the pervading Indian smell of manure and urine and the acrid smoke from dung fires.

The captain asked to be dropped outside the Great Eastern hotel by the queue of taxis. These were all open American tourers, Dodges and Hudson Super-Sixes and Studebakers, jammed bumper to bumper so that when a new arrival slammed into the back all the Sikh drivers jerked in their seats and the front vehicle shot out into a separate place ahead. The captain was going out to the SEI, the School of Eastern Interpreters, which was the cover name for the house where Force 136 debriefed and rested their agents after return from the field.

Force 136 had some pleasant quarters around the country. Apparently – I never saw it – there was a beautiful bungalow in the hills down in Ceylon where Mackenzie had his head-quarters, another by a lake near Poona, and a house with spacious grounds in Bombay which was owned by Jinnah, the founder of Pakistan, who used to come personally every month to collect his rent. The SEI quarters in Calcutta were well up to standard; they were located in the house of Rabindranath Tagore, the renowned Indian poet. It was a splendid white colonial mansion set by the river, with an islet of perfume in the garden where white jasmine had been allowed to sprawl all over a small wooden hut. There were fountains which could disperse a misty swathe of deliciously cool water, and lawns flat and smooth where you could dance with FANYs and local girls if you were lucky enough to be there on the night of one of their lively parties.

It was Colin Mackenzie who had arranged for the employment of the FANYs as officer cadets in India, where they were exclusive to his organization. Force 136 were lucky with their commander. Mackenzie, who had been a classical scholar at Cambridge where he won the Chancellor's medal for English verse, had lost a leg in the trenches during the First World War; subsequently he had been director of a major textile company at the same time as Lord Linlithgow who, when it was suggested in 1941 that an SOE organization should be set up in India, his viceregal domain, asked for Mackenzie to head it.

The job was of no great importance in an India peacefully remote from Hitler's war. There were only four or five of them in the unit, and the remit was vague – 'to help Lord Linlith-gow'. The area included the Persian Gulf countries which were at least on the periphery of action, and Mackenzie was up there establishing contacts when Japan burst into the war. Suddenly his job became of prime importance in the military activities on the eastern borders of India; the Gulf countries were dropped and the new SOE unit, now called Force 136, developed rapidly as it established political, economic and military missions throughout the five countries in the SEAC theatre of war.

Given the potential for dissension among all the separate powers and policies involved in that theatre Mackenzie was the ideal man to command a major clandestine organization. He had great personal charm which, coupled with an acute sense of diplomacy, meant that his projects could usually be activated without arousing the normal jealousies and opposition from the seekers and preservers of power in the top layers of command.

As opposed to the permanent secret service which seemed so often to make a deliberate effort to antagonize other services, Force 136 made deliberate efforts to cooperate. When the OSS first came to India, Mackenzie sent them a signal offering to help with all the resources at his command. Force 136 provided lists of the locations of their agents, and maps of the areas where the OSS might wish to operate. They handed over equipment and secret field reports which might be helpful in setting up OSS operations, and they provided them with an officer experienced in recruiting nationals of the various countries in our area. 'Mackenzie was personally responsible for the best relationship between the OSS and SOE of all theatres of war,' one American commentator recorded.

Mackenzie remained a civilian in the military enclave of SEAC. There was a period in his dealings with the Chinese, all of them generals, when officials there thought that the Chinese were not particularly forthcoming because SEAC had sent a mere civilian to discuss these important matters with them. Mackenzie and Mountbatten decided that the atmosphere in such meetings would be more congenial, and the outcome more productive, if he could carry the rank and uniform of major-general when dealing with the Chinese military – though remaining a civilian in India. So Mountbatten put the request through the normal channels.

It had to go to Churchill, however. He had recently decided that Lumley, who had been governor of Bombay, was the ideal man for a certain job in the Middle East but subsequently discovered that the army had made him a major-general in Holland, so he ordered no more civilians to be made generals without reference to him. For some reason or other the Church-illian approval never came through; Mountbatten disclosed this one day in his office down in Ceylon and Mackenzie, who preferred civilian status anyway, expressed proper regret for the effort that had been made. Then, when he got to the door, he suddenly realized one important benefit he had lost. He turned and asked: 'If I can't be a major-general, can I at least have the whisky allowance for one?'

It was almost double the ration he was then drawing as head of Force 136, on a brigadier's rating. Mountbatten agreed.

Mackenzie happened to have known Peter Murphy, who was Mountbatten's close friend and Personal Staff Officer, at Cambridge in the early 1920s, and it was SOE that had helped Mountbatten get Murphy to India and attached to his staff. The War Office were reluctant to allow this, but Colin Gubbins, the head of SOE, had solved the problem, as Mountbatten noted in a message to Murphy:

'. . . your presence is becoming urgently necessary, and I am glad to say that I have had an opportunity of seeing General Gubbins at the Cairo Conference . . . I told him my object was to have you out on my personal staff in a civilian capacity . . . Gubbins offered to have you appointed as his liaison officer with me. I must confess I jumped at the offer . . . because I do not have to get Treasury approval for your salary. I made it quite clear . . . you would become my Personal Staff Officer (PSO) and that you would not in fact be specifically employed on SOE duties on my staff but would keep in touch with Captain Garnons-Williams who is my coordinator for SOE, SIS and OSS . . . Have seen Mackenzie and Guinness, who run SOE here, and they are delighted to fall in with this proposal to let you be my PSO.

Despite the goodwill this cooperation must have created, on top of his previous contact with Murphy at Cambridge, only once in the war did Mackenzie ever appeal to him personally on a matter of importance. This happened later on in the spring of

1945 when Aung San, who commanded the Burma National Army, had become disillusioned with the Japanese and wanted to switch loyalties. All sensible people were delighted, since it meant that the Japanese would have not only the hill tribes but the whole of the Burmese people opposed to the occupation, and as a result our forces would suffer far less casualties in their advance southwards.

However, the colonial government in exile had branded Aung San a traitor, and made no secret of their intent to execute him. When they heard he was going to cross the lines to discuss collaboration they said he should be arrested the moment he was safely in our hands, but they were told this could not be done because he had been given a safe conduct for the meeting with Slim. Then they discovered that he had had to change the time and place specified for the meeting with the men who were to conduct him to Slim, so they claimed this negated the assurance of safe conduct, and demanded he should be handed over to them.

Mackenzie had arranged the meeting, we had dropped the agents to bring Aung San through the lines, and he was horrified when he heard this. Mountbatten was away at the time so he went to Peter Murphy and explained the position. The following day an order was issued from Mountbatten's office that no Burmese civilian associated with Aung San's mission was to be arrested without the personal permission of Mountbatten. The meeting with Slim proceeded without physical interference from the CAS(B) – the Civil Affairs Service, Burma.

Whatever difficulties there may occasionally have been between 136 headquarters and their men in the field, we on the squadron had few disagreements with the staff, and even when there was a complaint, as in the case of the misplaced drops that January, it was always muted, and invariably resolved through amicable discussion. The reason for my flight down to Dum-Dum that day was not to ask about the abortive *Elephant* drop; that was incidental, we had far too many unreceived sorties to query each. I had been called in because their air liaison officer wanted to discuss the possibility of landing a Dakota in Indo-

126

China. He could, and did in due course, arrange this sortie through the normal channels but he wanted to discover first if the plan was practical, and if there were any particular difficulties he should consider.

It was a mistake by some of the agents, such as the captain that day, to criticize the men in charge of the various country sections as career officers who had no idea of the conditions under which men in the field had to operate – just as it was for them to assume that all pilots were equally ignorant of jungle warfare. Mackenzie had chosen men of practical experience to head the Burma, Siam, Indo-China and Malay sections of the organization; they were people who knew the language, the people and the terrain.

Ritchie Gardiner, the head of the Burma country section, was a lean precise Scot in his late thirties who had been forestry manager of a major Burma timber company that included six hundred elephants among its work force. He was one of those who had escaped from Burma by walking out, a journey during which thousands lost their lives; his group had come out via the Chaukkan Pass, the most northerly route, which had never before been crossed in the rainy season, and Gardiner had been decorated for saving one of his companions on that trek at the risk of his own life. Force 136 had sent a rescue party with elephants into the hills in search for them, and when they finally encountered the group in the uninhabited mountains in the northern tip of Burma they probably had only a few days life left in each of them. Gardiner wrote about the final stage of the journey:

By this time we were all weakening, speech itself was an effort, and so indeed was thought. We were not cheered by the corpses, and those still alive by the track but too weak to go on further. Our legs were swollen with beri-beri and we would pick off a hundred leeches from our emaciated bodies during the day's march. Our daily food ration was a handful of mouldy rice, one mouldy biscuit and a half ounce of cheese. It was a big day when we shot a python which gave us a mug of soup and a rather tough cutlet apiece.

It was Gardiner who told me on that visit to 136 headquarters that our failure to make the *Elephant* drop the previous night had not been due to a blunder by staff, as the hitch-hiking captain had prejudged. The reason was that the field party had not been in position. This happened fairly often, and was understandable; you could not expect men who were being harried by a Japanese patrol to go out into the only open space in the area and blazon their location with enormous fires. But it turned out not to be the Japanese patrols who kept the *Elephant* group away from the site. They were busy on private affairs.

This *Elephant* group were as much a headache to Force 136 as they were to us in failing so often to be in position on the DZ. They were a mixed party of Chinese and Burmese, half a dozen of them, and we had dropped them to make contact with the local communist leaders and organize guerrilla bands. But the Chinese were Chiang Kai-Shek's men, not particularly friendly to the communists even in wartime, and Force 136 had reason to believe that the ones in *Elephant* were up to some private nationalist business; and the three Burmese were known to be trying to contact Aung San to discover if he approved the task for which we had landed them in Burma.

Half the time Force 136 did not know where the team were and what they were up to, and we kept arriving over sites that were devoid of fire and human beings. Even when they were on site they gave such tiny signal fires – on one occasion five candle ends set up in jam tins – that you needed the eyesight of an owl, and the luck of the devil, to discover their presence. If you failed to do so they would then complain that they 'made signal fires but the aircraft did not drop'.

Some of the men in the field, particularly the indigenous teams, seemed to think that the only possible hindrance to a successful drop was the weather over their DZ. They did not appreciate that to make a drop you had to have a serviceable aircraft, passable weather over the Chin Hills, and a mist-free DZ area, before you could even start looking for their lights down below. Only when you found them could you start working out how to get in and out of their valley for the drop.

Consider *Harlington*, for example. Admittedly this was in the

Hudson days, when the machines were old and unreliable, but it will give some indication of the problems that prevented us from arriving on time to serve the group waiting by their fires. *Harlington* was a plan to contact Seagrim when it was not known for sure if he was still alive down there among the Karens. The objective was simply to drop a Karen officer into the hills – without a wireless transmitter, because in those naive times the Kempei'tai were thought to be such a brilliant force that a captured transmitter would be deadly in their hands. The plan was that once he had landed and had established that there were no Japanese in the area, the Karen would put out a fire-signal one night and the precious transmitter would then be dropped to him. So down he went, one night in January 1943.

Now we come to the incredible part of *Harlington*. Every full moon from February to October in 1943 attempts were made to drop that radio, over twenty sorties in all, but not a single one made contact with the patient Karen waiting down there with his signal lights. Maybe two or three were navigation failures, and others failed to discover the reception, but the majority were due to weather, to mist covering the target or impassable monsoon conditions over the hills. After weather the next major cause of failure in the early days was aircraft serviceability – oil leaks, fuel-pump failures, runaway props, cowlings lifting off, soaring engine temperatures, and on one occasion a complete wheel falling off simply while taxying for take-off.

These dual problems of faulty aircraft and confounding weather are exemplified by a slice of the log book kept by Jimmy King, the most experienced Hudson pilot, dealing with his efforts to make the radio drop during one particular moon period. *Harlington* is the 'op.' he mentions in the log – but because this was during Wing Commander Moore's regime of muzzled security he was not allowed to put the actual code name on to paper.

25 Feb. Took off on op. Visibility 1–2 miles. Thick haze up to 700 feet. Port engine cut on take-off. Picked up, landed, tested, took off again. Cloud on hills. Failed to locate DZ.
26 Feb. Made another attempt on op. Visibility 1–2 miles.

Found valley okay but visibility so bad couldn't distinguish signals from ground. Saw bonfires but no torches. Did not drop containers. Duration flight 8 hours 10 minutes.

27 Feb. Met forecast prevented attempt.

28 Feb. Ditto.

1 March Took off on op. Weather same as previous nights. Reached Irrawaddy. Oil pump in auxiliary oil supply failed after pumping one gallon only into starboard engine. No alternative but turn back. Bengal completely obscured by thick ground mist. Could not get D'F assistance from Dum-Dum. Starboard engine oil pressure dropped, so cut engine and proceeded to coast. Found clear patch and force-landed in stubble field, 15 miles NW of entrance to Hoogli River. Transferred oil from auxiliary tank to starboard engine and took off again when weather sufficiently clear. Thirty mins. to Dum-Dum. Duration of trip 8 hrs 10 mins. No damage to aircraft, life or property.

Such a remedial emergency landing was not unique. Later that year over Assam I cut a Dakota engine instantly when, to my horror, I saw petrol streaming from a loose-capped wing tank and spraying all about the red-hot exhaust stubs. I landed on one engine in a paddy field, screwed down the cap properly, took off again without 'damage to aircraft, life or property' and completed the operation.

Another bar to a successful drop was the occasional intervention by the Japanese. As far as we know for certain, out of the twenty-seven aircraft we lost on Special Duties only one was shot down by enemy fighters. And as far as we know only two were hit by gunfire, both suffering only trivial damage. But enemy aircraft were seen from time to time and the pilots would then fly down low in the night or take shelter in cloud in daylight – we had no armament on the Dakotas, and even the Liberators were largely stripped of it. After such evasive manoeuvres it was not always possible to get back to the DZ again.

We met AA fire a little more frequently than enemy fighters. It bore no comparison with the fearful turmoil you encountered in Europe – our contact was usually just a single gun – but the flow of tracer from a Bofors-type or the thump of a single explosive shell can be disturbing when met for the first time, and almost all our crews were complete novices under fire. Most had been trained in Canada or Australia and had never seen AA from the air either by day or night.

In the early days such experience was provided for pilots before ever reaching a squadron; on flying training back in the UK in 1940 you had become used to seeing flak from almost your first night in the air, and a flight to India in those days would have been through hectic Malta and North Africa, so crews were already blooded on arrival. By 1945, however, aircrews were coming out to India in something like airline security; the fighting in Africa was over, the Mediterranean completely under our control. And even on arrival in an operational squadron such as 357 the sight of gunfire was still a novelty to be discussed on return; and although many crews had seen gunfire in some form or other by the end of their tour, not all recognized it as such on first contact.

I had a newly arrived navigator one night, flying with me for experience. We had been to Siam on a successful drop and had leaflets to disperse over an area east of Mandalay. It was such a calm and beautiful night, with very little mist, that I thought it would be a pleasant change to go down to a thousand feet or so when crossing the moonlit plain. So we were idling along on autopilot and I was trying to make modern pictures of the constellations – an aircraft of Sagittarius, a jeep of Pegasus – as we smoothed our way over the ashen-grey gridded islands of paddy lying in great black lakes of forest; all so still and serene in the moonlight. And then, just as I was developing Scorpio into a gramophone pick-up, a gun opened fire on us.

At least I assume we were the target. There was nothing else visible in the brilliant night about us. It was light AA, Bofors-type stuff, fireballs pumped in a languid stream that curved over in a slow arc to fade down and away again, a few hundred yards ahead and off line to starboard. Jerked into action at once I snapped out of autopilot, swung the aircraft away to port and continued directly away for a few moments before turning back

131

in a climb to see if I could locate the gun. It had stopped, however. By then the navigator had come scrambling up beside me to discover the cause of the sudden violent action. He had been just in time to see the last few flaming blobs hosed up and then fall lazily away until disappearing.

'Verey pistol, was it?' he asked.

'Light AA.'

'You think so, sir? Looked very slow to me.'

He did not believe me. When questioned he revealed that his only experience of AA was as a schoolboy, when he had seen a raid one night over Bournemouth. He listened respectfully to rank when I assured him that what he had just seen was genuine gunfire but I am sure he was not convinced. No one else had had time to see the shells. It must have been a Japanese gun, for we were a couple of hundred miles behind the front line. I have no idea why they had bothered to take pot shots at us; had we been an aggressive bomber they might well have suffered from such a disclosure. And it was only a jungle road below, not a town or airfield. We flew higher in a weaving course over the area to see if we could spot the gun but he would not open fire again. And the navigator remained convinced it had been a Verey signal – he did not mention it at debriefing.

I did see a Liberator one day under fire. It was a little later in the year when, although the monsoon had not yet started, the clouds were beginning to pile up every day against the Chin Hills. By this time our fighters had complete control over the Burmese plain, in fact there had been very little sign of Japanese fighters since the day some nine months earlier when the USAAF, seeking to ensure that our Chindit landing would not be molested, had made a major attack on Japanese airfields and destroyed nearly forty aircraft in one devastating assault. The Japanese air force never recovered from that disaster.

On this particular day we had flown a long way south down the coast before finding a cloud gap over the Chin Hills. Once through to the plain we were about to turn north to avoid crossing too much enemy territory in daylight when a big aircraft came lumbering out of cloud about a mile ahead of us. It took only a glance to accept it as a Liberator, and I was just about to turn away on our own business when heavy AA began to burst into little puffs of cloud about him.

We were close enough ourselves to hear the shell thumps, so he must certainly have done so, but the aircraft seemed to react with ponderous sluggishness, like some great beast of dim intellect. The pilot would have wheeled over at once but the message from the brain centre had to traverse the long neural trail out to the dinosaur's extremities, where movement was actually effected. While we, trailing behind, had already slipped wide out of range of the gun, the great wallowing creature was just beginning to respond to the pilot's urgent wheel-swing; like a drifting ship in a long-rolling swell, it tilted lazily to port, then slowly began to roll away from the grey shell-bursts. We had marked the gun and were set back on tranquil course by the time it had finally swung away out of range.

When shellfire of any type is close to the aircraft there is never any doubt about its nature, nor its malevolence, and pilots who met it for the first time were understandably apprehensive about staying in the area. But agents down on the ground, accustomed perhaps to sight of tracer and sound of gunfire, were not always sympathetic to such a reaction. The men dropped that January on *Mouse* for example had some hard words about a Dakota pilot who sheered away quickly when under attack.

We were never very popular with *Mouse* right from the opening drop. Their DZ was a hundred miles or so behind the lines of the Arakan front, and they were supposed to be landed to a reception by another team who had been dropped earlier and had the similar task of gathering intelligence for the army corps down there. However, the pilot could not find the reception when he arrived that night, and thus developed one of those mid-air cockpit conferences we all experienced at some time or other; the Joes would be urging you to let them go, whatever doubts you might have, and if you finally agreed they then had their own conference about a new order of jumping, loads to take, and action on landing. It was a process that took time.

While the discussion went on among the Joes in the fuselage

133

the pilot roamed about in search of a new site, fearing that the original one may have been compromised. The Joes finally decided that instead of one man going down alone in the first place to check the new site was clear, everyone – three British and three Arakanese – would go together. The pilot would then fly away for twenty minutes to give them time to get organized on the ground, and on return he was to drop the first six packages if they gave him a flashing light; he would wait ten minutes after that, then drop the final twelve packages only if again they flashed the signal.

I happened to be in the operations room on his return, having landed earlier from a trip to Siam, and stayed to hear his debriefing. All had gone according to plan; he had found a suitable site, dropped the men and seen them all land safely, then flown away towards the coast and returned after twenty minutes to a flashing of lights. He had dropped the first six packages, gone off for ten minutes, then on return had found not lights but three good fires now burning. He dropped the last twelve packages to the men visible down on the moonlit paddy field.

They were not however the men of *Mouse*. I had contact later with one of them, Jack Grinham, and he said that they never saw the aircraft again after the first six packages were dropped. They decided not to accept any more, pocketed their torches and went off into a safe bivouac. Whether the lights on the ground had been provided by the Japanese or by enterprising villagers – both were apt to try this snitch – the consequence was that 136 headquarters thought the team had received all their equipment, whereas among the missing items was the battery charger, all their food except for a few packs of emergency rations, and all their arms and explosives except what they had carried on their persons when they jumped.

'I hope the Dak pilot got a real right bollocking for what he did,' Grinham said.

He did not. An experienced crew might not have made his mistake, but it was an understandable one, and as far as I recall there were no queries about his action afterwards at debriefing. And at least the DZ where he had landed the party proved to be a good one. The village headman owned the paddy field in which the *Mouse* men landed knee-deep in water. He had been ill-treated by the Japanese and was vengefully eager to help the returning British. The team felt secure enough to follow his lead into a jungle hideout, roll up into their chutes, then sleep through the dank cold early hours until the sun was high and they could dry their clothes.

The trouble with AA gunfire followed two nights later when, in response to a signal from *Mouse*, we sent out a Dakota with a charger, food and ammunition. The pilot had trouble determining their drop zone, for the only light was a torch flashing the letter K – the team were surrounded by Japanese and dared not light signal fires on the DZ. A torch by itself, without signal fires to give location, is difficult to read as you circle an area at night, and without a figure of fires giving guidance you have to study the site and area before deciding your line of drop. The pilot made three runs over the site to check that it was really the *Mouse* party below this time, and to decide upon direction for the drop, then when he had it all right in mind he came in the fourth time low and slow to drop the single vital container they needed. That was when the Japanese AA gun opened fire at him.

'It must have given the crew a real dose of the shits,' Grinham said.

It may have, too – but that's surely not surprising. If you are on your first operational tour, circling low in the moonlight over enemy territory, trying to decide if the intermittent flashing that you glimpse from below is really someone signalling the letter K, you are under stress; you have never seen AA gunfire in all your life, and suddenly there are four flashing explosions close by the aircraft, the crackling thumps sound over the engine, the aircraft judders under the force of the blast, smoke goes scudding past and there is a stink of cordite in the cockpit, it is all a new, and very shattering experience.

The regular circling at low altitude had given the gunners plenty of time, as well as temptation, and after that third run they must have decided they had his height and speed in perfect check so let him have it. He was lucky to have escaped without being hit. Despite the shock of this assault however, he did still make an effort to get the container down to *Mouse*, as Grinham reported:

> He came across at twice the height, taps wide open, and dropped the container much too early. It drifted away towards the Jap AA unit on top of the hill. The Dak disappeared very quickly. If we could have got hold of that crew that night they would have been rendered incapable of reproducing the species – and made to walk all the way back to Jessore after we had finished with them.

They did recover the container fortunately, but it took them a tense day's search, for the Japanese were hunting them at the same time. So they finally had their battery charger, and something other than rice to eat.

Finally too, a long time afterwards, Grinham could forgive the hiccups, and speak with gratitude about the many times we did deliver on time and target to his group down there in the Arakan. For they spent six weeks behind the lines and supplied invaluable intelligence to the army; their successful record was to provide Force 136 with helpful argument when the army presently expressed doubt about their value, and suggested they might be better absorbed completely into the regular forces.

Both crews of the criticized flights lived to complete their tours of operation. They were lucky. Statistically the aircrews of our two Special Duty squadrons would have stood a far better chance of survival had we all jumped out with the first parties we dropped, instead of flying back to base and then returning night after night about thirty times to service them during their trials down there on the ground. Every third agent that we dropped cost the life of one of our aircrew.

A few of the aircrew at Jessore, just four in all, found the flights too terrifying to bear and were driven finally into refusal to take off on an operational flight. An agent who changed his mind about clandestine work was returned to his unit, none the worse in rank for the decision. Not so the airman. The RAF had a name, and a policy, for those who suffered such fear: it was called LMF – Lack of Moral Fibre. The rest of the unit knew when such a case occurred, the disgrace was inevitably public; the stricken man was reduced in rank and posted away out of sight.

When you imagine the terror of being dropped into the night over tropical jungle behind the enemy lines try to imagine also, if you can, what terror an airman must have suffered before he was driven to the public ignominy of the LMF procedure. Some might think such men deserved a medal for the fight they must have put up, before they were finally overwhelmed.

9

One of D Division's more macabre capers was our SEAC version of *The Man Who Never Was*, the body that was landed off the Spanish coast with documents to deceive the Germans about the invasion of Sicily. That was operation *Mincemeat*, and ours had the equally non-committal name of *Hiccups*; however, it would have horrified the name-givers in Delhi to discover that those of us who knew about it on the squadron always referred to it afterwards simply as operation *Corpse*. The pilot was Jack Churchill and I heard him being introduced one night in the mess with the words: 'He did the corpse job.'

It made him sound like a grave-robber, particularly as it was spoken in such a confidential tone. This was said in the high-security days of Wing Commander Moore – though certainly not in his presence – but there was never much talk about the operation at any time; it was staged from Dum-Dum and only a very few people on the squadron ever knew it was being mounted.

Fleming would have known about the European parallel, but the idea might just as well have come to him from a local source, for he might have heard about that Karen suggestion that the body of a European should be dropped so they could deliver it to the Japanese as Seagrim. I cannot recall asking Fleming about this, and in the notes I made on two meetings with him there is nothing on *Corpse*.

The first contact we had with it was not on the squadron but at Thornton's parachute school. A captain from D Division visited Thornton one day with an enigmatic request. Could he arrange a parachute which did not open?

Of course he could, Thornton told him. Just chuck it out

without attaching it to the static line. Then there would be nothing to snap the holding twine, and down the pack would come to clump on the ground like a free-falling sack of rice. Next question?

No, no, the captain told him. Thornton did not get the point. The parachute had to be launched normally and yet not open. It had to go out attached to a 'man-sized' load, down a Hudson slide like any other package or person, but then not develop properly. The failure must be so contrived that even an aeronautical expert who subsequently examined it on the ground would be convinced it was accidental; there must not be the slightest suspicion that any deceit was involved.

Still easy, Thornton said. Tell the pilot to drop from very low level – about twenty feet should do it. The parachute would not be fully open by the time the load smashed into the ground, but no one could tell this by examining the parachute afterwards.

That was no good either. People on the ground might well be watching, the captain said; in fact there was provision to encourage this to happen, so the load must go out at the normal height. No breath of suspicion, Major, remember?

In all the thousands of jumps Thornton had observed he had actually witnessed only one fatal accident, which was the one that happened with me the first day on the practice DZ. But he had heard of several such accidents when two parachutes became entangled, and the drill of despatchers ensuring people went out separately was specifically designed to avoid this danger. He therefore thought there would be little difficulty in arranging a parachute failure by this method. He prepared sacks of rice as his 'man-sized' loads and wrapped them in parachute harnesses. The two went out side by side over the practice DZ with Thornton waiting below to observe the tangled fall.

Both parachutes opened perfectly, safely apart, and the sacks sank down gently to the ground.

A further test produced the same result, and he realized that the parachutes must somehow be prevented from separating just after they left the slide, and the best way to achieve this was to twist both their static lines together. The two packs would then go out on what was effectively a single static line; the holding threads would thus be snapped more or less simultaneously and the parachutes open beside one another. He did this four times.

Twice there was a partial failure of one parachute; twice both developed fully and landed the two sacks of rice lightly on the practice ground. He tried a single static line holding two parachutes together and the result was the same – an occasional failure, but generally both opened normally.

Faced with such unreliability of failure outside the aircraft he concluded the job would have to be done before launching. After all, he reasoned, a parachute which has its holding twine broken before leaving the aircraft could not possibly be distinguished from one which had opened outside. So he broke the twine and opened the two parachutes, tangled the shroud lines thoroughly, then pushed them down the slide together.

Success. They both failed at first attempt, and the failures continued on a further two trials. He made a call to the captain at D Division to say his problem was solved. Did he want to see a test?

The test was never run. The captain came out from Calcutta next afternoon but when he discovered the solution being offered he said it was unacceptable. A second unopened parachute was not a permissible accessory. It must be a single parachute failure. He then added that a second parachuted load would be going out with his mysterious 'man-sized' package; but this was a genuine load and it was equally essential that its parachute *did* open properly. If that second parachute failed then so did the whole operation. One must open perfectly and deliver its load safely; one must fail so badly that its load was destroyed.

He himself offered a suggestion that afternoon. He said he had heard about a panel splitting open. Was this possible? Thornton had never in all his experience heard of such an accident but he and his men were running out of ideas by then, so he said he would examine the possibility. However, a brief examination of the seams showed him this was no answer. The stitching was such that a single snapped thread would not cause a run, each one would have to be cut through; to believe that each one of hundreds of stitches in a panel had been faulty would strain the credulity of the most naive investigator, so that approach was abandoned.

It was not surprising that the job should have been so difficult. For twenty-five years, ever since Irvin made the first descent by a manually operated parachute, brilliant minds had been working on improving the security of the device, and Thornton began to realize that most of his 'accidents' had been foreseen and obviated. No matter where a launching body finishes in the air, under or over or around the parachute pack, it still opens and the man finishes up dangling beneath it. And once opened it takes an expert a deliberate and sustained effort to collapse it again, something an inert 'man-sized' package clearly could not induce.

The tangled shroud lines seemed to offer the best possibility, and so he went to the parachute shed and helped pack one in which the shroud lines had been carefully tangled – without actually being tied; when this was tested it did fail to develop properly, and the inner sack of rice burst on impact (all rice was double-sacked, and it was always free-dropped; the inner sack burst on impact but the other one remained intact). When he did a second test, however, the shroud lines untwisted themselves and the parachute developed normally, as did another two out of three trials, so that was no infallible solution either.

The shroud lines seemed to be a possible weakness. Thornton abraded a few against an emery wheel so that little more than a thread remained. Yet the nylon was tough, it refused to snap and the sack landed softly as ever. He enclosed the whole parachute in a hessian bag but the pilot chute burst it open and down came the rice as gently as before. He packed the pilot chute inside the main one instead of on top, but out it popped and then dragged open the main canopy as usual. He tried dumping the parachute in water for a day but it opened perfectly in a spectacular spray, a flash of sparkling diamonds in the morning sunlight, and floated sweetly down to the ground with its load.

Then he was up in the practice hangar one afternoon and

141

showing a team how they should test the static line. He gave it a tug and said: 'Make sure it's as solid – ' and then he stopped in mid-sentence.

He had the solution.

It might seem strange that no one had thought of that solution at once, but given the very careful wording of the problem the answer was far from obvious. Thornton's brief had been to give D Division a parachute which would not open. He still did not know how they intended to use it, and even their own suggestions had followed that precise lead. But the solution was outside the parachute. It was to be found in the static line.

This strip of webbing is immensely strong and is attached firmly to a solid part of the fuselage, for it must stay with the aircraft; the far end clips around a piece of twine that holds the parachute pack closed against the pressure of the spring-loaded pilot chute. When the man jumps he extends the static line to its full length so that it snaps the holding twine, the pilot chute can then spring open to drag out the main parachute and the man floats down to the ground. Meanwhile the despatcher pulls back the dangling static line into the aircraft. If the clip which goes around the twine were to fall apart, from metal fatigue say, as the man went down the slide, then he would no longer be attached to the static line, the twine would not be broken and so he would go down with an unopened parachute. On the ground they would find still attached to the parachute the end piece of the snapped clip which would explain the accident.

At the aircraft maintenance depot in Barrackpore they broke the clip without much difficulty – it snapped under a tension strain of just over seventeen tons apparently. When the two pieces came back Thornton kept the top half with the report from the depot to demonstrate to, and reassure, future parachutists the strength of the link upon which their lives depended. The other broken half was affixed to a parachute and then the order from D Division was complete. A convincing parachute failure was ready for its 'man-sized' load.

It was at this stage, when he finally reported success, that Thornton discovered the load would be a dead body. It was

142

ostensibly to be the corpse of an Indian army signals officer, a captain. He would be a Muslim and carrying the usual identity card and body tags, as well as a non-compromising document or two such as an operative might illicitly carry – a payslip, a bill from Firpo's, a letter from a girlfriend, the photograph of an elderly Indian couple who might have had a son in his thirties. Agents were not supposed to carry such documents with them but this instruction was widely ignored, so the rule obviously had to be broken in this case also where it was essential to avoid any taint of irregularity.

It was normal practice for radio instructions to be carried on the person of the agent and not with the actual set; this was because both radio and agent would then have to fall into enemy hands before they would have any real chance of deceiving us with their transmissions. So among the documents on the body was the usual sheet with radio details, frequencies (the actual crystals were with the set), ciphers, list of schedules, call signs and so on, including even the security check; for some reason or other this was often recorded on paper, despite the obvious danger of compromise. D Division were confident that with all this material ready to hand there was no Secret Service in the world that would miss the opportunity of establishing contact with the enemy.

The plan was to land the body complete with its plausibly unopened parachute beside a road in Burma, and close nearby would be the developed parachute with its safely landed package containing the radio. All the Japanese had to do was to take the papers from the body, use the simple code to send out the safe-arrival signal, and there would be an immediate and delighted response from India. They would presently send out the security check, which could be passed with confidence by the Japanese, and trusted contact would thereupon be established. D Division could then start eliciting information from its catch, and feeding back misleading intelligence in return.

Once the parachute problem had been solved all that was needed to complete the scheme was the corpse. One might think that in the midst of the poor starving millions in Bengal –

and there was a serious famine as usual that year – there would be no problem about picking up a dead body among the thousands dying every day in Calcutta and the surrounding countryside. But there are very few Indians, however destitute, who would carelessly yield a family body to be subjected to some strange European rites; the poor have a human dignity that transcends even the primitive drive of hunger, and neither money nor power can prevail against it.

The odds were against any accidentally discovered body being suitable for the role, because Hindus make up the majority of the population in the Calcutta area and the candidate had to be a Muslim. The documentation had been so prepared. Muslims are circumcised and Hindus are not, so the religious distinction could not be ignored, even on a dead body. Muslims do predominate in northern Bengal however, and millions migrate to the city, so they were bound to be represented in the daily mortality count of Calcutta. The problem was to obtain a suitable one.

Even where unclaimed bodies were to be found every day, at Howrah Station lying among the sleeping hundreds in the main hall and on the platforms, it would be difficult to cart one away without recognized authority. The babu clerks, who subsist on documents, would have to be fed the correct diet of forms, and the usual procedures, such as attendance of the official vehicle and the men in their customary uniforms, would have to be followed, all ensuring acceptance by a thousand observers of the rightful collection of the corpse. It would not have been easy.

I heard subsequently, from someone whose word I trust, that he had been asked to help although he was not in D Division, and that he and a friend did produce the emaciated body of a man which they had picked up off the streets of Calcutta one night. It was rejected as unsuitable, whether for religious or other reasons was not known. My confidant had an idea that one or two others had also been co-opted in the search and may have submitted candidates. If so they were equally unacceptable.

It was not only the religious specification that would debar such candidates, it was also their physical condition at the time of death. It is most unlikely that a suitable body could be found lying in the streets; D Division did not want to drop into Burma the body of a man who had clearly been starving, and probably to death. They wanted one that could have been an army captain. You do not find such corpses among the street sleepers.

A hospital offers far better prospects, and that is where D Division had their main hope. They had to wait. They had a contact in the military hospital, and he had an Indian doctor friend in the civil hospital, so their coverage was wide, but nonetheless several weeks went by without them coming up with a suitable body. Patients were dying in dozens every day, men and women and children, but D Division had to have a fully grown Muslim male. The majority of these on offer, however, were far too old, and a few of the right age could not be used because they had died with stitches still in place from surgery. Finally, and this was the major hold-up, nearly all the dead had relatives who claimed the bodies for the proper rites of disposal.

Their contacts in the hospitals had already been waiting for some time before Thornton started work on the parachute problem and it was shortly after he found his solution that D Division also found their body. It was a Muslim in his middle thirties who had suffered a heart attack in a tram as it trundled along Chowringhee, and was dead on arrival at the civil hospital. The body was still unclaimed after the customary three days in the cold chamber and it was about to be sent to the medical school to be used as a teaching cadaver when at the last minute an army officer arrived – from D Division of course – to identify the dead man as his missing uncle. He paid a sum of money for the corpse to be moved to the military hospital; there, so he claimed, his uncle's body would be kept in the cold chamber to await the arrival of other members of his family for the funeral.

So all was now ready. The squadron was officially, and very discreetly, notified that D Division wished to launch operation *Corpse* as soon as possible. It was set down for a Hudson drop on the opening night of the next moon period, which was about a fortnight later.

During the waiting period D Division had completed most of the documentation but there were some details that had to await delivery of the actual body. A uniform had to be made for him, an Indian army captain would never be clothed in the issue bush-jacket of heavy khaki, and shorts which were wide like a divided skirt – far cooler incidentally than the tight shorts worn by the navy – so a sastri had been put on standby to await measurements. They had brought in several sizes of army standard boots, for nearly all officers wore these in the field, but the final selection had to await the actual fitting. Socks would be bought for him from the Army and Navy department store in Calcutta.

On the day before the operation was to be mounted they took delivery of the body in a box-coffin, then moved it to a house they had rented out near the golf course to complete their work. A photograph and fingerprints were taken, the measurements supplied to the sastri, and the body was provided with a wristwatch, identity discs, and underwear. I was told that at one stage the conducting officer sent a young lieutenant into the storeroom to 'ask that Captain Mukerjee if he would like a drink' and that the lieutenant came clattering back wide-eyed and trembling, babbling that the man was dead, but I am sceptical about this and one or two other stories later heard; D Division took their stunts seriously, and they had put far too much work into this one to treat their prize with such frivolity.

By the following morning the uniform had been made to measure and all the documents finalized. They completed the dress, distributed his memorabilia and official documents between his pockets, and for the moment put into a sack the rest of the equipment he would be carrying; the usual webbing and belt, ammunition pouch and revolver, haversack and so on, the normal oddments carried by an agent when he jumped. It was about midday when they set off on the circuitous drive from their private mortuary to Dum-Dum, as they still had a few items to be collected from their office.

It was mid-afternoon when they arrived, and by then the body had been out of the hospital for almost two full days in the oppressive heat of a Bengal summer. It was then put into the oven of a Hudson fuselage, parked well away from the main buildings, so that the final preparations could be completed in privacy. Take-off was not until nine o'clock – the time of the drop was dependent on the moon, so it could not be put forward – and this was unfortunate because the conducting officer had already begun to think on arrival that their calculations about the deterioration of the body might have been optimistic.

They were. The body should never have been put into the aircraft. You could get temperatures over 170 degrees in an aircraft in summer and, not surprisingly, by sunset that day – three cooking-hot hours after arrival – the two ground crew brought to Dum-Dum to check the Hudson off had decided there was something not very pleasant about the load.

After the conducting officer had completed his preparations, fitting the webbing, revolver, haversack and so on, he covered the body with a brown fly-sheet from a tent. However, the covering did not hide the shape, and it was inevitable that the two ground crew soon knew what was there in the fuselage; either their imaginations then decided that the air was tainted, or the sustained heat was finally taking effect, but either way they thought the doctor, who had already spent some time in the fuselage, should be alerted to their scented apprehension.

He arrived with the conducting officer and after quick examination suggested that the best answer was to splash some carbolic on the fly-sheet; this would not only overpower any odour that sensitive noses might in fact detect, but also discourage less sensitive ones from trying to do so. The conducting officer at first refused outright to allow this. He was worried that the uniform might become impregnated and that this would arouse the suspicion of the Japanese, but when the doctor said the aircrew might justifiably make an official complaint to him about the state of their cargo he agreed to consider remedies.

They visited the aircraft again. Apparently there was no positive impact on entering the fuselage, but if you hung around the statuesque pile by the slide you had a queasy little start every now and then, and the two airmen claimed that such queasy little starts had grown more frequent as the afternoon

147

advanced. The conducting officer did admit, after nosing around for a while, that there were occasional wafts of unpleasantness but said this was only when you sniffed for them and, as he would be closest to the body on the trip and was not worried, he saw no need to take any action. He had a bottle of eau-de-Cologne and proposed to use it on a cloth mask he was taking with him, and he was happy to provide the despatcher with the same relief. Certainly he would not allow the body to go out reeking of carbolic.

When the doctor pointed out that the Japanese were unlikely to get to the bait for perhaps twelve hours after it was dropped, by which time any smell in the clothing would have been overpowered by the output from the body itself, the conducting officer did accept the point. His one stipulation was that no carbolic should touch either of the loads or their parachutes.

So they settled for this compromise. Some hessian sacks, liberally doused in the antiseptic, were placed around the body as a smell barrier. When the crew arrived a few hours later the only odour noticeable was that of antiseptic, with just the occasional hint of cologne when you got close to the masks, and when they knew why the fuselage smelled like a women's hospital ward just before visiting hours they were happy to have that instead of the alternative.

Churchill entered the fuselage first that night, just as the conducting officer stepped back from his latest adjustment of the tent-fly covering. Churchill happened to bang the side of the door with his parachute and this rocked the body slightly; he glanced towards it uneasily and was horrified to see an arm become dislodged out of the covering. It flopped down and started swinging in slow pendulum. He turned away quickly from the sight, shutting it out of mind as he hurried forward to his seat, and, like the Coleridge man who knew a frightful fiend was following him along the lonely road, he never turned around to look back again that night.

He had had some discussion with the conducting officer that afternoon about the arrangement of the drop. The distance between the landing marks of an opened and an unopened parachute on a DZ can be up to two hundred yards, and although the impression had to be given that the dead man's parachute had failed accidentally, and therefore the opened parachute with the radio could not be close nearby – a failure must fly further ahead than an opened parachute – it was still essential to get both well within the clearing. If either one landed outside, and was lost in a bamboo thicket or an overgrown chaung, the whole operation would have been a waste.

Most of us would, on such a drop, do the job in two runs. The package would go down first and be used as a check on drift, then the man would go down with any adjustment that the package drop had shown to be necessary. Although drift was of no interest in this case, it was decided that the normal procedure would still be best to follow; for the radio package with its parachute lying on the moonlit paddy field would be a good marker on the second run when the body with its failed parachute would be dropped. Churchill, a pilot of considerable experience, had done some of the rice-sack drops on Thornton's trials and was confident he could land the body not merely within the clearing, but also at a credible distance from the opened parachute.

The DZ was in an area near Toungoo where the Japanese were reported to be present in strength, but there was no fixed installation which might call for heavy AA protection so they had nothing to worry on that score. The actual site was a triangular patch of paddy beside a well-used spur road that branched off from the main valley road to a large village less than a mile away. It was reasonable to assume that with so many Japanese in the area they would discover quickly, if not actually observe themselves, that a drop had taken place, particularly as Churchill planned to dither about the area for a few minutes like a pilot unsure if he were over the correct site. I have heard that a flare, or Verey light, was fired for the same purpose, but am not sure about this; such flagrant advertising might have evoked suspicion.

They were not worried at D Division about the possibility of a local villager stealing the package. After all that fanfare leading up to the drop it was most unlikely that anyone would dare risk such a theft. The thief would risk not only his own life but those of his fellow villagers whom the Japanese would go on executing in continuous sacrifice until the missing package was recovered. Anyway, a radio transmitter was of no more use to a Burmese villager than was the dead body.

The RAF component of operation *Corpse* went more or less according to plan. Churchill found the DZ without difficulty and after pottering about noisily for five minutes, ensuring his activities were being attended to, and perhaps sending down that fiery signal, he dropped the radio package and saw the parachute land safely on the paddy fields. He then made a wide leisurely circuit to give his despatcher and the conducting officer time to get the body on the slide.

When he finally made the run however, the despatcher came up beside him, just as he was about to give the green light, and reported they were not yet ready; he asked Churchill to roam about for a few minutes so they could get organized. It appeared that in handling the body on the slide the bush jacket had been pulled open, and the conducting officer was insistent that the corpse must go out 'properly dressed'.

So Churchill circled the village and the forest area where the Japanese were thought to have their depot, while the two behind him in the fuselage pulled their dead parachutist back up the slide and buttoned up his bush jacket properly again for departure. Then they moved him carefully back on to the slide, with the broken clip attached to the holding twine of his parachute, and told Churchill they were ready. He circled into position, made the low run-in, the green light flashed, and *Corpse* was finally launched.

When Churchill returned that night from his eight-hour flight in the carbolicized aircraft, he and the conducting officer reported that the drop had gone exactly as planned. D Division were delighted. On the off-chance that the Japanese had been drawn to the paddy field immediately, they set up a listening watch the very next morning.

This was the limit of optimism. More rational calculations suggested a period of patience. The corpse and the radio had to be found, and they then had to be delivered into the hands of the Kempei'tai who might not even have a unit stationed locally. Once they finally did get the documents, they would have to be translated and then studied before they would be able to utilize the potential of the treasure delivered to them out of the skies. It would take at least a week, surely? Ten days, say – and by then the Kempei'tai should come on the air and start transmitting to D Division. Then all sorts of riches would follow for our cause.

The riches were slow in coming. A fortnight passed without a single squeak of Morse from Burma, and D Division began to search for hope amid this expanse of silence. Damage to the transmitter on landing was an attractive explanation. The parachute may have opened perfectly as Churchill had said, but how often had it occurred that a radio was landed apparently to perfection to a reception party, yet was actually damaged beyond use!

It was always happening . . . well, it had definitely happened once. Almost certainly that was what had occurred in this case. And bear in mind also that the Japanese technicians – if in fact any were available locally – were dealing with a radio they had never met before. It could take them another week or so to sort out all these difficulties.

Even when a month went by with no Morse bleeping out to them from Burma the optimists still managed to find an explanation. The transmitter must have been irretrievably damaged, and the Japanese would still be trying desperately with the best technicians available to effect repairs. In case the task was beyond them, and to save time anyway, it would be better surely to give them a replacement transmitter. It could be delivered with suitable reassurances that this was not a peremptory demand to the Japanese that they accept without further delay their assigned role as the fall-guys, but rather that it was a prearranged plan with the operative whom we, in our ignorance, still did not realize had had a fatal accident on landing.

So another transmitter complete with crystal was packaged with great care and included with it was a note that was sufficiently enigmatic to be accepted as genuine clandestine language: 'The promised back-up. Same schedule.'

Just in case the documents had not been recovered they included full copies of them all in the package. The priority for *Corpse* had weakened in the long silence. There was no question of sending out a special aircraft on such a sortie, so D Division had to beg humbly for space on another clandestine's mission. Force 136 was helpful, as usual. They were happy to allow D Division to include their package as a small diversion drop on a sortie planned for *Badger* in the next moon period. It was duly delivered from six hundred feet on a brilliantly clear night and it fell perfectly in the first row of paddy fields beside the road, the parachute settling wide like a huge mushroom. It could not fail to be noticed by anyone passing along that well-trodden road, even by nocturnal travellers.

By this time D Division were so anxious for reassurance that a Liberator flying out to Siam the following night, on a track that took it close by the area, was asked to divert and check the site. The pilot did so, identifying it without any doubt, and reported that the paddy fields were absolutely clean. Had there been a parachute on the ground it certainly would have been visible. It must have been collected, and would surely by that time have been in the hands of the Japanese.

But the blockheads would not use the thing. It was infuriating. D Division were in despair at such professional incompetence. How could you conduct any sort of intelligent espionage operation with people who did not understand the simplest principles of the game? Every night at 10.30 and every day at 11.30 the operator in Calcutta kept listening out for a response, but never a bleep came from the decoy. Weeks passed, the excuses for the silence became muted, hopes became fainter. On the squadron we heard nothing more of *Corpse*.

I never asked Fleming what he proposed to do about this slackness by the Kempei but feel sure that his lively mind continued to devise new schemes to prod them into utilizing the gift he had so laboriously provided for them. Suddenly, however, a miraculous alternative contact was then provided by the Kempei in Malaya. Down there they had more intelligent people in intelligence. This was the moment when the astute

Ibrahim brilliantly capitalized on being netted by the Japanese, and Force 136 handed over the play to Fleming. He and his deceivers settled back happily to deal with this more professional troupe of Kempei in Malaya. On the Burma front our *Corpse* was dead.

After hostilities ended Fleming did apparently make some enquiries in the area as to what had happened when the body was delivered, but it appears none of the locals contacted knew anything about the matter. The Japanese must surely have been drawn close enough to the site both that night and on the subsequent drop to be first to claim the booty, but if so and if they ever made any written record of the incident, it seems to have been lost with all the rest of their records when they were trying to escape before the crushing advance of the XIV Army. Our *Corpse* disappeared without trace.

The European 'man who never was' did apparently achieve an important deceit of the enemy. Not so our man in Burma. He remained true to his nature throughout. In the hierarchy of nonentity our man was far superior – he not only never was, he also never did.

10

The most dangerous periods of any flight are the take-off and landing. This is when the aircraft is closest to the ground and at its slowest, and is therefore most vulnerable to the slightest deviation from normal in weather conditions or the performance of the machine itself. Airfields are designed with a clear flat stretch at either end of a strip so as to extend the chances of recovery from an unexpected incident or, at the least, to minimize the consequences of the unavoidable crash landing.

Aircraft working with the clandestine organizations had to take multiples of those risk periods on every moonlight operation. In order to deliver men or supplies to a tiny clearing down among the trees you had to make the equivalent of about five extra take-offs and landings on each operation, in terrain where weather conditions were nearly always abnormal; and far from having a safety margin at either end of these slow low-level runs, the tiny clearings could be within a tumbling mountain mass where twisting valleys would provide the only means of getting down close to the ground, and the only escape route back up to safe height afterwards. But any unusual incident when you were down in the valley manoeuvring close to stalling speed could be disastrous. That was the vital difference between making a drop in a valley DZ and putting down at an airfield.

One afternoon, that February 1945, we saw a Liberator falter in its landing approach at Jessore. Sometimes in the afternoons when flying was over for the day, rather than go straight back to our quarters I would take the circular route southwest of the strip. There the low-lying land was daubed with pools and lakes formed by the lush green trails of the Ganges, with only a sprinkling of villages embedded in the islet groves of bamboo and palms and dark green mango trees. It was a vacation drive, you were temporarily distanced from service life and war, and that afternoon I was with Egerton-Eves, one of the first pilots to have joined me on the Dakota flight, talking, among other things, about golf courses in southern England.

We stopped at the first lake. There was a narrow band of reeds beside the causeway, then the water stretched away for about a quarter of a mile over to a grassy shore where a cluster of mud huts was embedded in a grove of leafy dark trees. As I stepped down a tonga came clopping along towards us and we held ourselves close against the van to allow it to pass. It went by with a grating of wheels and a visual shock in the form of two rear-facing women passengers in clashing saris, one a livid purple and the other an electric blue. They were each gripping a side of the tonga with two plump hands to avoid sliding off on to the road, and after they had passed there was a pleasant tang of cinnamon in the air. Then the Liberator came blundering over our tranquil scene.

It came rumbling in from the north, about four hundred feet up, with wheels already down for landing, and then, just as he started to cross the water in front of us, an engine cut. We both looked up sharply at the explosive coughing sound and saw the aircraft, with terrifying instancy, begin to slant down towards the water. You would have thought even at slow speed he would have had some help from impetus but there was no sign of it; he slanted straight down as if ricocheting from the actual impact of the stoppage. The faulty engine was on the far side from us; we could not tell how quickly he feathered the propeller, but the effect of the failure was so frightening in speed and attitude that Egerton-Eves called out:

'He's had it!'

Not quite, as it happened. By the time he reached the far end of the lake he had scarcely a hundred feet left, but then at last the thunderous roar of the other reawakened engines began to have effect. He flattened out just before reaching the palms that lined the road over there and, although he seemed to have survived as he disappeared from sight, we both waited, watching and listening for the space of a tensely held breath, before finally letting it out with a whistling sigh of relief.

He landed all right, and was unconcerned that night in the mess; after all, he said, an engine failure was only one lost out of four. But the few hundred feet that saved the aircraft that afternoon would not have been available on a moonlight drop down in a valley in eastern Burma. At least in such an emergency the Dakota would respond far more quickly to increased power, and it was far more manoeuvrable anyway. I had as much admiration for the Liberator pilots as I had for the agents who jumped out over distant jungles, and could never understand the quixotic behaviour of Bob Hodges in flying them almost exclusively during his whole time on the squadron.

It was not only mechanical hesitancy that could bring disaster during a drop; indeed the majority of our crashes probably derived from natural causes. You expect to lose aircraft, of course, if you fly into monsoon storms, but other quite normal weather conditions suddenly become dangerous when you are flying very low at slow speed in mountainous country.

Low flying at speed through a mountain valley can be an exhilarating experience. You sway joyfully into the high-speed turns, and feel lifted up in mind as well as body when you go zooming up to cross so low over the ridges that you set the branches flaying. But then do it again with speed cut back close to the stall, a quarter flap down, wallowing through on currents and swirls and troughs of unpredictable winds, and there is no joy in the experience; the passage has suddenly become a fatally serious business.

Strong wind is of no consequence at height, but it will buffet the aircraft around in a valley leaving you with only minimal control. Wind direction can change abruptly just below a ridge and can cut a vital ten per cent from your dangerously low airspeed. Wispy cloud can come swirling across a ridge and envelop you or obscure your moon light just when you are aiming for a valley outlet. And simple human error or misjudgement which at height or speed would be of no importance could be fatal down there in the narrow darkness where safety margins had had to be abandoned.

The only agents ever killed in a crash on flying operations were six who died with the nine aircrew of a Liberator, which hit a tree on take-off one night from Jessore, and an OSS agent who died with five aircrew when their Liberator was shot down by a Japanese fighter. An agent's outward delivery flight was a risk that he had to share with the aircrew. Statistically, it was the most dangerous part of his whole operation. Once it was over, and he was safely delivered to the ground, he had no part in those subsequent servicing flights where the major risk was incurred.

It was on these flights, supplying the agents once they were securely in place down in their jungle hideouts, that we suffered almost all our losses. It was then that pilots were free to take risks. The men down in the jungle were always exerting subtle unconscious pressure on you to make the drop; you sensed them there on the far side of that massive cold front, or down there under those racing clouds, or tucked tightly into that turbulent valley, waiting there in utter dependence upon you, their lifeline. So you tended to take risks you would never take with them on board. There was no compulsion then about safe drop-height, you got what height you could under the clouds and if a parachute did not have space to open it mattered little. You had at least got something down to them that night.

Occasionally there might be direct pressure from the men in the field. It was not unknown for a clandestine headquarters to tell us if one of their parties was in desperate need of medical supplies or food or ammunition. To be told, for example, that 'the plasma is urgently needed, tomorrow will be too late' is not conducive to a cautious objective approach to a cloud-covered DZ; nor was the message from *Hebrides* in Malaya after they had had no drop for a month saying they were near starvation.

Lee, the Canadian flight commander of the Liberators, had an experience of such pressure when he took off one night for the *Bison* site with, among his load, one particularly precious package. He was told it was 'vital to deliver' it that night.

Lee had a hard night's flight on that one. *Bison* was engaged entirely on intelligence; the men had a hideout overlooking the road to the north of Mandalay, and were reporting the movement of all Japanese traffic – a particularly important task because at that time the army were preparing to advance on the town. The actual DZ for *Bison* was in a valley several miles back from the road, with peaks up to five thousand feet within just a few miles of it. On previous flights the Liberators had had to drop from two thousand feet but on the night that Lee had his 'vital to deliver' package he made a determined and prolonged effort to get down closer to ensure it landed on site.

After a study of the site, and two failed attempts to get down lower than usual – it was full clear moonlight fortunately – he did finally manage to sidle down the slope into the valley and drop that particular package from about fifteen hundred feet but, as he told me afterwards, he felt sure he was not going to be able to get out of the valley alive.

'We opened all the taps wide and prayed,' he said. 'I swear we went between two trees to clear the ridge.'

He thought the vital package had been a piece of equipment essential for some special operation, and it was only by accident that he learned some weeks later what it had actually contained. It had been a parcel of meat; the urgency for delivery had been to ensure that it arrived fresh.

Sometimes the pressure to ensure perfect delivery could come from a most casual remark. We were going out one night on a double drop in the northern area, and learned at the briefing that two Liberators would be joining us at the first site for the *Cheetah* drop. We would be alone on the second DZ, however. This was *Badger*, and I had never dropped there before, but from the information the intelligence officer gave us the site seemed to call for caution. However, there was a major from Force 136 headquarters out on a visit and he subtly negated that warning thought when he said: 'The Libs can't get in – you're their only hope for this stuff.'

I do not know what the actual load was – there is nothing in my notes about it – but those few words in the operations room gave a special importance to the sortie, so it was one of those about which I did make a note afterwards.

It was a smooth trip out, not a cloud in the brilliant night sky, and with the familiar patterned landscape of hills and plain extending out to a misty horizon that blurred dividing line between earth and sky. We were settled there in the heavens some ten thousand feet above the moonlit landscape, like being on a rope suspension bridge that was swaying gently as we looked down at a weed-covered stream flowing slowly underneath, with a few straight sticks of roads, and occasional clearwater stretches of open country.

On the far side of the Burmese plain we caught silvered flashes from the twisting Shweli, and then crossed a final band of paddy fields that looked like grey paving stones laid close against a dark ridge, the first of a series of ridges that faded away within that ghostly haze of the horizon. The hills were scarred with pale patches varying subtly in colour – dove-grey, ashen, ivory, frosted bitumen – ridge after ridge drifting back slowly under our wings until suddenly a pinpoint of bright new colour appeared out of the haze. It developed into clearer view as a line of glowing dots set down in the black lifeless landscape, and when nearer still it became a string of rubies flickering on the leather-tan rectangle lying across the slope. We had arrived at the DZ.

The fires brightened through orange into writhing pyres of flame as we glided down, and wispy smoke veils began to waver between us and the sparkling stars. Down and down, greeted at about a thousand feet by a torch flashing a short and three longs, the letter J as briefed, then continuing our spiral down to about four hundred feet – and still the horizon all about us was littered with stars, nothing to impede our circling flight.

Cheetah was the highest DZ in the area, a smoothly curved hill covered in the whitened grass that marks exhausted soil in the border hills. Here the lumbering Liberators could circle safely as low as they wished, and here one night I had seen one of them leave behind on the centre of the site a cluster of mushroom-like blobs as neatly fashioned as a fairy ring on an English garden lawn. We were first that night, and after two smooth runs all our eight packages were scattered in a wriggly line almost the full length of the fires. Then the first of the Liberators arrived to exhibit their expertise but we did not stay for a lesson. We had to go on to *Badger*.

The Liberators could never hope to reproduce their *Cheetah* patterns there. As we approached the site, the ridges began to flow more quickly beneath, a deep jade green on the moonlit side, velvety black in the shadow, crowding closer and closer until when we finally ended our dead-reckoning run the linear pattern beneath us had disappeared altogether, and we were circling over dark chaos. There were great clods of mountains tumbling about the main ridges, and the ridges themselves were indeterminate in line and height, split into jagged spurs and crumpled into erratic peaks; a landscape which appeared to us like a newly ploughed field must appear to an ant. And down in the depths of a tumbled furrow, deep beyond range of the slanting moonbeams, a triangle of fires flickered into light. This was *Badger*.

We moved in warily. That casual remark – 'You're their only chance' – was subtly impelling however, and as we slid down between the hills I was peering out through the open window for a possible line to a low accurate drop. The site itself was in shadow, down beyond reach of the mid-high moon; on the first trial run we flew out of moonlight at the end of the tiny clearing and the air was suddenly dank as we sheered through shadow, then we shot up clear of the ridge and were once more free in the clean bright light of the moon.

On such a still night it was possible for a Dakota to get down to six hundred feet over *Badger*, but you had to work for it. We had nine packages and the best we could do was to get three out on each run. We approached by a gentle dive down the valley, well below ridge height, straightened out for a three-second green light when the despatcher managed to clear the three packages over the tiny clearing, then the instant the red was called I opened the throttles fully and started a climbing turn to starboard, avoiding the high ground ahead by cutting through a tree-covered saddle on our right. It was a manoeuvre that had you tensed ready for contingency every instant of the run.

You could relax on the downwind leg. We were out of sight of the DZ then, as it was blocked by the tree-covered ridge, but in order to get down low over the site again you had to do a tight steep turn between two pinnacles at the far end. And so it went on for three runs. Then, after the last drop, we continued the upward swoop after crossing the saddle, up and up and up until the stars were all about us again, and I could then lean back in the seat, take deep long breaths, and start thinking of coffee, and the relaxing drop of leaflets yet to come.

On the *Badger* site afterwards I dropped from above the level of the ridge, some five hundred feet higher than that first night when we were 'their only chance'. The DZ was far too dangerous to tackle at normal dropping height; it was sub-conscious pressure from that casual remark in the operations room which fouled up my judgement that first night.

After climbing up into the clear we flew north a little way to drop leaflets and then, on sudden impulse when glancing at the chart with the navigator, I asked him for a course that would follow the dotted line of the Tropic of Cancer all the way back to Jessore – it passes within a few miles of the airfield. The track took us directly over Kutkai, a small advance airstrip on which we could see clearly one of the little L5 aircraft parked by a tent. The whole vast area east of the Irrawaddy down to Lashio had by then been recaptured by the allied forces under the American General Sultan, with his vital hill flank protected by the 101 OSS guerrillas, but the little L5 planes had been landing behind the lines in that area for over a year by then.

The Kutkai strip was short but in the dry season there was ample length for a Dakota to land if need be. It so happened such a need did arise shortly after that moonlight glimpse of the airstrip. A colourful Chinese gentleman had to be landed there.

This was a ferry trip, not an operational flight, for the only Japanese left in that area were isolated parties trapped in the hills. The Chinese passenger was some sort of emissary. He looked impressive in a silk turquoise shirt-coat outside a black ankle-length skirt, and he carried a leather saddle bag that jingled every time he moved it. He was fat, soft-fat, with wodges of flesh under his eyes, and fingers so flabby that a ruby ring he wore seemed to be embedded, just the jewel showing and the gold circlet invisible until you peered for it.

The trip was either for D Division or E Group, I am not sure which. Its purpose, so far as disclosed by our Chinese passenger, was to pay a sum of money to a local war lord for what was said to be 'assistance to Indian prisoners'. Mercenary fee or ransom? I don't know. When we reached Kutkai strip in the late morning a Sikh officer and sepoy were waiting in a jeep and they drove our colourful passenger off southwards towards Lashio, which was about thirty miles away.

A Civil Affairs officer was at the strip. These people belonged to the Colonial Service, part of the government in exile which had been opposed to all clandestine activities ever since the invasion of the country. They had tried to stop Force 136 leaving men behind in the hills, they had tried to prevent all contact with the emerging nationalist forces in Burma, and they had been fiercely opposed to the arming of the guerrilla groups. The man who came up to us that day at Kutkai had no badges of rank. He wore a topee, was tall and thin, and announced himself as 'the CAS officer in command here'. He then went on to incite opposition: 'You people should stay on the airstrip.'

He gave no reason for this order and when I questioned him it seemed to me it was simply an officious act of petty authority. Up to that moment I had had no intention of leaving the strip but it suddenly became an attractive thought. I told him there were 'certain secret intelligence matters' which might require my presence in Kutkai village, refused to give him any details, and made no answer when he said that I should check with him before making any such move. He indicated a small basha hut at the far end of the strip as his headquarters.

The rebellious urge to go into the village did not long survive his departure. It looked to be a walk of about a mile. The road was dusty with jeep traffic, and the scene was not inviting. It was a dreary landscape, not green and tropical but sage-coloured and arid; the hills rising all about the village were almost completely treeless, covered in pale brittle grass and scoured by brown eroded channels, the consequence of poor cultivation techniques. We walked across the hard whitened grass to the canteen where an American sergeant offered to lace our coffee with rum but this did not appeal just then.

One or two trees around the strip looked like potential additions to my tree book so I decided to check them out.

Leaving the others with the convivial sergeant I strolled over towards the nearest one, dense with foliage and a possible mulberry, passing a basha hut outside which a group of uniformed men, whom I took correctly to be Kachins, were squatting in conversation. I called out the Kachin greeting, 'Kaja'e,' and was continuing on to the tree when one of them suddenly started up towards me. He spoke with rapid excitement, white teeth flashing, in a tongue I took to be Jinghpaw and of which I knew no more than a dozen or so words. Then, when he saw I could not understand he beat his chest and said: 'Jessore. Jessore.' And he pointed at me, nodding rapidly.

I guessed what it was all about then. He had a better memory for faces than I had, and when the others, with a little English among them, joined us I discovered I had in fact dropped him further up north in December. He had then been with *Cheetah* but had now joined 101 OSS, to which they all belonged. I asked them about Pete Joost whom everyone knew. He had moved to the south by then, but with the name of Lazum Tang I was luckier. He had been in Kutkai that morning but was due to go down to Lashio and maybe had already left. They insisted, however, that I wrote my name, which I did on a piece of signal pad they produced, and then my Jessore friend went loping off across the dusty strip towards the village. Half an hour later, while I was having yet another lesson in Jinghpaw, Lazum Tang himself arrived in a jeep.

It had been a year since Lazum Tang and I had walked the Kachin hills together. He was now a major in the OSS, in command of over a thousand guerrillas. He was a neat and dapper figure, as if prepared for parade, but even when I knew him at the height of the monsoon in flooded jungle he had always been so. He said he had been sad about the demise of his Chindit group, but not for long because when the OSS took them over he had been promoted major, given far more pay and responsibility, and had encountered a host of friends.

When he asked if I would like to have a look at Kutkai I was happy to agree, mainly to cross the CAS officer. We drove up the dusty road and stopped at one of the Chinese tea houses in the centre of the straggly village. It was a bamboo structure and we sat in cane chairs under a sparsely thatched roof that let in slits of sunshine to line the bare grey earth, while just outside on the road a large lemon yellow butterfly was wavering over a scatter of mule droppings. We talked of his present job, and it was then that he told me about the ambush of the Japanese patrol mentioned earlier; he went over to his jeep to collect the book with the pressed flowers and the photograph.

Outside in the dusty street the passers-by were mainly Chinese, and included two women who hobbled past with feet like tiny hooves, the result of having been bound in childhood. Most were in grey homespun dress but one elderly woman wore a silken jacket of irridescent blue-green, like the head of a mallard in early spring. There was also a younger Burmese woman in a long cherry red lungyi who moved past us in that smooth gliding motion that Eastern women perform with such artless grace in their saris and lungyis; with hidden feet at the base of her straight skirt she went throbbing past us as we watched in grateful silence. Lazum Tang told me that about half the population were Chinese.

His feelings about the Chinese were ambiguous. The Kachin people had suffered much from marauding Chinese over the years and although most of these attacks had come from bandit groups, or local war lords, the Chinese army had also wrought havoc in the retreat of 1942, and even at this time several incidents had been caused by the regular forces advancing down the Irrawaddy valley. Lazum Tang and the rest of the Kachins would have preferred to fight with the American forces alone but this was not possible within the northern command; General Sultan's multinational force comprised two US regiments, a British division, and the US Kachin levies of 101 OSS, but his major manpower came from the Chinese First and Sixth Army groups, so the Kachins could not be selective in alliance. If they were opposed to the Japanese, as implacably they were, then they were inevitably on the same side as the Chinese troops under Sultan.

This alliance, however, did not necessarily include all

Chinese along the border areas, for the bandits and war lords still troubled the villages in the hills. But some of the Chinese regular army officers were sympathetic about this perennial problem, much to the surprise of their marauding countrymen. On one occasion a platoon of Kachin levies returning from a reconnaissance for General Sun's First Army passed through a village where a group of Chinese bandits had commandeered most of the village store of rice, paying for it in worthless Japanese paper currency. With several months to go until the harvest, the villagers were fearful of the future, so when the levies caught up with the bandits later that day they took them down to the road to a First Army unit in the hope of helping the villagers.

The bandit leader had not fought this decision. He said he had paid for the rice, and seemed confident his countrymen would support him against the Kachins. However, the Chinese major ordered them to take back the twenty baskets of rice to the villagers, and he sent a section of his men with them to see that they did so.

The bandits duly handed back the rice to the headman, took back their worthless currency, and thought that was the end of the matter. But the Chinese soldiers had not finished with them. They ordered all the bandits to kneel down in front of the Kachin headman and bow their heads in apology for what they had done. When their heads were bowed the soldiers shot them. They marched off straight away, roaring with laughter, and leaving the Kachins to deal with the six bodies.

The Chinese seemed to be dangerously capricious allies. The Kachins were wary of them in Burma, the French found them mostly unhelpful and obstructive in Indo-China, and Force 136 at least had all sorts of problems with them over Siam, as indicated for example in this report:

Our first contact came from Thais who were sent out by the political opposition to the partly quisling government. They were sent out via China as being the only possible route. At the same time the Chinese were entirely opposed to these messengers, as they aimed to control the future of Thailand

165

. . . In one or two cases they went as far as poisoning them. The death of one of these Thais in hospital at Kunming was attended by our [Force 136] senior representative in China and before he died he was able to give valuable information to our senior Thai representative, Prince Chin Subha Sucasti, whom we sent to China for the purpose.

The Force 136 group *Reindeer*, working in collaboration with the OSS levies, had close contact with the Chinese troops in the northern area. Rubenstein, one of the Jedburghs who had come out to Asia, was dropped in to this group, and he had a meeting with an officer of the Chinese First Army one day at a village. He recorded the following brief conversation:

Chinese soldier: You American?

Rubenstein: No, me English.

Chinese soldier: English velly good.

Rubenstein: Chinese very good. Japanese no good.

Chinese soldier: No, Japanese no fucking good.

That was the limit of their common language and common cause. They parted the best of friends on that simple basis.

Rubenstein told me of an earlier, equally laconic, conversation with the British General Festing whose division was fighting under American command in the northern sector.

'He came up to me – cheery old bugger, grey hair and gimlet blue eyes with a sparkle. Said, "You knocking the Japs about in the hills, eh? Bloody good show! Carry on!" Then he went off on his way.'

He sounded like Sassoon's general, the 'cheery old card' who presently finished off the two passing soldiers with his plan of attack. Rubenstein survived his general greeting.

When Lazum Tang drove me back to the strip that day at Kutkai my Chinese gentleman had already returned, no longer carrying his jingling saddle bag. With him and the Sikh officer were now nine Indians all in new US battle dress. We started the engines and a few moments later I saw the CAS officer come striding towards us from the far side of the strip. We did not wait for his arrival. I waved goodbye to Lazum Tang down by his jeep, then a hundred yards further on taxied close by the

CAS officer standing in rigid disapproval on the dry yellow grass.

I blew him a kiss, but he did not respond.

11

In the winter months you expected to fly over the Chin Hills without any weather problem; there might occasionally be haze which would affect long-range visibility, and there was always a likelihood of mist gathering in the valleys to obscure a DZ, but these were calm weather conditions. It was only when the monsoon began to build up in May that the weather became a continuous fearful threat.

However, every one or two years a frontal system would develop over the Bay of Bengal during winter and bring fierce tropical storms into our area of operations, then for a few days you would be in for a tense and tumultuous passage if you had to take the direct line over the Chin Hills. With peaks such as Mount Kennedy at ten thousand feet you had no hope of getting through underneath the weather, and with cloud tops well over the ceiling of our aircraft no hope either of climbing above it; so the only way forward in those typical monsoon conditions was to fly through the cloud mass. And once inside the swirling darkness you had no idea where the storms were raging until one suddenly engulfed your aircraft, overwhelming it with blows that sent you swaying and hurtling about in a black maelstrom where an evil force seemed intent on wresting the controls from your hands.

On such nights there would be many unsuccessful sorties. And this was acceptable. The other flight commander and I, and likewise Bob Hodges above us, would keep telling pilots to abandon an operation if they met violent weather conditions, particularly if encountered anywhere near the DZ, for almost certainly the site would be cloud-covered anyway so the risk of flying through the storm was without purpose. You kept

168

stressing that an abandoned sortie was only a postponement, a few days here or there made no difference normally to the men in the field.

Very occasionally however, so rarely that some pilots never met the circumstances during their whole tour of operations, time did become of the essence. Then you had to deal with the weather, to fight a passage through the fury of a tropical storm in order to reach the DZ which was suddenly so important. Such was the situation, with timing crucial and weather threatening, the night we sent four Dakotas out on D Division's *Cloak* operation.

A little military background is necessary to appreciate why timing was so important in this instance. A vital date in the Burma campaign, one of annual importance throughout the country, is 15 May – the traditional start of the rains. The monsoon has arrived. If by that date in 1945 the XIV Army had not captured Rangoon, with its port of supply, then they would be fighting at the end of a six-hundred-mile supply line which was impassable most of the time because of flooding rivers and inundated roads. Meanwhile, as opposed to that perilous task, General Kamura's army would be holding solid defensive positions in the two great valleys that had to be the lines of our advance, and the Japanese supply lines to the capital would be close at their back.

So Slim had to capture Rangoon before the fifteenth of May.

One of the major obstacles to this crucial schedule was the Irrawaddy river. He had to get his army across that great barrier. To prevent this General Kamura had assembled over 100,000 men in the Mandalay area ready to move quickly to any of the likely crossing points. Slim's plan was to make the apparent main crossing some miles north of Mandalay, drawing the enemy forces into battle there, and at the same time an army corps would loop around in a wide arc to cross the river a hundred miles south; once over it they would move quickly across the plain to cut through the Japanese supply line back to Rangoon. The added advantage of this plan was that at the point of the planned rupture, Meiktila, there were three airfields which would be invaluable for the further advance southwards. Meiktila was the key to the corridor that led down to Rangoon.

It was General Messervy's IV Corps which was given the vital task. For his secret crossing he chose a spot which, once over the river, would give his tank force an easy run of fifty miles due east over open country to Meiktila and its airfields. His plan was a miniature of the main one; he would make a decoy crossing about fifteen miles north of the chosen spot and so distract the local Japanese forces from concentrating against his real passage. He called in D Division to arrange this decoy, and D Division called on us at 357 Squadron to carry their plan into effect.

The weather was normal winter—gentle during the five days build-up to the operation and in this phase, as part of the overall plan, it was hoped to use our Lysanders in a deception role; unfortunately the aircraft were still in crates – they did not begin operating until after the fall of Rangoon – so the USAAF took on the job instead with three of their remarkable little L5 aircraft. The Japanese had withdrawn to the east bank of the Irrawaddy, and on our side of the river D Division laid out a paddy-field airstrip which was hidden from direct view of the enemy by low hills along the bank.

For five days the American pilots kept buzzing their little aircraft about the strip, flying up to the river and back again, circling above the area, landing and taking off more or less continuously throughout the day and even doing night-flying practice. Though only three aircraft were involved their fury of noisy activity throughout the twenty-four hours was such as might be made by a couple of squadrons. They carried no armament and took no photographs; their sole purpose was blatant activity.

During this period D Division doubtless had their double agents in India making a contribution to the *Cloak* deception, but their channels of communication were so complicated at the Rangoon end that most messages reached the Japanese as corrupt nonsense. As a more reliable radio contribution therefore, D Division had positioned four signals men at the actual fake site on the Irrawaddy bank, and for a week beforehand these radio operators kept up continuous voice and Morse transmissions over a whole range of frequencies. It would have been impossible for anyone with a radio within twenty miles of the site not to know that there was exceptional activity taking place in the area of the decoy crossing.

In addition to all this ethereal activity, they also had some signallers using Aldis lamps along the bank at night. There was also a team felling timber along the bank and using noisy power-saws which were churring and surging away most of the day, they had a single tank clattering about in full view of anyone with field glasses on the far bank, and there were a couple of jeeps raising dust all day in and about the thin indaign jungle of the west bank.

Two actual drops were made during this period. The first was one to a non-existent agent near a village about a mile back from the river over on the Japanese side. This was a 'replacement radio for the one with the faulty receiver', and although there was sufficient information to enable a good intelligence organization to utilize the set, D Division had probably abandoned all such hopes by now; the purpose of the drop was contained in the enclosed orders to the imaginary operator, giving him the name of the divisional staff officer to whom he should deliver his report immediately the area was in our hands. The clear implication was that the crossing would be made very near his post at the decoy site. For good measure there was also a love letter from the agent's imaginary girlfriend which gave incidental information about troop movements towards the area.

The second drop was made by a Dakota one moonless night about ninety miles north of the decoy site. The aircraft free-dropped a load of material which could possibly have come from an aircraft that had exploded in mid-air – there were bucket seats, engine cowlings, most of an elevator, unopened parachutes, kitbags with personal belongings, and one haver-sack containing divisional orders and maps concerning the crossing at the decoy site. The aircraft bits and pieces had come from a Dakota crash, so they were authentic; they were tossed out in bulk over the Japanese positions on the far bank, together with a grenade that exploded in mid-air to draw attention to the falling debris – and to explain it.

The staged crash followed. A few seconds after delivery of the haversack and the associated debris the aircraft was over the river and there it let fall a bomb container filled with explosives and flares. The contact fuse resulted in a spectacular explosion when it hit the river; the flash must have been visible for miles around and the sound have carried almost as far. It was hoped the Japanese would find the documents and assume they had been blasted clear in the mid-air explosion that apparently sent the aircraft crashing into the river. The fake aircraft crash is reminiscent of the car crash Fleming and Calvert had staged two years previously in the retreat from Burma.

While all these activities were taking place in Burma, D Division had been assembling the material at Jessore for the actual decoy crossing. We had four Dakotas assigned to the task, for although the total load was only about eight tons it was bulky and complicated, requiring an extra despatcher to help eject it, and it had to be carried within the fuselage; external containers were of no use on this operation, because there would be no ground party to receive the drop and to open the packages. It was all to be landed on the site of the decoy crossing, an area on the far bank that was covered in dense secondary growth and coursed by twisting overgrown chaungs where the only way through was by laborious cutting of a track.

The eight tons of packages were largely made up of 'bicat' crackers, 'paragons', 'pintails', and 'parafexes', all of them conspiring to give the impression of a parachute bridgehead landing which was giving rise to an untidy and complicated battle. The 'bicat' crackers, of which each aircraft carried ten sacks, were timed explosives, each unit being made up of fifty crackers to a fuse length. There were two types of 'parafexes': one simulated rifle fire, the other faked grenade explosions, and these were landed by parachute. 'Paragons' were dummy parachutists, human-sized figures which fell like normal parachutists and carried a variety of pyrotechnic devices on delayed fuses for post-landing ballyhoo. And finally there were the 'pintails', which were Verey light signals, the normal three colours of red and white and green, but in this instance fired off with a usefully noisy bang.

All of these devices were fitted with time fuses, so set that the variety of battle sounds would continue from late that first night right through most of the next day. The following night, by which time it was hoped all enemy forces in the locality would have been drawn into the noisy trackless decoy area, the real crossing for the Meiktila assault would be taking place fifteen miles to the south.

Such was the design of operation *Cloak*.

I had originally set myself down as one of the four on the job but then the weather problem arose, and I decided to switch jobs with Read, a young warrant officer from Sydney, whom I had originally detailed for an operation far over near the Siamese border. This was to the ISLD *Bloodhound* site, located some two hundred miles beyond *Cloak* in the Wa States which are tucked into the mountains of the Chinese border. There were eight agents to be dropped, Chinese and Karens, and their task was to gather intelligence about the activities of the Chinese communist groups which had begun to surface among the Wa tribes that straddled the border.

The briefing that morning followed the normal routine. There were about eighty aircrew in the room, and a layer of blue tobacco smoke was settled about three feet above their heads like a false ceiling when I ascended the platform with Bob Hodges. Standing by the huge map at the back of the stage I was above the layer, and the faces of those at the back of the room were merged into the blue haze like ridge trees on the horizon in late Burmese spring. The meteorological officer gave the weather details I had already heard from him; an extremely active cold front moving across from the northeast was already covering the area of *Bloodhound*, and was expected to reach the Chin Hills during the night.

When the met. man had finished I took the floor to brief the Dakota crews. I addressed myself mainly to the group on *Cloak*; it seemed likely that the cold front, which was going to trouble us in the distant sites, would not get down to their area until some hours after their drop, but they would certainly meet it on a direct route back to base and I suggested they pass south around it if the going was rough. This was not an order; we never instructed pilots to follow a specific line against weather, the decision was always theirs to make as they felt fit at the time.

While the met. officer was answering questions Bob Hodges had a quick word with me about *Cloak* timing, and we decided to put forward their take-off by three-quarters of an hour; this put them on target just after dark, giving the maximum margin against the chance of the cold front reaching their DZ before they dropped. So after the signals officer and flying control had finished, and Bob and Peter Farr of 358 Liberators had dealt with squadron matters, I gave the altered time to the *Cloak* crews and we then dispersed, some to stay behind and work out courses or adjust crews, some back to offices, and some down to the flights to prepare their plans or make their flight tests.

When the crews were clambering into the trucks I plucked out Read and took him down to flight headquarters in the van. He had only learned about the switch when he arrived for briefing and knew nothing about the background of the operation, so on the drive down to our offices I told him the story given to the others the previous day. My interest in the purpose of our flights, which Moore had discouraged when in command, was not just idle curiosity; I am sure all the crews felt more involved when they knew why they were making a particular trip.

It was mid-afternoon when we assembled down at the flight hut for the evening's operations. As the timing of our take-off on *Bloodhound* was of no importance, for we were bound to hit the bad weather anyway, I had delayed our own take-off for half an hour so that I could check the *Cloak* crews away. Had there been any problem I would have been happy to dump our ISLD operation and take over one of the four, for timing was vital in their task, but they all arrived down fit and ready, and there were no problems with any of the aircraft.

After they had been driven to their aircraft I went outside to check them away. Standing on top of the grassy slope of the empty dispersal pen next to our flight hut I could see the other pens further back from the strip, and watch the truck deliver the crews one by one. Presently the engines began to cough into life and the twonk-twonk-twonk of the coppersmith bird in the distance was overwhelmed by sound as the pilots revved up in their cockpit checks. It was a cool bright afternoon, the sky a pale baby blue of cloudless purity, and just beside me down the bank a huge butterfly with cinnamon-barred wings was lolling about in the still air above a cassia bush on which the pendulous sprays of pastel pink flowers were just beginning to appear. It was difficult to accept there could be threatening weather anywhere in such a tranquil world.

The first aircraft came thundering along the taxi-track with a splutter and popping of exhausts, I waved to the Canadian pilot who responded with a thumbs-up sign and then enveloped me in a miasma of quivery petrol fumes as he continued on past the pen to the strip. The others followed within a minute or so, Read the last, and he responded to me with a grin and a wave of his hand out through the open window of the cockpit. I waited on the top of the slope until all four were airborne, watched one of the Liberators stagger into the air from the last yard of the strip, then walked back to the flight hut and joined my crew. We collected our parachutes and piled into the truck to be driven down to the lush green semicircular mound within which D-Dog was parked; the crimson flags of the control locks were hanging limp in the cool air of the calm afternoon.

Charles O'Brien was already at the dispersal pen with his eight ISLD Joes. He too had heard the weather report and was anxious about his night's sleep, for he would have to be on hand if we brought them back.

'Think you'll be able to do the drop?' he asked.

I told him to wait there in the pen until we arrived back, when we would be able to give a useful answer.

The trip turned out to be every bit as bad as threatened. We had a dreadful night of it. Over the Chin Hills the cloud was already piling up in great frothy clumps, a thrilling but menacing sight with the sun behind us; the topmost crowns at ten thousand feet or so were a blinding white, and below that they ranged through deepening pinks to orange until down close to the hills the basal structures were crammed together into a dark solid mass. We flew above in the still air but all the time as we continued eastwards, and the stars began to pierce through the steely blue sky, the cloud tops kept rising steadily and crowding closer about us. At last, somewhere over the Burmese plain, we had to give up our attempt to stay in the clear, and before it became too late I chose a gap and we plunged down the chasm into the darkness beneath.

After that it was a struggle all the way across the plain and into the hills of the frontier. For a time there were gaps in the black void, but then the clouds finally closed on us and we never saw the moon or stars again all night. Apart from the flashing instants when lightning gave brief glimpses of the swirling tumult that had engulfed us, it was all blackness, a violence of blackness.

There was never a chance of finding our DZ. We reached the area, still without sight of sky or ground, still being hurled about within the turbulent mass, so I abandoned the operation at once and fought a way round on to a reciprocal course back to India. By this time it was a tense physical struggle to keep even vaguely on course and height. Flying the aircraft was like trying to quell the struggles of a mad beast; you needed strength and speed to react to the savage jerkings and twistings of the control column. Finally, when we were suddenly caught in a down-draft that slammed us down more than three thousand feet in a breathless drop, with the altimeter hands twirling around like a spring-balance dial when the weight is removed, I had had enough.

'Stuff this!' I called to the navigator. 'We'll put down.'

This was not as difficult as it may seem. We had been given a line bearing on the radio and that coupled with a timing check gave us a rough idea of position. On that basis we set course for the area north of Mandalay, the widest part of the Irrawaddy plain, and after about a quarter of an hour on that heading through boisterous blackness we reckoned we were at about the centre of the low land. There we circled down as gently as the turbulence would allow and finally came clear under cloud, flying through intermittent rain squalls with vague patterns faintly disturbing the darkness below. Then came a more definite touch with ground as we glimpsed a light or two, and we circled wider and wider in confidence until we finally discerned the great river glinting down in the blackness. After that it was easy. We followed it northwards, found Myitkyena flare path temporarily clear of rainstorms, and there we lurched and bounded and swayed about in a diving approach to finish at last, the first time for five hours, in straight level movement as we ran to a stop at the end of the strip.

Every single one of the eight operatives had been sick, most of them untidily so. And most of them repeated the action next morning when we found enough gaps at twelve thousand feet to make a bumpy but clear passage across the Chins and back into the limpid clarity of a Bengal winter morning. We landed at Jessore to learn that Read and his four crew had failed to return from *Cloak*.

The operation had been successful. All four aircraft had reported back to base that the decoy crossing-site had been positively identified and their devices landed precisely on target. Having had a comparatively clear outward trip they had all started on the same direct line home to Jessore, but by then the cloud mass that had caused me so much trouble some hours later was already piling up over the mountains, so they found themselves having to thread a passage between churning heads of cumulonimbus which were towering above the Dakota ceiling. All encountered violent turbulence, hail and lightning, when climbing through to height and Read could well have blundered into the centre of the fury. You need luck to survive those encounters. Such tropical storms have been known to tear a wing from an aircraft.

When I spoke to the other three pilots not one of them said he had thought of turning back from the violent weather and looking for shelter in northern Burma. Nor would I have done so on my first operational tour. You take risks then because you know others will do so, you do not want to be the one who has chickened out at a challenge. You care too much what the rest of the group will think. I turned back because I had no such care. Those times and fears were past; I had aged. Bob Hodges would have done the same. You would hear some young Liberator pilots telling how they had managed to weave a way into a valley for a low drop over a difficult site, and Bob would shake his head and tell them that on that site he had dropped from a thousand feet higher. After his record on operations in Europe he felt no need to prove himself to the group.

I took off on the search with a scratch crew next morning but the clouds were still in a turmoil along the line of the *Cloak* flight-plan and it was impossible to work systematically. We had to confine ourselves to the places where we could find gaps in the cloud mass; once below it we hunted about what clear space was available, mostly only a single valley, then had to climb above cloud again to search for another gap that would allow descent. Even below cloud, when bouncing and sliding and thumping about in the turbulence, the landscape below filled you with despair; down in those dark green tree-covered ridges, where even the streams were not visible in the bottom crevice, a thousand aircraft could plunge into the jungle morass and disappear completely from aerial sight.

This was not an operational flight, so it is not on record in the Operational Record Book which lists individuals on each sortie, and none of the Dakota flight was on board, just a navigator and two radio operators from a disbanded squadron whose crews were idling at Jessore awaiting posting. The only record of the trip therefore will be in our personal log books, so no one can be publicly embarrassed if I tell what happened towards the end of our search that day. The navigator was a young officer who had never flown in the monsoon, and he had no experience of the low-flying activities normal to the specialized role of our squadron, so the weather that day and the way the machine was flown must have been a terrifying revelation to him.

Flying low in bad weather within mountain valleys, with wind-ripped clouds being flung at your machine, can be fearful or it can be exciting. You slide and slip and bounce and judder in the wild wind gustings, hurtling towards tree-tops, and then suddenly you are hit by an air rebound and smashed back clear with a thump you can actually hear – like the noise you get when you kick a soft pillow. The unexpected uplift squashes you down into your seat, and your grip clamps in spasmodic reaction on the control column. You see the tree trunks go flicking past like roadside palings, you swirl over the top of the ridge and then down the other side as if borne on a wild surf; it can be exhilarating if you have the controls, speed in hand, and the confidence born of experience in those conditions.

That day, however, the task was too serious for idle enjoyment of the bouncing ride. All the time I was peering down between the mounded tree-tops looking for a glimpse of angular shape or metallic flash. The actual chance of sighting any such evidence of the crash was remote beyond reason but the search had my concentrated attention. Which was why I failed to notice the navigator's behaviour.

He must have been suffering for some time before I finally noticed it. After a couple of hours over the area, I was just about to abandon the search when I saw another gap away to starboard and made a diving turn to plunge through it. It was as I glanced past him towards the cloud opening that I saw he had his hands held up close by his face, his fists were clenched and he was beating them violently against his cheeks. For a moment I was too busy to pay attention, but once we were safely below cloud base and being flung about in a wide valley with plenty of safe space all about us I could take time off to contact him.

It was clear he was terrified. Distraction seemed to offer the best sedative and I asked if he had any idea where we were.

He would not, or could not, answer. He had stopped beating his cheeks by then and his arms were lowered against his chest, but they were still shaking so violently I could hear the thudding sound and see his shirt fluffing from the blows. I leaned over to bang him on the shoulder, not a nudge but quite a hard whack, and told him to go back to his desk and check our position – there at least he would not have to bear the sight that was so terrifying him. But he shook his head quickly and turned away from me to face the side window, and I suddenly decided we might just as well finish the job anyway so I rapped him on the back.

'We're going back,' I called. 'Give me a course for base.'

He did not move at once but at that moment my attention was distracted. We had been flying up the valley with gaps overhead and only a scattering of clouds covering the ridges. Then, in a matter of seconds, there were no gaps above, and cloud was pouring into the valley from the northeast; it was as if a great cloud-dam had burst somewhere in the mountains up there, releasing the contents which came rushing down in riotous volume and threatened to engulf us in the flood. The ridges on both sides of us had also been covered now, except for one possible escape to clarity on the western side; there a narrow gap of light remained between the torn edges of cloud base and the palisade of trees along the top of the ridge which was a few hundred feet above us. I flung the wheel over, opened the throttles in a climb, and we bumped and swayed into line for the gap of yellow light leading to the plain.

We were within seconds of the ridge and I had to squint against the clear light of the low sun directly ahead of us in the west. Then a long streak of cloud suddenly flayed off the torn mass just above, and in an instant the ridge was covered. I pulled back the stick very slightly, just enough to make sure of missing the trees but not so as to climb too high into cloud, and held it for perhaps half a minute which I reckoned would put us over the ridge. The aircraft was being flung around so violently in the swirling whiteness it was a strain of muscle to keep the control column aligned as I eased it gently forward, and then we came sheering out of cloud in a sliding downdraft on the far side of the ridge, in the clear.

It was only then that I realized the navigator was holding my right arm, reaching across and clutching it with both hands and whimpering with fright. We could see only one more low ridge ahead, and it was clear in sunlight with open paddy fields beyond. There was no longer any flying concern, and after a quick glance across at him I had a sudden fellow-feeling of sympathy, thinking how stricken I would be had anyone seen me in such a condition. I did not like to look again in his direction until he was composed, so I made a business of adjusting the throttles and pitch, resetting the gyro, checking the petrol tanks and then fussing with the trimming wheel until he had had time to recover. Finally, in a casual voice and still not looking at him, I asked about the course for Jessore.

'I'm going to it, sir,' he said. 'Right away.'

He was more or less in control by then but it took him a few fumbling moments to undo the seat belt; he then checked on the course I was steering and went back to work out something more precise. It was of no importance really, I could find my own way across the plain in the gentle light of the setting sun.

One reason why I had felt so much sympathy that afternoon was because less than a year earlier I had myself suffered an attack of fear just as severe as his. It was when I had to lead a patrol down a jungle path where the Japanese were known to be present and had already killed one of our column in an ambush. It was the inaction I found almost impossible to bear that day, just walking along slowly and waiting to be killed – unable to fight, to run, to shout; absolutely nothing to do but just walk steadily forward to the certain death that terror insisted was waiting for me at the next bend.

It is a common fallacy, particularly in the armed services, that action and courage are inseparable. The men who are awarded medals for valour have always done something with a gun or a ship or an aircraft; stories and fantasies, too, will concentrate on energetic violence as the hallmark of bravery. But I realized that day in the Kachin hills that the man who can take action in a desperate situation is the lucky one; blasting away with his gun he obliterates fear with sound and fury, he escapes its threat. Not so the poor wretch who has nothing to do in a terrifying situation. He has to exist with the fear. The men who really deserve the medals in a fighting action are the inactive dependents: the aircrew sitting idly in their seats, the cooks down in the battleship galley, the army signallers waiting at their radios with no messages to send and none to receive.

I frighten easily, but I sensed no fear at all that day when we hunted for the missing aircraft. There was far too much on hand and mind to dwell on danger. The poor wretched navigator, the radio operator and the despatcher were the ones who had time to suffer the fearful test. But if a medal had been awarded for that flight it would have been to me it came . . .

'Despite the appalling conditions Squadron Leader O'Brien pressed on with his mission. Disregarding all danger, and

181

showing courage of the highest order, he continued with great determination to persevere with his task and . . .'

It is an absurd system.

The missing Dakota was not located for several months. When it was finally discovered it was found to be lying on its back, not crumpled as if in a diving crash but just crushed down flat into the trees. The likelihood was that it had been caught in a downdraft that hurled it straight into the mountainside.

One of the most unhappy tasks associated with the loss of an aircraft is writing the personal letters to the next of kin. What on earth can you say which will give any degree of comfort to a mother who has lost a son? Does it really matter to her that he died bravely, foolishly, accidentally, or to no purpose? You have never met the parents, you have no idea how best to present the awful event, and sometimes you know almost nothing about some of the men who died in the crash. To be on a Committee of Adjustment, having to go through the effects of those who were killed, is always a poignant task, but at least you have a formula to work to, and practical details to organize. There is no such distraction when you sit down alone in the office to write a personal letter to the parents of a young man who has been killed. I used to dread the task.

Apart from killing thirty-three of our aircrew at Jessore during that February–March moon period, the weather also, inevitably, had a serious effect on the success rate of actual drops. The huge frontal system which had penetrated into Burma had also covered most of Indo-China and this caused a serious setback in the planned build-up of operation *Bazaar* in that country.

Bazaar had come into being after a visit by François de Langlade, who headed the Indo-China section of Force 136 in Calcutta. We had landed him inside the country three months earlier in order to discuss resistance plans with the French military authorities. Like that French group who had gone in from China, he had also worn an RAF uniform while in the air, which in his case was to avoid risk of being shot as a spy if the aircraft force-landed. Once on the ground he consulted with the Gaullist supporters in the French army, who were anxious to start operations against the Japanese, but he advised that no overt action should be taken at the moment. The immediate objective should be to build up a large supply of arms in the northern area, where the Japanese were not present in great strength, and only when the forces were well supplied, and the time convenient within SEAC plans, should direct action be initiated against the Japanese.

The build-up plan was put into effect immediately de Langlade returned. We were notified of some fifty DZs where reception groups could be positioned, and more than a dozen radio stations were established. Once we began to increase the sorties however, the Japanese quickly became aware of this increase in nocturnal activity, and intelligence reports suggested they might take preemptive action before the resistance forces were fully armed and ready. To counter such a threat it had been decided that a major effort must be made for that February–March moon period, and the bad weather therefore was particularly disastrous for Indo-China operations. Noise had been made over the area for no return, for not a single one of the ten Liberators allotted to *Bazaar* that month had been able to deliver.

Moreover the pressure to deliver had resulted in the loss of those additional aircrew, twenty-eight dying in the three Liberators which failed to return. It was the weather that destroyed them, all crashing in the mountainous northern area during the period when that massive cold front came in from the South China Sea.

It was an ominous warning of what we could expect when such conditions became normal once the monsoon arrived in a few weeks' time.

12

The resistance movements within the occupied countries in South-East Asia were predominantly communist and, despite opposition from the Foreign Office and its dependent Colonial Office, it was the deliberate policy of Force 136 to collaborate with these underground movements. This action was not taken in disregard of the consequences, but was calculated on the basis of saving lives in the war against the Japanese armies of occupation. The moment the armistice was signed, however, the Foreign Office was able to get its own back on SOE, dismantling the organization completely and seizing all its records – and downgrading the honours and awards recommended for its leaders.

In Malaya the communists formed the core of the AJUF (Anti-Japanese Union and Forces) and Colin Mackenzie, the head of Force 136, was well aware of the threat they posed to the colonial administration on its return. Malayan police officials who had joined Force 136 advised him of this but 'they also agreed that while our support might contribute to strengthening them [the communists] it would be worth taking the risk if it also helped us to learn more about them, more about their characters and relative positions in the party, and more about their organization in general.' In the end, after months of argument, permission to arm the AJUF was finally given.

Our first successful drop in Malaya had been the OSS *Cairngorm* already mentioned, and just ten days later Ken Jones, commander of the Liberator flight, made the first drop for Force 136. This was *Hebrides*, led by Dobree who had been an agricultural officer in the Malay civil service. He quickly established liaison with the communist guerrilla forces, and, by

184

the end of February, had built up a network of intelligence units, was training his own force of a hundred men, and was arranging DZ receptions for other landings in his area.

One of those we delivered to him was the *Beacon* party, led by Doug Richardson who had been in the Malayan Survey Department. Richardson was one of those parachutists we landed in a tree. Had it been a blind drop he probably would not have survived, such was his plight, but luckily Dobree's reception party was waiting for him that night and, even more luckily, they had an expert visitor on the site. Richardson was caught high up in the tree, dangling helplessly from a branch and unable to do anything for himself except shout to the searchers down below; even so it took them some time to home in on his calls, so densely packed were the trees in the area, and it was only by flashing torches up at the canopy that eventually they saw him.

But how could they get him down? The tree was without any branches at all up to about thirty feet, impossible for them to climb, and to no purpose anyway; Richardson could never make that bare-trunked descent without a rope, and they had no ropes with them. They did, however, happen to have a fascinated spectator, an aborigine who had watched the wondrous event of a drop from the sky, and it was he who casually solved their seemingly insoluble problem. He must have wondered why these supreme creatures who had mastered flight did not themselves take the obvious course to get their friend to the ground.

He examined all the trees in the vicinity and chose one that was easy to climb and much shorter than the monster from which Richardson was dangling. He climbed the tree almost to the very top, which was at about the level of the branch on the other tree where the canopy of the parachute was caught. He wrapped his arms tightly around the pinnacle of his smaller tree, clamped to it like the star atop a Christmas tree, and began to set it swaying in the direction of the other one. With a great swishing of branches he gradually built up the tempo and range until finally he was able to reach out and grab part of the canopy.

After that it was easy – in principle. He climbed down while keeping a hold, first on the rest of the canopy, then on the shroud lines, and finally drawing Richardson himself close against the little tree. Once Richardson had firm grasp of a rescue branch he hit the release of his parachute harness, and was then able to make his own way down the easy tree to the ground. The aborigine, who could see no problem in recovering the parachute, was delighted to receive it as a gift.

In Siam the arming of locals had been delayed while the Foreign Office continued to quibble about cooperation with a government with which we were officially at war. The OSS, untroubled by such protocol, arranged with the RAF to have one of their men implanted in Bangkok while Force 136 was still trying to bring from England the man they wanted to work in the capital with the Regent.

However, this OSS initiative was not universally popular in the American command. General Wedemeyer, the US chief in China, was not at all eager to become involved in the intricacies of Siamese politics. He told the British representative in Kunming that he would be content to leave Siam entirely to Mountbatten, 'but this should not be mentioned to any American'. When this report reached Mountbatten's headquarters it probably went into one of those numerous files marked 'for UK eyes only'.

In Burma the plan to supply arms to the AFO, the Anti-Fascist Organization, had brought Mackenzie into bitter conflict with the government in exile. In their opinion the AFO were nothing but communist terrorists, and they managed to persuade General Leese, commander of all land forces in South-East Asia, to issue an outright ban on the supply of arms to anyone associated with that organization. This meant in effect that we could not drop arms to anyone at all in Burma, even to the fiercely pro-ally hill tribes. How could one tell if a villager, whether from the plains or the hills, was associated with the AFO or not?

Nothing could have persuaded Mackenzie to accept such an order. Operation *Character* was just about to be launched in Karenni and, although Slim had stressed that it should be

186

concerned solely with gathering intelligence, the recruits would certainly have to be armed. The Karens had suffered grievously the previous year when their families were executed by the Japanese for not betraying Seagrim; on that occasion they had had to bear the agony in silence, unable to offer armed resistance, so they would have to be armed and trained to fight if they were to provide the intelligence service the army required. Otherwise, they might well not cooperate at all. And who could blame them after their experience the previous year?

Mackenzie informed Mountbatten that to deny arms to the partisans in Burma, even for self-defence, could well be to condemn them to death. He could not be a party to such a policy. He declared that he would be forced therefore to cease all operations behind the lines in Burma.

That argument was decisive. It meant, as he well knew of course, that either Force 136 must be allowed to drop arms to whomsoever it wished in Burma, or that the comprehensive intelligence service just about to be launched for Slim and his XIV Army would have to be scrapped. Mountbatten, who was in sympathy with Mackenzie anyway, responded promptly and rescinded Leese's order. So the plan for *Character* was put into effect.

In Indo-China we did not supply arms to the nascent communist forces under Ho Chi Minh; he was the protégé of the Americans, and it was the OSS in China who nurtured the development of his organization. Our dealings were with the French army; they were the major resistance force in the country, there were no political objections to supplying them with arms, and so we flew guns into the country night after moonlit night in the early part of 1945. Thousands of guns, as I saw myself one afternoon at Jessore.

It was in the late afternoon in February and I had been out with Barlogie, an Australian who was second-in-command of the Dakota flight, to see the duck come flying in to the large lake just north of the airfield. The sun was setting as we drove back along the metalled road, scattering in brilliant blue flight the rollers perched on the swooping telephone wires, and passing a long row of betel-nut palms that flicked line shadows across us to give a sort of visual corrugation to match the juddering road surface. Even after months of the dry season this area remained green and flashing with water. We kept clattering over little wooden bridges across the shreds of the Ganges, and saw white egrets picking their delicate paths along the edge of the roadside pools. On one large lake a fisherman standing in water up to his thighs looked like a torso sliding about the glassy surface when he threw his net.

A figure appeared ahead of us on the road, arms waving, with a three-ton truck beside him on the verge. He was a sergeant from 136 stores depot – the truck had a fuel problem and he had sent the driver on the four-mile trek to the airfield for help. He asked us to collect the driver and take him straight to the MT section, for he himself did not want to be out at night with this particular load on the truck. As he was talking I had walked across and looked over the tailboard at the load that so concerned him.

It was an extraordinary sight. There was a great tangled mass of sten guns piled up in a slope that rose from just below tailboard level to about five feet high against the cabin. They were not in boxes, just the bare primitive stens in an untidy heap; they reminded me of a picture seen as a child of a vast pile of crutches and sticks that a nun told us had been left by people who had flung them away at Lourdes after being miraculously cured of limb disabilities. The sergeant explained that the guns had been in sacks on arrival in Calcutta but as they were going to be packed into parachute containers at Jessore they had simply been tossed into the back of the truck as the spring action of each was given a check. There were over a thousand guns in there.

We picked up his fat driver waddling along in a sweat-dark shirt and shorts about a mile away and dropped him off at the MT section where they dealt with the problem. In the mess that evening I discovered the guns were urgently needed in Indo-China. A French conducting officer told me that the reason we were putting up so many flights just then was because most of the French army in the country had shifted loyalty towards de Gaulle; once this became clear to the Japanese there would be trouble and the army had to be ready to fight. Then he went on to rail against the Americans for their anti-French policy.

The impression given from documents now released is that the Americans were often embarrassed by the problems arising from their anti-Gaullist policy and that they really would have preferred to have nothing to do with Indo-China at all. Roosevelt, at the Cairo conference, offered to give it over complete to Chiang Kai-Shek, who declined the offer out of hand as he had no desire to become involved in the age-old differences between the Vietnamese and Chinese. And General Wedemeyer was reported to have included it with Siam in his gift offer to Mountbatten, but nothing seems to have come of that either. So the Americans, seemingly against their wishes, were stuck with the pursuit of their anti-Gaullist policy.

This resulted in one casualty in the top echelon of Force 136. Colin Mackenzie's deputy, Brigadier Guinness, had been responsible for ordering our trip with de Langlade into Indo-China to organize the resistance. Unfortunately, when sending a signal to London about the trip, Guinness mentioned that de Langlade was also taking a personal message from de Gaulle. That was disastrous. And surprising too, for Guinness would surely have known about the business of hiding French identity with RAF uniforms, and the background to such subterfuges. Mackenzie, who was in London for consultation, saw the signal and was horrified. 'The very last name he should have mentioned,' he said.

American dislike of de Gaulle meant that his involvement in any action automatically rendered that action suspect. The letter was really quite innocuous, it simply urged support for the resistance, but the American deputy director of P Division had not been told of a de Gaulle association with the mission. He might well have vetoed it had he known this, and felt that he had been deliberately deceived. Mountbatten decided that the blunder was too provocative to pass over and so he sacked Guinness. When Mackenzie was told the decision on his return he was not surprised, for he knew at once that when P Division saw de Gaulle's name on that signal heads would have to roll.

We made the first Dakota drop to Indo-China that critical

February. Three of our aircraft had been fitted with long-range tanks built into the cockpit bulkhead, but for this Indo-China flight an additional six tanks had been laid out on the fuselage floor. These were made of a black fibrous material, coupled up to one another and the wing tanks with an array of red valves and copper pipelines that made the Dakota fuselage look like the deck of an oil tanker. Once fuel-loaded, the air in the fuselage was heavy with the murderous stink of petrol from the ominous black cylinders.

These additional tanks were only fitted temporarily for the *Satirist* operation which I flew that February moon period to a DZ about fifty miles west of Hanoi. We took off from Myit-kyena just after six one afternoon and were airborne until nearly eight o'clock the next morning when we landed back at Jessore. Compared to the twenty-four hour trips the Liberators were making to Malaya it was of little account, but nearly fourteen hours for a Dakota was a record in South-East Asia.

The task of the *Satirist* group was to contact General Sabat-tier, the leader of the resistance, and open a radio link between him and Calcutta. With such a quantity of fuel our Dakota payload was limited to six men, and their personal kit in separate packages; the rest of the equipment was carried in a Liberator which travelled directly from Jessore, and was due to arrive at the DZ a quarter of an hour before us. Because there were several Japanese airfields to be crossed *en route* to the DZ, we waited at Myitkyena until sunset, once we had topped up our tanks for the long flight over Indo-China to the Pacific coast.

I saw the clouds of little green parakeets again that evening. Nine months earlier, after being beaten back from the river with heavy casualties, we were trudging across the flooded paddy fields in the late afternoon when I saw the parakeets for the first time. Tired and silent in defeat, just the creaking jangle of mule harness and soft thudding steps as we plodded back with our wounded, I suddenly heard a strange rustling sound, like autumn leaves being whisked along a dry road. As I looked up the noise changed into a screeching twittering sound, and I saw the little birds like a myriad of arrows darting overhead, dark fir-green shapes streaming past under the lowering monsoon sky. Now, in the cool clear light of the February evening, they flashed bright and splendid in passage, reminding me of a field of lucent green grain-shoots flickering in a breeze.

The sun sank into a glowing ember sky and we took off in the shadows, climbing up over the slate-grey Irrawaddy into a second sunset where we could see the green-silvered ridges of the Kachin hills rising clear as islets in a sea of purple valleys. Ridge after ridge they drifted past beneath us, like a tidal flow of debris, the shadows in the valleys rising steadily all the time until there were only isolated peaks of lighted green down below; then at last the shadowy flood welled over them also, and darkness covered all the land. Overhead the sky began to prickle with stars.

On this occasion I had a second pilot, the Canadian Cooper again, and after an hour or so I left him in control and went back to check on our Frenchmen. There was a wooden catwalk down the centre of the fuselage between the black fuel-tank cylinders, and all six parachutists were sprawled about the flat area near the door. The leader raised himself and waved a hand as I grabbed a static line to steady myself into a crouching position beside him.

'Tout va très bien?' I called.

This was something of a *tour de force*. The words were the title of a French song that Timmie, my fiancée back in England, had taught me on our last leave down at the cottage in Sussex, and my knowledge of French sound came almost entirely from a few such songs and phrases picked up from her. The written language which I had been taught at school by a Christian Brother who came from Coonabarrabran, and the accent acquired from him, together with my rudimentary vocabulary, would always produce a strained look of concentration on French faces. With the parachutists that night however, as so often, goodwill bridged the deficiency.

I gathered from the captain's reply that he had no problems and, though not understanding an additional comment, I did manage to grasp his question about timing, and was able to get through to him the simple message that we had another four

191

hours to go. The rest of them all leaned forward with that familiar brow-wrinkled concentration as we continued our loud exchange, with me able to respond in some fashion or other to simple practical questions dealing with height, airspeed, wind and so on, but whenever they made a comment between themselves I was almost invariably lost. Nonetheless when I left them and went back up the catwalk, gripping the roof cable to balance, I remember feeling pleased at the performance.

The moon rose as we flew over the southwestern corner of Yunnan province and presently the jade-green ridges were once more standing clear in relief against the valleys. Then over Tongkin the shadow-edged hills smoothed away at last and we were over the vast flat rice fields of Hanoi province – like a netting stretched over the land – with wooded settlements blurred by smoke, and moonlight flashing from the irrigation canals. It was nearing midnight when we arrived at the DZ, by which time the despatcher had removed the door panel, the Frenchmen were all humped ready with parachutes, and the first package was ready with static line attached and standing by the open doorway.

The moon was full, so brilliantly clear we had no need of the C of fires which began to flare before we actually reached the site. It was so bright you could perceive colour – creamy rectangles of open paddy, a dark tan square of bare earth, and among the dozens of men on the ground one was wearing a wine-red cloak or blanket. There were no opened parachutes on the site and we could see no sign anywhere of collected chutes or stores; this was surprising because the Liberator should have dropped fifteen minutes earlier, and the site could not possibly have been cleared so completely in that time. I told Cooper to keep a sharp lookout, for to share a drop site with a Liberator was always apt to be dangerous.

As we passed directly over the fires we had a signal. Within the gap of the C of fires two men were standing close together and one of these flashed what I thought was four dots – the letter H. The correct identification was supposed to be N. When we had passed on over the site, and banked to bring the signallers into view again, the flashing continued, and he persisted with

192

this meaningless series as we circled watchfully, the moonlit shadow of our Dakota jiggling across the paddy bunds of the site.

'That's sure no N he's flashing,' Cooper said.

It certainly was not. So we had a problem. We had been told that the Japanese had recently become suspicious about French intentions; the activities of our Liberators had not passed unnoticed and there was always a possibility that the Japanese might light a decoy sight and trap a load of parachutists as soon as they landed. They must have known the regular pattern of fires used in the area, always the semicircular C instead of the usual Burma T pattern, so it would have been easy enough to copy; but they would not know the recognition letter because that was changed for every drop on every site. To avoid agents falling straight into the hands of the enemy therefore, we had been specifically warned not to drop to a faulty recognition letter.

I was not inclined, however, to obey this sort of order without question. We had travelled over a thousand miles to get to the site, and to reject it because of what might have been a misunderstanding would be stupid, whatever the staff might have ordered. The first thing to do was to make a further check on the site, for the absence of the Liberator did suggest that we might have made a mistake. So I flew over to the railroad near Hanoi and there, from an incontrovertible pinpoint of a rail junction and bridge, we made a carefully timed dead-reckoning run back to the map point marked as our target. Exactly on time we were back over the same site, the same fires, and greeted with the same meaningless series of torch-flashes. There could be no doubt that we were over the correct DZ.

There were two reasonable explanations for the faulty signals: either the ground party had been captured by the Japanese who now controlled the site, or there had been a misunderstanding about the recognition letter to be flashed. There was only one way to discover which of the two explanations was correct and that was for someone to go down there and make a positive check. It was my logic which produced that decision, but I had no intention of risking another man's life to implement it; the only man to make that decision was the man to make the test. What I had to do was to explain the situation to the leader, and he would then decide whether one of them should so risk his life, or whether the operation should be abandoned.

Explain to him. In French. With a man's life dependent upon our understanding. There was no way out of it – we had no other apparent channel of communication, no one else in the crew spoke French. I was the best we could provide.

I called for a signal pad from the wireless operator and then handed over the controls completely to Cooper. My whole mind had to be given to this problem of communication. I had to keep the message simple, within the constraints of my Australian schoolboy French, and yet make certain it was understood. So I planned it out in short separate sentences. These I wrote down in capital letters so that I could point to them if misunderstanding arose. It took about five minutes to get it all ready and then I asked the navigator to go back and bring the captain up to the cockpit.

When he arrived I addressed him as 'mon capitaine' (the phrase sounded vaguely familiar) and drew him up close by the throttle box so that he could see the site, for we needed all the visual help that was available. I also turned up the cockpit light, for I had the paper in front of me – and still have it today – and counted off the sentences with raised finger, which also served to pound down any attempt at interruption from him:

'Une: La lettre juste est "N". Dah-dit. "N". Vous comprenez?'

He did.

'Deux: Il ne transmitte pas "N". Vous voyez?' I pointed to the flashing lights. He agreed it was not 'N' and said something else which I refused to hear.

'Trois: C'est possible qu'il est un Japonais.' As feared, this produced a voluble dismissal of any such possibility, but I hunched up against the noise and waved him to silence. I had to keep rigorously to my track. Once diverted we would be in a quagmire of misunderstanding.

'Quatre: Je ne vais pas faire tomber tous les hommes dans

cette danger.' 'Faire tomber' was the best I could do; it seemed unlikely that a verb 'dropper' existed. He appeared to understand and, from his gesture of dismissal, to feel this was a ridiculous caution.

'Cinq: Je puis faire deux choses – A. Je puis retourner à Jessore avec tous le monde. B. Je puis faire tomber un homme seulement. Si tout va très bien avec el, nous verrons la lettre "N". Si tout no va très bien, et nous verrons encore cette dit-dit-dit-dit comme ça (pointing down to the meaningless flashes still continuing from the DZ), je ne vais pas faire tomber les autres.

'Bon. C'est tout. Qu'est que tu veux, mon capitaine?' The 'tu' slipped out – the whole phrase was one that Timmie often used to say to me.

The conversation seemed to be a complete success. I did not understand precisely what he said but had no doubt he understood the arrangement perfectly; and that in beating his chest and repeating 'Moi – je vais' that he himself would go out and make the check.

So we shook hands, he patted me on the back and wished *me* 'Bonne chance', while I was still fumbling for words to wish him good luck. Then off he went to prepare for the drop. Cooper, impressed by my performance, spoke enviously of such facility with the language. I took over the controls and was sitting there all aglow, tightening the circuit to bring us into line for the drop, when the navigator came up beside me with one of the Frenchmen in tow. The man spoke to me in faultless English with a public school accent:

'The Captain asked me to check with you, sir. Is the arrangement that he will drop alone in the first place, then we follow only if the correct letter "N" is flashed from the ground?'

This chap had heard my strained efforts to communicate when we were grouped down at the back of the fuselage earlier in the flight and had not given a hint of his expertise. Why on earth hadn't he told me? He was quite hurt at this sharp question; he thought I wanted to practise my French, he said, so he had not interfered. He had only come up now, he explained – doing so with brutal clarity:

'Because the captain was not sure he understood what you were trying to say, sir.'

So much for my Coonabarrabran accent. Cooper diplomatically busied himself peering closely at the instrument panel after the Frenchman had gone, and there was no further reference to linguistic expertise that night.

We proceeded with the operation. As usual the despatcher dropped a single package on the first run and this landed at the far end from the gap where the signaller was standing. I made the necessary green light adjustment on the next run and managed to land the captain just inside the top of the C of fires. In a tightened circuit we watched him closely in descent. He rolled on the ground and we saw him shed the parachute immediately he was upright, then he started running towards the C gap where the signaller was standing. From there a palely dressed figure moved across to meet him.

The torch had stopped flashing during the drop but the signaller now began sending up the same nonsensical series of dots as before. But the captain, drawing the paler-dressed figure behind him, closed quickly on the signaller and when they came together the flashing stopped. There was a pause of a few seconds and then the torch was directed surely towards us with a slow deliberate signal:

Long-short . . . long-short . . . long-short. The letter N.

The other men followed the captain down, then we gave them their packages. After that there was the customary low farewell-run directly over the site, the despatcher probably waving from the open door, and then we climbed away towards the clustered diamonds of Cassiopeia, underneath the moon in the deep blue velvet sky.

On the return journey the radio operator picked up a transmission of music which for a few minutes came through with thrilling clarity. It was the Mendelssohn violin concerto and it swept me back to a night on leave in Sussex when we were listening to the concerto on a portable gramophone out on the lawn, while above us a little pipistrelle was converting the music into flight. Like the violin, it darted and swerved with effortless ease in a vivacious aerial dance of gay abandon, diving and glancing above our heads in an ecstasy of flight. But on this night over the mountains of Yunnan the music was only a taunting memory, for it suddenly began to fade; despite the efforts of the radio operator it became fainter and fainter until finally it passed beyond ear-strain, and at that poignant moment a Chinese male voice broke in with a high-pitched tirade that shattered all memory and brought me sharply back to the business of flight.

The sun was rising behind us in the east as we passed over the Chin Hills, a clear, clean, cloudless dawn. For a little while the colouring was exquisite, a deep orange glow as if from a vast fire beyond the dark violet ridge, the mist a soft pink on the slopes, and golden wedges of sunlight splitting the forest in the transverse valleys. The light expanded quickly to blaze away the colours, and as ridge after ridge passed beneath us the mist was seared away steadily by the sun, and the bulges of forest began to emerge glossy green in the clear morning light; then the last of the hills ebbed behind us, and in the distance, beyond a thin strip of patchwork plain, we could see at last the wide blue water of the Bay of Bengal.

There had been no sign of the Liberator all night. We discovered the reason when we landed back at Jessore at eight that morning. They had, as briefed, reached the site about a quarter of an hour before us, but after circling the faulty signals for a few minutes the pilot had rejected the reception and turned back for base – as he had been specifically ordered to do in such an event. A two-thousand-mile journey wasted because of a misguided order. I felt sorry for the pilot and that night Bob Hodges, who was always sensitive to a crew's disappointment at a failed drop, called him over to share a drink with us. He told him that he had been entirely correct in his action.

'Don't take any notice of what the squadron leader did,' he said. 'He's an ignorant Australian, he doesn't always understand orders.'

The following week the Japanese army of occupation suddenly abandoned all agreements with the French forces, and in a midnight coup they seized control of the key points in all Indo-China. Meetings had been arranged with French officers in garrisons throughout the land, a carefully planned scheme which found thousands of them suddenly taken prisoner in the midst of a social gathering, and the majority were then immediately executed.

'Mon capitaine' died that night.

13

I first met Colonel Peacock one morning in mid-February when we took him on a practice jump. He was waiting outside the aircraft, the nine others in his team lined up behind him as if on parade, and when I introduced myself he jerked my hand in a firm grip and made a critical comment:

'They told me seven o'clock.'

It was five past. In the dispersal pen across the taxi-track the crew of the other Dakota were greeting Major Turrall's group as they tumbled from their truck, then they all massed together about the fuselage steps in a chattering throng. Ours, however, was a solemn group. Colonel Peacock, slightly below my height but about fifty pounds heavier, a solid square chunk of a man, bristly moustache, eyes narrowed under bushy eyebrows as he glanced in disapproval towards the other noisy group, stepped aside to let me mount the steps. He had nothing to say.

Ten minutes later I banked the aircraft steeply to watch him make his descent on the practice DZ, the first of a stick of five. He tugged the shroud lines, landed with flexed knees exactly as in drill, then immediately stood upright and thumped the parachute release. The colonel was not a man to go rolling about on the ground to ease a fall.

Peacock was in his fifties, born in India, and had spent most of his working life in the Burma Forestry Service. He had started his war in scouting and intelligence duties, work for which he was well qualified because of his knowledge of the jungle – he wrote a book on Burmese game – and his supreme command of the language; an old Burma hand told me Peacock was the only European he could never distinguish from a native in speech. By 1944 he was in command of a large guerrilla group operating behind the lines on the Arakan front, and the importance of that front happened to diminish just when Colonel Gardiner at 136 Calcutta headquarters was planning *Character*. He decided that Peacock would be the ideal commander.

However, the nature of the operation changed presently, and a single commander was no longer practical. The XIV Army finally decided that Force 136 could be useful, not in guerrilla activities but in gathering intelligence, so *Character* was expanded to cover three separate areas in the Karen hills, each an independent command. Peacock would be in the centre, Major Turrall in the southern section, and Colonel Tulloch would follow later in the north. Peacock had not been happy about becoming part of a trinity, having already commanded his own guerrilla force, and at the planning meetings in Calcutta he tended to carry on as if he still held the stage – 'a real prima donna', Gardiner said wearily.

The plan was that on the opening night we would fly four Dakotas with fifty men to the Peacock DZ, and two more aircraft with twenty-four men to Turrall's site. I decided to take Peacock in the lead aircraft, not so much because of the importance of his entry but because on blind drops you sometimes had to discuss a difficulty on site with the leader, and it struck me that when circling a DZ at night the colonel might be a problem up in the cockpit if your view of the situation, and final decision, did not accord with his. It seemed right I should be the one to face that problem if it arose.

When I first saw the aerial photograph of the DZ in the operations room I had misgivings. It was an abandoned rice clearing, a taungya, and it had patches of scrubby growth unlike anything I had known in my jungle trek – I had no idea if it was a danger to parachutists or not. The site was too narrow to give a safe line clear of the patches, and after studying the photograph with decreasing enthusiasm for some time, I decided to have a chat with Peacock.

Force 136 had three basha huts for their people out to the west of the airfield. At the far end of the huts was a single amherstia tree, and at this season it was covered with an immense number of vermilion flowers, the petals tipped with gold – it reminded me of a Christmas tree, all its tiny candles alight. Colonel Peacock was sitting outside in a chair by the tree, oiling his revolver. He nodded a silent greeting and went on pushing the cleaning rod down the barrel of the .38 as he waited for what I had to say. With his head lowered I could see through his black hair a long pallid scar across the skull where a dah had nearly ended his life in a Burmese uprising in 1915.

'I'm not very happy about your DZ,' I told him.

His manner changed at once. He banged the gun down on the oily rag and raised a huge first in vehement agreement. Just what he had told those fools in Calcutta! A stupid choice! It was rugged country, there was a 9000-foot peak only a few miles from the DZ, there were few villages around – all unfavourable factors in trying to raise quick support against the Japanese. But the idiots in Calcutta had refused to change the DZ. Maybe I could make them see sense?

I was not going to be drawn into his battle with Force 136 staff; my concern was merely the safety of the drop site and I wanted him to tell me something about those bushes. However, all he would say was that he had not liked the look of them himself in the photograph and then he went on again to urge that the whole force be landed on the Turrall site. When I told him we on the squadron could not interfere in such matters he became curtly uninterested in further conversation – until my Wingate experience happened accidentally to emerge, and then his manner abruptly changed again. He looked up in approval.

'You're a jungle wallah, then?'

He began to talk. Most of his work had been in central Burma but he had been in the Kachin hills during the First World War so we had memories to share. He seemed to know every creature in Burma that walked, crawled, flew or swam; to have shot, trapped or hooked them at some time or another, and to have eaten them cooked in a variety of ways. His knowledge was practical; what fruits and plants could be eaten, what trees were useful – teak for ship decks, pyinkado for railway sleepers, padauk for gun carriages. I told him about an afternoon when we had halted by a padauk in flower: the delicious fragrance had been draped down like an invisible veil you could walk through as if passing a perfume counter in a large store, and he said:

'Can't remember the smell myself but they make a good yellow dye.'

I thought he would admire Wingate, an enthusiast of jungle warfare, but he dismissed our campaign as an extravagant waste; with five per cent of the manpower and material lavished on Wingate, he said, he could have stopped Japanese traffic throughout northern Burma – got some practical benefit for the resources involved. In particular he ridiculed the punishment Wingate set men who committed grievous offences while behind the lines – banishment from the column with just a rifle.

'Damn sight *safer* by yourself than thumping about with hundreds of men and mules,' he said. 'With a rifle and ammunition you can live like a lord in the jungle.'

Just then Major Turrall came out on to the veranda, attracted perhaps by the sound of Wingate's name. Turrall was a wiry little man in his fifties who had worked as a prospector; he always wore a huge sombrero pushed down on his head and would peer up at you from under the shady brim. He had been associated with Wingate in his Abyssinian venture, then again on our Chindit operation in a D Division-type stunt; Turrall had gone off into the jungle with a small unit of men and animals to fire machine guns, set off explosives, cut conspicuous tracks through the bamboo and leave trails of mule dung, all designed to give the impression a full Chindit column was in the area.

He and Peacock seemed to have little in common. There was sharp disagreement between them that afternoon about Wingate – Turrall was a fearless little man, rank carried no weight with him – and it only ended when a flight of duck passed low across in front of us. The drakes, as opposed to the drab ducks, were a spectacular flash of colour, chestnut breast and blue-grey wings, white-streaked heads that gleamed like burnished copper in the low rays of the setting sun – a magnificent sight. Peacock gave a quick keen glance, identifying them on the instant.

'Garganey,' he said. 'Not very good eating. Small and bony.'

Turrall disagreed again. He said all duck were tasty, it was a matter of knowing how to cook them. Peacock said the best way was to fry it with plenty of nga-pi, the pungent acrid sauce used in most Burmese dishes, which, like Bombay Duck, is based on fish left to rot stinking dry. Turrall did not think much of that; he said the only way to cook duck was to roast it. I left them disagreeing.

There were no difficulties about Turrall's operation. The plan was for his two aircraft to fly together to their site where the first plane would drop Turrall's party who would then show a torch line for the second group. The chosen site was a huge clearing with no high ground nearby, a perfect DZ.

The difficult Peacock site, however, called for a more studied approach. I would take off in the lead aircraft, and the other three would follow at quarter-hour intervals. Once Peacock's team were safely on the ground I would fly ten miles south to Nattaung, an 8800-foot peak which was a menace in bad weather but a useful landmark in clear moonlight. The other three aircraft would fly there direct and contact me on RT for final advice on the drop. If there was no word from me they had to abort.

On the afternoon of 20 February the sun was setting when we drove down to the flight hut for the launch of *Character*. I had Peacock and Turrall with me, the others were already waiting outside by the truck. Turrall went across first and started waving his hands and shouting as he tried to separate his men, and then Peacock, who had been strapping a map case to his chest, said:

'I'll divide mine into the four aircraft loads.'

It was fascinating to see the effect of his entry into the straggly crowd of British and Karen parachutists. It was like that of a magnet passed under a paper that holds some iron filings, which swirl around in instant reaction then stop abruptly in a neat pattern imposed by the magnetic field. Peacock simply moved through the throng and then four compact groups were suddenly standing ahead of the truck, while the other twenty-four men with Turrall were still swirling all about the taxi-track.

We were airborne just after dusk. After about an hour's flight, when darkness was just beginning to highlight the stars, the navigator returned from a fuselage check to report that Peacock and his men were all stretched out to sleep in a row down the floor, using their parachutes as pillows. We flew steadily on through the calm bright night across the silver streaks of the three great rivers and the trellised paddy fields of the plains, then followed the valley road eastward from Toungoo into the Karen hills. There, after a five-hour flight, we came to our DZ.

It was a shocker. The brick-shaped clearing was on a far steeper slope than suggested by the photograph, with the narrow axis running across the slope. That meant we had to head down the valley to drop, missing the first quarter because of those suspicious growth patches, then we would have to slam on full throttle in a steep climb to clear the opposite ridge. It would be impossible to let more than two men out on each run, for overshoots would fall into the precipitous valley which, from its impenetrably black shape, seemed to be solid jungle. With that sinister threat alone I might have rejected the proposed site.

There was, however, an even more compelling reason to abort. This was the evidence of human presence. On our first approach, slanting down from ten thousand feet, a number of small fires had been visible. Taungya jungle clearings are burnt off in a line blaze and can leave scattered smoulderings for a day or two afterwards, but these were not dull red broken lines. They were bright little individual fires. There were groups of men down there.

The fires had been doused by the time we made our low-level inspection but figures had been clearly visible scattering from them. I could think of no reason why Karens would be out at night in abandoned taungya, land on which crops could not be grown for another ten years, but it was easy to imagine a Japanese force lighting fires to cook rice and warm themselves five thousand feet up in the hills on a February night – and dousing those fires instantly on the approach of an inquisitive aircraft.

Instead of calling up Peacock, who would now be hooked up and waiting near the marker package at the doorway, it seemed worth doing a wide circuit so that both he and I could check out any alternative sites in the area. I did so, but could find nothing of promise, so after a few minutes' fruitless search I decided that our major section of *Character* would have to be aborted. The navigator went back to call up Peacock with the news and I prepared for battle.

There was a short delay – he had to unhook his static line from the roof cable, and divest himself of parachute harness and all his gear – so I flew on a steady course to give him a flat platform for this dismantling process. When the cockpit door finally opened, the roar from the open fuselage surged in upon us and I waited until he had come up beside me at the controls before breaking the news.

'I can't let you go. Two reasons: the site is too dangerous, and I'm pretty sure there are Japs camped on it.'

'It's your decision, but I think you're right. Those fires looked fishy to me.'

That was all there was to it, much to my relief. We were on the same side. He refused the offer of coffee when he learned there was not enough in the thermos for all his men and then went back to tell them to take off their parachutes and relax. I called up the other aircraft, told them the operation was scrubbed, and we flew back to Jessore where we learned that Turrall's group had been successfully landed, the two aircrews had already been debriefed and were by then content in their beds. We had only an unsuccessful sortie to enter in our log books.

However, in one sense, vitally important for the whole *Character* operation according to the Colonel, the trip *was* a success. He wrote:

The wisdom of this cancellation was seen shortly afterwards when Major Turrall's group, which had landed safely, found from the local Karens that the place was indeed an enemy camp. There can be very little doubt that, had the drop been attempted then, the result would have been disastrous, not only for those actually jumping, but for the operation as a whole . . . there is no doubt that the first stick on to the DZ would have been at once attacked by the enemy encamped there, and would have been lucky to escape into the jungle with their lives. Such a scattered few, if indeed they got away at all, would have been without wireless communication, and with only the barest essentials that were on their persons when they dropped . . . And consider what would have been the chances of Turrall if the locals, instead of seeing us follow him into their area, had heard the attempted landing at our DZ had been summarily put down by the enemy. Such news would have spread like wildfire and there surely would have been no rising. *Character* operation would have failed at its inception.

The conclusion is egoistic. I do not know what we said on our return. I did make some notes on this sortie but they finish with our departure from the DZ, and the Operations Record Book does not even mention it (historians should note there are many omissions in the ORBs). But certainly I would not claim to have saved *Character* operation by my decision to abort. I think it equally certain that Peacock himself did believe his presence was essential for success. But although he did make a major contribution to *Character*, he was only one of the several separate commanders who did so, and even within his own group there were good men who could have assumed efficient command had the need arisen. *Character* was far too diffuse in nature to founder because of the loss of one man, however important his role.

The morning after our unsuccessful sortie there did seem some evidence of the operation being critically poised. Turrall reported the Karens dithering about support and one can sympathize with their caution after the sufferings they endured when helping Seagrim. It was all very well for Turrall to say that this time many soldiers would come to train and supply them with arms, but they would like evidence of such wholesale commitment before again risking those murderous Japanese reprisals.

Ritchie Gardiner, back at Calcutta headquarters, was fully aware of the importance of landing the rest of the party. Once he had my report about the lack of alternative sites in the vicinity of the original choice, he immediately signalled Turrall to accept the others on his site. This was the height of the moon period, our aircraft were already committed to other operations and we could find only two spare Dakotas that following night, so it was decided that Peacock would go in with half his group and the rest would follow when we had planes available.

I was already committed to an ISLD sortie that night and saw no need to change the arrangement; with the colonel going to a prepared reception there should be no need for any final consultation. Nor, in the event, was there any problem, and all landed safely. The advent of Peacock and his group, together with a supply of arms, tilted the scale in favour of Karen support. At a village meeting the same evening the local chiefs decided to accept the offer of ten rifles for static levies in each village, and to allow young Karens to join up as mobile levies on full army pay. However, the purpose of *Character* was still to gather intelligence only; arms were solely for defence.

To complete the launch of *Character* four of us took off the following night for Turrall's site, two carrying the rest of Peacock's band, the others loaded with ten tons of arms and ammunition. Among the Joes we carried that night was Duncan Guthrie, in my aircraft. He was a huge man, well over six feet tall and heavily built, a most impressive figure with a black beard of solid growth. He had been lucky to survive when dropped the previous year as a Jedburgh – parachutists landed behind the lines in France after D-Day. He and his companion had been landed miles away from the reception party and when they started hunting for the maquis next morning they met up with a Belgian on the same search so invited him to join them. They came upon the maquis presently but were met with fierce suspicion which seemed justified when presently, under questioning, the Belgian was revealed as an infiltrator. The maquis shot him then and there.

Why they did not shoot the others also, for they had arrived as a unit, Guthrie never knew. There was some delay, however, during which he was able to persuade them that he could prove he and his companion were genuine British agents; he said that if they listened to the BBC that night, when the personal messages were sent to various operatives in Europe, they would hear one for Guthrie saying: 'La lettre issue du lit'.

Fortunately the BBC did put out the prearranged message that night, and thereby saved their lives.

We had another brilliant night for that final stage of the *Character* opening. The ridges of the Chin Hills were silvered in the moonlight, the valleys velvety black in shadow, and the geometrically cut figures of taungya were like brown suede patches sewn on the mountain slopes. One or two of the taungya had already been fired, though we were not yet in March, and the sites were like pools of lava, with glowing embers breaking through the grizzled crust and streamers of smoke wavering up the dark slopes. I had a second pilot again, so that gave me an opportunity to go back at one stage and check on our group. Again most were asleep on the floor of the fuselage, but Guthrie and another officer, Ansell, were awake, and I spoke to them for a few minutes about the usual things . . . time of arrival . . . weather prospects . . . present height, and so on. Both were looking forward to the jump.

Returning to the cabin, shutting the door with that soft fluffing sound that cut you off from the noisy uproar of the metal fuselage, I had again that vague feeling of guilt about the discrepancy between their situation back there and ours in the cockpit. It was dark and hard in the fuselage, there was a smell of sweat, a sprawl of bodies, a litter of equipment; but once the door was shut I was in comparative quiet and luxury; carpeted floor, cushioned leather seat, softly glowing instrument panel with the needles all steady in symmetry, a smell of leather and coffee, and outside the clear wide windows the diamond-studded immensity of the Burmese night. And we would be staying up there with the stars when they went plunging down into the jungle.

The DZ was on a ridge. From the pinpoint of an arrowhead bend in the silvered trail of the Yunzalin Chaung we could pick out the grey crescent clearing about ten miles away. At our approach a T-shaped series of tiny glowing embers began to emerge from the pale moonlit curve amid the dark hillside trees; as we planed down the fires brightened into lively flame, and when we flew low over the site the grey drifts of smoke were set swirling like flimsy curtains against the starry background. A torch at the head of the reception flashed a short and two longs, the letter W. It was clear to drop.

Our marker package fell almost in the centre of the DZ. With such a good opening we could afford a long green on the first drop of Joes, which Ansell was leading, but after those first four landed perfectly things started to go wrong. Only two went out next time because one of the Karens slipped as he moved forward, so the despatcher had to hold back the others, and in the final run the man immediately in front of Guthrie hesitated at the doorway and, despite the despatcher's thrust, managed to keep a grip on the frame. This was when Guthrie dealt with the little Karen problem by 'winkling him out'.

All he probably did was lean against the slight Karen – with his huge figure that was persuasion enough. Unfortunately by that time the red light had flashed and Guthrie himself was too far committed for recall. He landed beyond the end of the T stem, which should have been safe enough anyway, but there were a few scattered bushes whose shadows were merged deceptively with substance in the moonlight, making them look more solid and menacing than they actually were.

'I thought they were trees,' Guthrie told me later. 'I remembered being told that if you were going into trees you should always cross your legs, otherwise you might never have children. So I crossed my legs. That was my mistake.'

'Why?'

'Because they were just little bushes. They would have caused no problem with future parentage, or with my ankle, had I done a normal landing. But I crashed down into one with crossed legs and that was it. I broke my left ankle.'

His mistake might have been less injurious had he not been so heavily overladen with complete webbing, packed pouches, pockets stuffed with rations, a full haversack strapped to his chest, and a carbine slung around his neck. With that load he needed great expertise, and not a little luck, for a safe landing. Even experienced parachutists are wary about night drops, and moreover this was 5000 feet up where the air is much thinner, so altogether the chance of injury must have been high.

Such was the difference between these overloaded night landings at height and the daylight jumps at Jessore that some people less experienced than Guthrie would claim afterwards we had dropped them from too low. Ansell applied no such blame in his report on the drop:

> The next stick parachuted down. Perhaps it was the thin air at that altitude, perhaps only imagination, but they seemed to drop like stones. One came down with a rush near me, landed flat on his back, bounced, and lay still. It was Rifleman Ba Tun – wrapped up in his parachute cords like I had been, but otherwise all right. He was soon disentangled and directed to the RV with the rest. Not all were so lucky, for there occurred two bad accidents, Captain Guthrie and Rifleman Lu Dan sustaining severe injuries to the ankle, from which they were unable to stand at all, let alone walk.

It took Turrall and his men a few minutes to come to Guthrie's aid for they had assumed he would walk back to join them, and meanwhile the second aircraft dropped Lu Dan, who broke an ankle, and the leader Major Poles who cracked a rib. All the Joes carried a little phial of morphine; they administered these to the injured and after that, Guthrie said, all was euphoric. He could not have cared less about his ankle, about a nearby Japanese patrol, or the war or the world. He kept telling Turrall that they could carry him to the planned base, which was twenty miles away and across mountainous ridges; Turrall, looking at Guthrie's bulk and knowing what the trail was like, had little to say during this airy description of his morphian scenario. But by the time the other three aircraft had all dropped their loads the effect of the drug was beginning to wear off and Guthrie himself suddenly realized the absurdity of his fancy.

'You'll have to leave me,' he said. 'It's impossible to carry me that far.'

'I'm glad you said that,' Turrall replied. 'I was going to tell you that's what we must do.'

So they did. They put him in the care of the locals, together with Lu Dan and the radio operator who had burnt himself badly with a signal flare. The three were hidden in the jungle, the others moved off to their operating areas, and when the Japanese arrived two days later they found not a trace of the fifty men who were the nucleus of *Character* operation.

Up in the air that night we knew nothing of the accidents. We had a problem on the final run. The last package had a faulty static line, so short that when the parachute opened the shroud lines caught the tailplane so heavily that the stick jumped in my hands. It was exactly the same sort of jolt you get when a control surface is hit by gunfire, but not having heard nor seen any flak I rejected that explanation. A night fighter was equally unlikely. Although the controls still seemed quite solid I kept worrying about the cause, testing elevators and rudder, as we set course for base. It was a relief when the despatcher, having pulled in the static lines and replaced the door, came up to tell me about the faulty parachute.

We landed in the misty pre-dawn, had our debriefing session in ops, tired but quietly content with the night's work. Then it was to our quarters with the dew glistening on the grass and Indian bearers drifting about the paths between the huts . . . sleep till late morning . . . roused by the heat to shave and shower and dress . . . down to flight headquarters comparing notes and consoling those that failed . . . to Bob Hodges's office to discuss the coming night . . . he asks about *Character* and you say it went without a hitch . . . back to the mess where you are having a drink with him and Lee who commands the Liberator flight when Bunny Warren comes in to join you at the bar:

'You *did* make a cockup of it last night, Pat, didn't you!'

It is then that you hear the field report. Just the bare sad facts sent through on radio, broken limbs putting three men out of action, nothing that might explain or excuse an apparently botched job.

It was a long time later that I heard Guthrie's account of his landing that night and read Ansell's report on the drop. Only then did I discover I was not to blame, but by then the blame had been absorbed; the truth was no longer of any use.

14

Politicians and staff officers produce the documents that military historians rely upon for their studies of old campaigns, and participants in such events can often be mystified by the picture those authentic documents present. You read of dissension between groups which you observed working in harmony, of collaboration where you witnessed opposition, of policies said to be in effect when you saw they were ignored in the field.

The US Secretary of State directed that the OSS should not have any association with Force 136 but the OSS accepted with thanks the help offered by Colin Mackenzie. A British staff officer filed a report about the Kachin levies' misery when they were switched to American control, but the leader himself told me they were delighted with the change. The XIV Army recorded a complaint about lack of intelligence from Force 136 the same week one of its own corps commanders thanked them for that specific service. Sadly staff files do not carry postscripts from those directly involved in the decisions and incidents noted in the official records; history might be a little less cut and dried as a consequence, but then so is life.

The following could be considered as an example of such a postscript – in this case to the official record of operation *Dracula*, the plan for the seaborne capture of Rangoon. When I raised this subject with General Browning some years later, he said there had been a 'squabble between the USAAF and the RAF' about dropping parachutists, and the staff had had to intervene to sort it out. This is not true, but I can well believe he had such information from the official record. It would, I imagine, read something like this:

213

The American commander declared that his unit could guarantee that the reception party would be landed in the designated area. The RAF officer disagreed and said this was not possible. It was necessary to intervene in their disagreement . . .

Another version of this 'disagreement' between the USAAF and RAF participants is the one I noted down a little later at Jessore after that meeting.

The first phase of *Dracula* was to drop a parachute battalion south of Rangoon to destroy the guns protecting the sea approaches. The USAAF were to do the drop but some Eminence (I never discovered his identity, Browning refused to discuss it) decided that the battalion must be guided in by a reception party previously dropped by two Dakotas from our squadron. I did not know about this at first: all that the air commodore at our group headquarters told me was that we were to drop the reception party and the USAAF would follow with the main body. When I said I thought this a queer arrangement, he told me my job was to carry out orders, not criticize them, and sent me off in a staff car to the planning meeting at command headquarters.

Later I was told that our intrusion had been inspired by the failure of some USAAF aircraft to land airborne troops accurately during the invasion of Sicily; there was a story that some units had finished in the sea, well short of the coastal AA guns, and this VIP (Mountbatten? Browning?) was determined the same would not happen at Rangoon. Whether this was true or not, I was certain the commander of the troop carriers would regard our RAF intrusion as an insult to his professional capability, as would I if two USAAF aircraft of his crowd were brought in to show us the way, so I had sympathy with him even before we met that afternoon in Calcutta.

He was a colonel in immaculate uniform – called 'Fen' in my notebook. He merely nodded when I was shown into the little office to await our call. He sat rigidly upright in the chair, stony-faced, staring fixedly at the Japanese aircraft identification chart on the wall as we waited for the conference, and answered

214

curtly when I tried to get a conversation going. I managed, however, to discover that he knew the basic insult in the plan – hence the frigidity – and when I said that I intended to say it was a dotty scheme his manner changed at once. He leaned across towards me, eagerly agreeing with my arguments and adding others of his own. We were allies.

Fen was a regular officer, and proud that his unit had been chosen out of all allied transport groups in India to undertake this special operation, but only that morning had he discovered the stipulation that his aircraft were considered to need guidance from an outside group. Although for us it was just another typical blind drop, he was so keen to have the job that I began to nod agreement with the importance he was attaching to it, as you will about the enthusiasm of someone whom you like.

Oh yes, a vital task . . . Exactly, the high point of the whole campaign . . . True, true, the capture of Rangoon depends on it.

Such eagerness in a senior officer – he must have been at least ten years older than me – was touching, and I wished him luck as we were called into the meeting.

We were faced by two officers. At the desk was a young American brigadier who looked worried, and standing beside him was an RAF group captain who, unfortunately, I antagonized at once. He was wearing a starched bush jacket with the belt so tightly drawn that the lower half flared out to join the line of his very wide shorts; the effect was that of a ballerina's tutu, and with his short plump figure he brought to mind the *Fantasia* hippos in their tiny voile skirts, prancing about in 'Dance of the Hours'. It was a diverting picture but he must have seen the happy reaction on my face, for he was suddenly glaring at me. I sobered up at once and paid close attention to the brigadier, but the damage was done.

It was clear that they were as unhappy about their orders as we were. They did not disclose the source but spoke in intransitives or made the plan itself an authority . . . 'it has been decided that . . .', or 'the Plan lays down that . . .', as they groped for a compromise that would more or less conform to the embarrassing order yet somehow have the USAAF run the drop. However, the incompatibles were not easy to merge. After laboriously preparing the ground the brigadier said:

'We have decided on a slight adjustment. We'll take one aircraft from your outfit, squadron leader. It will fly in formation with the colonel's aircraft which will drop the first eight men. Then you go in and drop eight men from your aircraft. What do you think of that?'

It seemed a muddle to me. The group captain flared at this summary dismissal but the brigadier waved him down and invited me to give reasons, though he must have been well aware himself of the snags. I said that night flying in formation with an aircraft from another command that had other practices was a recipe for confusion, and Fen gave his eager agreement. In my innocence I asked why they were dragging us into it. We were under pressure by the clandestines, they wanted every aircraft we could spare, surely the sensible plan was for the colonel to take his own US crews in the formating aircraft?

The two of them spoke together in low tones for a moment then went scrabbling through a file for something. The ceiling fan kept up a regular wheezing as it wobbled around on its long stalk, and outside in the garden a crow was cawing a single melancholy note like the cry of a lost soul. Unfortunately they could not tell us that they were trying to fiddle their way out of an Imperial order, and as neither Fen nor I knew that at the time we could not help. Our reaction to all their suggestions was the innocently obvious:

It's a stupid plan, so why not change it?

The situation was aggravated by the antipathy I had provoked in the group captain. He kept snapping every time I tried to discover more about their constricting brief, so pretty soon I turned sour and obstructive. Had it not been for that vision of the dancing hippos we might have relaxed and perhaps discovered their dilemma, and I would have been happy enough to play along with whatever scheme we could jointly concoct. But the animosity between me and the group captain finished any hope of friendly cooperation. My attitude was: the hell with him and his problem!

The American brigadier was the more imaginative of the two and he kept coming up with tortured compromises – that I go independently and drop to a reception by the colonel's group, that I go off first and therefore technically in the lead but drop after him, that I fly as second pilot to the colonel in his aircraft. In each case they asked for my comments – their orders must have had some such requirement otherwise they would surely have just announced their plan, and told me to shut up if I tried to speak. After one of my rejections the group captain bent down and muttered something to the brigadier (probably 'Shall I cut O'Brien's throat?'), but otherwise he played only a glaring part in the scene.

The breakthrough came when Fen declared that as all his aircraft were equipped with 'Loran', a radar navigational aid which could give the pilot a perfect fix on position, he could still drop accurately even over cloud-covered land. I told them the only signal aid we had was 'Rebecca', which required a man on the ground as operator; even then we worked by moonlight, and to ensure men landed safely we had to be able to study the ground. The brigadier pounced on this escape.

'That means you cannot guarantee to drop the group on that site the night of D minus one?'

I agreed. Fen however claimed 'Loran' was accurate enough to ensure parachutists were landed in the exact designated field, whatever the conditions. He was pushing his luck – the landing site would have to cover squares of miles to be sure of such accuracy – but I made no challenge; he had stayed friendly all the time they had been shaking us together to start a fight, he was anxious to do the job, so I accepted his claim without a murmur of doubt. That settled the discussion. He went off happily to his unit but I had to wait behind.

It took them about ten minutes to arrange the wording. When I was called back the group captain was completing the minute sheet as the brigadier spoke to me. He said that they had considered 'the disagreement' between Fen and me, and decided that as I could not guarantee to carry out the operation they were forced to pass it to Fen's squadron. When I tried to point out that there had been no disagreement with Fen the

217

group captain interrupted to insist there had been . . . I had said it was not possible to guarantee a landing on the DZ and Fen had said he could do so . . . that was a disagreement . . . thank you very much, squadron leader . . . you may go.

Their filed minute was probably the 'squabble between the USAAF and the RAF' that Browning recalled. If that file survived, the group captain's report on our 'disagreement' becomes documented fact, the stuff of history; and even in the archives, as Mackenzie discovered, such misinformation can still be protected from being challenged by the participants.

Dissension did occur occasionally between the clandestines, most commonly when ISLD was involved. Even after that reprimand from P Division for sending me out with just a radio set, the ISLD conducting officer would still niggle about a strange package or two among their own sacred load. The Psychological Warfare people, the poor cousins among the clandestines, never had an aircraft allotted solely for their propaganda sheets, but had to rely on charity from the big boys. They often had difficulty getting space out of ISLD.

The conducting officer on an ISLD sortie also filed a complaint when D Division took some space on their aircraft one night. The amount of space taken, and the weight, could hardly have been more insignificant. The total addition was just one dead pigeon.

It was a Fleming idea, as one might expect, a simple deception stunt; you tossed out a dead carrier pigeon with a message attached and hoped to hook the Japanese. This particular night we had an ISLD team to be dropped blind in the mountains along the Chinese border. Charles O'Brien was conducting officer so he had to be told about the pigeon which had been delivered to us in a brown paper bag. He made the expected fuss, then settled down happily to compose mentally his critical report as we droned on over the Chin Hills towards China. I believe the pigeon's message contained a radio frequency for a non-existent agent; it was hoped the Japanese would read the message, then try to make contact on the frequency suggested. It was a wild hope, but then it only cost D Division a few rupees to buy a pigeon in the Burrabazaar market, so they could afford to fling one out every now and then. For we did repeat this stunt.

The basic ISLD operation that night was a failure – and perhaps it was out of resulting petulance that Charles did actually file his complaint about the D Division intrusion. It had been a map-chosen DZ, no photograph had been taken, and the area turned out to be solid jungle. There was not even the filament of a track showing within the dark matted growth of the moonlit mountainside, and though I tried to persuade Charles to consider a good clearing about ten miles away he dared not diverge from his brief. So the Joes had to come all the way back to India just in order for him to have his brief changed.

As for the dead pigeon, it was supposed to have fluttered down dead on the Sittang valley road and after a few minutes' low flight I found a suitable target; there was a mound set back from the road, on it a little white pagoda shaped like an ogee arch, an enchanting cake-decoration piece pinned on top of the knoll and all agleam in the moonlight, with a narrow ashen path joining it to the road. I flew over at about fifty feet, flashed the green light when directly opposite the little pagoda, and we delivered our offering. It had been a ten-hour flight, and all we had done was to drop a dead pigeon.

D Division did have five radio links with the enemy through double agents, Indians whom the Japanese had sent to India where everyone without exception had finished up working under D Division control. A major problem with these links was that their radio channels had to course through the Indian National Army headquarters in Rangoon, where that 'cashiered' officer finished after we dropped him. Messages passed through inexperienced Indian and Japanese cipher officers, then had to be translated – a tortured process that meant it was almost invariably a garbled version of the original that finally reached its destination. This was a constant irritant to D Division. It must have been exasperating to have a double agent send off your perfectly coded prize story, wait weeks for the enemy response, then finally discover from it that your original message must have become so corrupt in passage that the response was useless nonsense.

D Division actually made money on some of the stories planted with Indian agents. They sold a false guest list of a Chinese reception party in Delhi for several thousand rupees, and the Japanese were equally grateful for a freighter's manifest which included gliders in its spurious cargo. Such fabricated artifacts could not be passed on a radio link, they were routed to the Japanese through China; the Chinese had a highly professional Secret Service, and D Division had one of Chiang Kai-Shek's staff attached to their office in Delhi to speed up the passage of fabricated top-secret documents, such as false itineraries of senior commanders and faked banquet menus with forged signatures of VIPs. All these went to China where the Japanese made a useful contribution to our war effort by paying for them.

Unfortunately this channel, though efficient, was too slow and ponderous to help tactical deceptive action in Burma. To persuade the Japanese to alter troop dispositions and adjust defences the deceits had to get to local command more quickly if they were to be of benefit to commanders in Burma. So D Division had to rely on their inefficient local radio links, or entrust us on the squadron with such material as cashiered officers, crashed parachutists, brigadier's caps, dead pigeons, fake love letters, and broken bits of aeroplanes.

It must have been heartbreaking for Fleming and other top deceivers to see their painstaking and artistic productions so often wasted on the inefficient Japanese Secret Service. Most of their masterpieces disappeared without a ripple. One, an artist's sketch book which showed officers with their unit badges prominent, was known to have reached an authority and was much appreciated, but whether it achieved any useful purpose it is impossible to say.

The risk of attracting enemy attention to a real objective the army had in mind was ever present. D Division came into conflict with the army again about this in March when they prepared a document which purported to show the preparations for a major concert being given by Bob Hope, Bing Crosby and Dorothy Lamour on a visit to Burma. The document gave the list of formations to be present at each of the six performances over three days; the purpose was to persuade the Japanese that a huge force was being assembled on the coast of lower Burma to start a drive across towards Rangoon. The completed document was about to be allowed to fall into Japanese hands when the army belatedly saw a copy and instantly ordered its suppression, complaining that once again D Division had stumbled upon an actual contingency plan. Fleming told me they had even had posters with pictures of the famous trio prepared for unit display.

We in the squadron were sometimes the unwitting cause of friction between different ground parties. Over on the Chinese border there was an ISLD party named *Bulge* that failed four times in March to accept a drop assigned to them. They were being hounded by a Japanese force and kept having to make a rapid getaway from each DZ they prepared; after ninety hours' flying time not one Liberator had flicked a spark of fire out of them. Then one night the *Bulge* men did manage to get to the DZ as arranged, but with the Japanese pursuers still close on their trail they cautiously confined the signal fires to four torches in line.

These were not enough to attract the searching Liberator, then teetering on the limit of its endurance, and in such a weakened state it was an easy victim for the seductive bright lights of a nearby Force 136 group. This group had missed a drop recently because of bad weather; they had assumed the searching aircraft was an unannounced replacement and so they set fire to their great piles of wood. The Liberator picked them out from miles away and as the ISLD were known to be under pressure not much attention was paid to the recognition letter that was flashed, so the 136 men collected the drop. When I spoke to one of the *Bulge* men later on he told me he laid no blame on our squadron for what happened; the culprits in his eyes were 'those bloody Force 136 crowd; they deliberately pinched our drop'.

Another ISLD team, *Brave*, was dropped by mistake to a Force 136 reception that month. In this instance it was the 136 group that suffered. They wanted food, not four Chinese agents.

Conflict about a drop could arise even between operatives of the same organization. Tiny Lewes, who was on *Walrus* laying ambushes for Japanese troops moving south through the hills, had a drop one black cloudy night and left the fires burning to give light for the collection. He was still collecting when another of our Dakotas spiralled down, the way a vulture will when it discerns a fellow bird on the ground gorging itself, and the site then had a second drop. A few miles away another 136 *Character* group, the rightful owners of the cargo, had been slow to put match to their fires and to their fury were unable to distract the aircraft from its mistaken target.

In fact, they were lucky it was an unarmed Dakota making the drop. Had it been a Liberator the ground party might well have received a burst of gunfire, being taken for a Japanese group trying once again to steal a guerrilla drop. The Japanese air force also shot up reception parties taking a drop, but I believe there were no casualties from these attacks; curiously, in the two cases reported, the enemy aircraft paid no attention to our planes making the drop.

The most common disagreement to arise was between the men in the field and their own base headquarters, but the staff were not always to blame for mistakes and omissions in deliveries. An E Group and ISLD party both signalled criticisms of their headquarters that moon period in March, but the real blame in both cases lay with two pilots who unwittingly swopped targets – despite my admitting this later to the E Group leader, he still insisted his own 'fat box-wallahs' must have somehow been to blame.

The title, E Group, like that of Force 136 and ISLD, was specific to South-East Asia Command. In Europe MI9 was responsible for helping prisoners to escape, and MI19 collected intelligence from enemy prisoners and refugees; the two worked in close collaboration, for much of the information collected by MI19 was of special interest to our own men trying to escape back through the enemy lines.

The same system operated in India up till mid-1944 and then it was decided to divorce the two units; there were so few Japanese prisoners and refugees that the work of MI19 was left to a small section of the Intelligence Directorate in Delhi, and all operations concerning escape and evasion within enemy territory came under an enlarged separate organization known as E Group. One of their operations which benefited us in the RAF as well as others was the setting up of an escape line out of Burma. We dropped their operatives behind the lines, usually to a Force 136 DZ, and they established a network of native agents who would go to the scene of a crash, hide any survivors from Japanese investigators, then contact base to arrange retrieval. They were bringing back to safety an average of fifteen airmen every month in early 1945 by this method.

One of their major successes in SEAC was operation *Vancouver*, which started with a team being dropped into Yunnan to establish contact with several labour camps holding Indian prisoners of war in the frontier area. The E Group specialists worked with Force 136 guerrillas in freeing groups of men from the camps and moving them across the hills into Burma, with us making nocturnal drops at a midway staging post; so successful were they that before the Japanese finally closed the camps the E Group team had managed to clear a total of 580 prisoners back to Myitkyena, whence the USAAF flew them out to freedom in India.

E Group had the distinction of forming an organization surely unique in SEAC in which the Americans and French worked together in harmony. This rare sweet concord was achieved in an Anglo–American–French combination of the British E Group, the American escape organization MIS-X, and the French DGER (the *Direction Générale d'Etude et Recherches*, code name for the French SOE). The task of the joint group was to investigate prisoner-of-war camps in Indo-China, and in April we dropped the first of their mixed teams into that country; others followed quickly so that by the time of the armistice they had teams in contact with every POW camp in the country.

Locating prisoner-of-war camps was an important part of E Group's work because the Japanese refused to notify the Swiss where the camps were situated. By this time American bombers from Pacific bases were attacking targets throughout Asia, from northern Japan down through China to Singapore and the East Indies. At 30,000 feet, even by photographic interpretation, there is little to distinguish an army camp from a prisoner-of-war camp, and it was a vital task of E Group to ensure that the allied air forces had the distinction clearly established before they despatched bombers to their targets.

Collaboration between E Group and Force 136 was particularly effective. We dropped five E Group teams along the Burma-Siam border, for there were several enormous POW camps in Siam, including those associated with the construction of the infamous railway of death. These teams went in to Force 136 receptions, particularly to *Character* in the south and *Hainton* in the northeast, both of which had operatives straddling the border and were able to provide guides and information for the E Group teams on arrival. All made their separate ways over the border and, as far as I know, established contact with the camps.

One group in the northern area did not have a radio and had to send their information back over a hundred mountainous miles to John Smallwood, whose *Lynx* group operated near the triple border junction of Burma, Laos and Siam. Smallwood discovered the existence there of an age-old system of passing information; if the message was accompanied by a chilli the headman of each village was bound by custom to pass it on to the next village, and if it was sent with a chilli and a feather then it was passed on with all speed possible. He was able to keep in effective touch with the E Group team by this method.

The OSS were actually the first to get a non-Thai into Bangkok, landed offshore one night by an RAF flying boat. The OSS wanted to establish teams in the northern area also, and Force 136, which had men on the ground there already, offered to provide reception parties on their sites. In this instance, however, the American State Department stepped in to forbid such a friendly association, so a plan for cooperative effort was again frustrated. The discrimination applied only to the field operatives; we in 357 Squadron were apparently approved allies by the State Department, so were able to drop

OSS *Siren* to set up a chain of informants in central Siam.

It might be imagined that joint operations between the clandestines would reduce the potential for disagreement, for you cannot steal another group's drop if they are present with you on the DZ; but as far as I know there was never a joint air sortie between the major groups. There was a joint submarine sortie to Malaya between 136 and ISLD in the early days but another one subsequently planned was never finally mounted because of disagreement between the planning staffs. The same thing happened when a joint air sortie was considered for Malaya that March; problems arose when the groups came together for planning discussion and they finally decided to go their separate ways. So we had to send out two aircraft to two different DZs to accommodate the staff differences.

Finally, to end this account of collaboration and conflict between the clandestines in early 1945, there was a misunderstanding between Force 136 and ISLD down in Malaya. In this instance staff were not to blame; Boris Hembry, who headed the ISLD Malay section, had a friendly relationship with Force 136, and the difference that arose in the field caused him some distress, particularly as he had gone out of his way to be of service to the 136 field group who were having difficulty communicating with base.

The 136 group was *Gustavus*. This was headed by John Davis, the senior British officer in the Malayan underground who had been appointed Mountbatten's representative to deal with the communist MPAJA (Malay People's Anti-Japanese Army. Davis had landed eighteen months earlier but had been without radio during all this time – his first set was captured by the Japanese, and a replacement sent in by submarine arrived without effective batteries. The MPAJA tried to help, filching car batteries and attempting generator repairs, but up to the end of January 1945 Davis still had no contact with India. Without a radio to arrange DZs with us he could not implement Mountbatten's directive to provide the guerrillas with arms and finance, and we could not drop the radio as we did not know where he was.

Hembry saw a possibility of helping with this problem by a

gesture which infringed the jealous spirit, if not the actual regulations, of the exclusive Secret Service. Just then he was planning *Evidence* for ISLD, a team to be based near a rubber plantation he had managed before the war. They would be gathering intelligence of all types in the area and a slight change of location would not damage their prospects, so Hembry told 136 he would move his DZ nearer the Davis party; he knew the area intimately and was confident about finding a suitable DZ. His men could then take in an extra radio, contact the MPAJA for the whereabouts of Davis and arrange delivery. Force 136 gratefully accepted his offer. The *Evidence* team joined us at Jessore presently to do their parachute training and prepare for their drop.

About a week before their take-off however, John Davis down in Malaya had a stroke of luck. His radio operator managed, after weeks of tinkering, to repair the generator to the extent that when coupled with a car battery it transmitted a signal that was picked up by Ceylon. Force 136 at last, after nearly three years of silence, had contact with the Malayan underground.

The *Evidence* team, then making their final practice jump at Jessore, knew nothing of this. Presently, after the 136 stores officer had added the Davis package to their load, they took off in a Liberator one afternoon on the twenty-hour trip to Malaya. The sortie was successful, the team landed safely near Hembry's old plantation as planned, and at once sent a message to Davis through the communist guerrillas saying they had a radio for him and would he please collect. A week or so later there came back a scribbled note which Davis had rushed off while on the move along a jungle track. Naturally, therefore, it was brief. It said:

THANK YOU BUT WE DON'T WANT YOUR WARES.

The brevity of his reply and the unfortunate choice of a rather derogatory last word – for security reasons the word 'radio' had to be avoided – gave a bad impression. The overall effect was of a brush-off, and the ISLD team were upset by what they took as a curt rebuff for the considerable pains they had taken to be good neighbourly spies. So there was no further contact after

226

that initial approach, and when subsequently they had little cooperation from the MPAJA, who stuck faithfully to the agreement signed with Davis and were mistrustful of this other secretive organization, they blamed Force 136 for influencing the guerrillas against them.

This little difference between the two organizations was not helpful to us on the squadron. Much as we would have liked to – saving a lot of trouble and expense as well as putting the lives of only ten aircrew at risk in a single aircraft instead of twenty men in two – we were never able to mount such an economical joint drop for the *Gustavus* group of 136 and the *Evidence* team of ISLD. They were conveniently close in space for us, but unfortunately, far too remote in sympathy.

15

In the spring they set the taungyas ablaze in northern Burma. These jungle clearings are made in winter, a patch of trees felled and left to dry on the hillside so that by spring the brown geometrical figures show up like patchwork on the dark green cloth of the jungle. Then, just when heat haze is beginning to blur the clarity of winter skies, visibility is further reduced as the taungyas are fired to make ready for planting, and smoke swirls up to diffuse in the haze like blood flowing from a wound under water. Consequently, for a few weeks when you fly over the ranges you have a scent of burning wood in the cockpit and all you can see clearly is the ridge directly beneath your aircraft. And every day as the spring advances the monsoon clouds mass higher and more menacingly in the sky.

It was precisely then, with the threat of the oncoming rains governing almost every decision being made by the XIV Army, that we were called upon to make our greatest effort for the clandestines. In the month of March our two squadrons completed over two hundred and fifty sorties for them. There were nearly fifty different sites in six different countries for these operations, and they cost us forty-nine lives – one dead airman for each site that we visited.

Among the five aircraft that crashed was one taking off with a guerrilla unit, the only time a British clandestine group lost any of their men in transit (one OSS agent died with our airmen in a monsoon crash, another American was killed in a Liberator shot down by Japanese fighters). I was out on operations that night, and it was late morning when we landed back at Jessore. Driving up to the operations room we were held up near the store shed by a three-tonner backing across the track to unload.

It seemed to be carrying cupboards, about a dozen of them stacked neatly within the framework of the open truck, but then when it passed close across in front of us I saw they were coffins. Our driver explained:

'We had to send a truck in to Cal at dawn for them. They only had eight coffins left in store after those prangs last week.'

It was a typical Liberator crash: just a slight loss of power in take-off was enough to put the lives of all aboard in immediate peril. A Dakota could have one dead engine, yet climb away fully loaded on the other one, but a Liberator taking off with a full load needed every unit of horsepower the engines were supposed to deliver; such was the condition of many of the aircraft, however, that this maximum was not always available. A contributory factor towards our several take-off crashes was a grove of tall trees up to three hundred feet high, sal and peepul and other great Indian types, less than a mile from the end of the runway. The trees could not be cut down because they were revered by the villagers living nearby – the peepul particularly, as the sacred bo-tree under which the god Vishnu was born – so we had to live with the hazard; consequently a southern take-off at night with a full load was always a tense business for Liberator crews.

The funeral service that day finished in disorder. The graves were not ready when we assembled at sunset and the villagers still had three to dig when the padre started the ceremony. To give the gravediggers time the bugler played the Last Post for each burial, but this so delayed proceedings that it was dark night, the moon yet to rise, and the last service was still under way. By then the filling in of the graves had still not caught up with the ceremony.

We were standing in warm darkness, sweating in our best khaki, as the villagers filled in the graves with whispered instructions, a clinking of shovels, a scuffling of earth, and every now and then a solid thump of rock on wood. Then suddenly, as if on a switch, the bushes at the far side of the graves began to flicker with the cold light of a thousand fireflies, and some of the grave-fillers stopped work and began to murmur disquiet. At that moment from across the field beyond the ghostly bush a jackal gave three startling yelps, the final one trailing away in an unearthly diminuendo that broke the nerve of the villagers. They downed spades and fled away into the night. We completed the covering of the graves ourselves.

Although we in the Dakotas were spared that particular take-off concern at Jessore, we did share with the Liberators the far greater hazard of cloud over a DZ, and that was the cause of our single Dakota loss that month. Any aircraft such as ours, with a ceiling below 20,000 feet, was at risk from violent turbulence in tropical cloud, but Special Duty operations were particularly perilous because we had to go down close to the ground in those conditions. The job was to get under the cloud, circle in the valley for the drop, then climb back through the cloud to escape. That was where our Dakota failed.

This was a sortie for BAAG, the British Army Aid Group which was operating two thousand miles away in China. They helped prisoners out of Hong Kong, and in this case there were three Indian escapees and a US naval airman shot down near there. The flight had to be staged through Kunming and there our pilot, Hunter, teamed up with a Dakota of the US 322 Squadron to make a joint drop. The 14th USAAF ruled that the site was too dangerous for a night drop, but a daylight flight was even more dangerous because of a Japanese airfield in the vicinity; they therefore wanted a day with cloud cover throughout southern China except for a clear gap over the DZ, a condition that put a strain on hope. Not surprisingly, hope was dashed.

The two aircraft went off in formation, above a layer of low cloud which offered protective escape from fighters, but the same conditions persisted in the DZ area so they flew south to the China Sea to make a safe descent through the overcast. Once this had been achieved they were down to about fifty feet above the water, flying along the coast through scudding rain clouds in search of the estuary that led back inland to the DZ, and the American pilot soon decided that conditions were far too dangerous. He pulled up into the clear and went home, but Hunter stayed below and continued to search for the inlet.

He never found it. A few minutes after the separation he

crashed into an islet that jutted up a thousand feet out of the sea only a few miles off the shore. He and his crew of four were the first casualties we suffered on BAAG; a few weeks later we lost five more lives in another attempt to assist this group.

An account of the remarkable work of Doctor Ride, the Australian surgeon who escaped from Hong Kong then ran the BAAG operation in close cooperation with the Americans, was written by his son. There was no mention of our squadron nor the ten men from it, British, Canadian and Australian, who died in their service. The BAAG men knew of the crash; they sent a team to the island to bury our dead.

This was one service the clandestines did sometimes render us in return; they would go to the site of a crash and help any survivors or, more usually, bury our dead. When an aircraft was missing we would always ask groups in the area for information, but unless they had actual wreckage to report they were rarely of help. One appeal we made for news did, however, yield a most precise response; I cannot recall the exact words but it went something like this:

2040 hrs. Aircraft, possibly Liberator, to north of our area, travelling east.
2310 hrs. Similar type and route to 2040 hrs aircraft.
0120 hrs. Unknown aircraft travelling northwest.
0140 hrs. Aircraft, possibly Dakota, north of our position, travelling northwest.

Nothing further heard that night.

Anyone who knew him might have guessed that John Hedley sent that signal. I knew Hedley from the early Wingate days when we had been in 111 Brigade together. He was an old Burma hand, lean and tough, a man of exhausting vitality and a voice that would reverberate even in an open-flapped tent. I had no idea he had joined Force 136 until we met by chance again one afternoon at Jessore.

This was late March, the margosa trees were now in creamy white blossom, and I used to drive back to the mess that way in the late afternoons to catch the sweet fragrance trapped in the

231

avenue along the paddy fields west of the strip. I had stopped by the roadside to enjoy the scene, the paddy fields that stretched flat and rice-shoot green to a palm-ringed village by the river. It was a cool clear day with just two feather-like plumes of silky white cirrus stuck above the southern horizon. Walking along one of the transverse bunds was a woman trailing three girls of descending height, all in coral-red fluttering saris, with brass waterpots on their heads, and some distance behind was a half-naked man with a wooden plough angled about his shoulders. Brilliant blue-green parrots were fluttering noisily about the lower branches of an Indian laburnum below me, the clusters of drooping pink flowers were shaking under the onslaught, but when I started towards the tree to check what the fuss was about, they at once coagulated into organized flight and sped away in a twittering tumult of colour.

In the ensuing quiet I heard the sound of thudding footsteps and turned sharply. A tall thin figure was striding down the centre of the road, arms bunched in grip of the straps of a huge pack on his back. There was something familiar about those long raking strides but before I could make out, let alone identify, the face beneath the green jungle hat, a thunderous voice called:

'Me, John! You, Pat!'

It was John Hedley. It was typical of him that he should be taking not merely an afternoon stroll but rather a vigorous exercise. He came striding up to me like a car doing a brake test, stopped suddenly to halt, then thrust out a hand with the vigour of a punch. I discovered he had just arrived, was due to start parachute training next day and had decided to do a little training march. He refused a lift back. I promised to take him up for his practice drops then he went striding on his way down between the margosa trees, his lengthened shadow flitting across the grey trunks, and monkeys chattering at him from the branches overhead.

I took him on his two practice drops and planned to take him also on the night of the *Squirrel* operation, but that was the day I had to attend the conference with Fen in Calcutta, so I missed his operational flight. After the drop he and his team of four

Burmese established themselves in a hide just ten yards from the side of the main Mandalay–Maymo road and from there the reports he filed of Japanese traffic were of such staggering detail as to mark a sudden appreciation by the XIV Army of the value of Force 136 agents behind the lines in Burma.

Hedley did not merely report the number of trucks that used the road on any one night; he attempted to give details of each particular truck in the convoy, its tonnage, its contents, the enemy unit associated with it, and anything else that his senses could detect or his intelligence deduce. His passion for detail was renowned. On the Chindit campaign he came across a parked truck one night and it never occurred to him simply to return to his column and report it. When I asked him why, he seemed surprised at such a question:

'I had to find out what was in it first, of course.'

There was a Japanese driver in it, to start with. The man was drowsy, deadly drowsy as it happened, for presently when he relaxed into sleep Hedley crept up to the truck and killed him with a single shot through the head. He examined the man's uniform, extracted what papers he possessed and what he could find in the cabin, then climbed into the back of the truck and, by use of a torch, his fingers, his nose, and even his tongue, he catalogued in detail every item that it contained. Hedley spent two months behind the lines after our drop and the information he filed was, in the words of his citation, 'absolutely invaluable in the assault on Mandalay'. Jack Masters, then on the staff of 19 Division, told me a few weeks later that he knew Hedley was with Force 136 when he read an Intelligence Report from them one day. It bore Hedley's distinctive hallmark.

'It even had the *name* of one of the Japanese officers in the convoy,' he said.

It was due perhaps as much to Hedley as to anyone that the XIV Army was no longer expressing criticism at the lack of intelligence reports from the clandestines. On the contrary there was a signal of praise for the reports being filed from the *Character* network set up in accordance with Slim's directive; such was the standard that the army were confidently requesting such explicit information as,

> WANT URGENTLY TO KNOW EXACT LOCA-
> TION OF LARGE JAP HQ IN MOULMEIN

and

> FIND OUT LOCATION OF 49 DIVISION AND
> 14 TANK REGIMENT.

However, although reacting with such successful obedience to the army instruction to concentrate on gathering intelligence, the original *Character* purpose of guerrilla activity was still very much in mind at 136 headquarters. All that month we were flying in massive supplies of arms and armaments for the Karen levies being raised so vigorously by Peacock and Turrall.

Peacock, in accordance with his final brief, was in fact gathering intelligence for the army but at the same time quietly developing a guerrilla force that was to become the largest in Karenni. Turrall, an impetuous man, was not so attentive to that brief, and about ten days after landing he attacked and drove out the small Japanese garrison of the nearby village and established a People's Committee to run the place. The move was much too premature; the Japanese sent up a platoon the following day and the People's Committee had to flee into the hills with Turrall. That abruptly ended the disobedient aggressive action by *Character*. Turrall reverted to his briefing and the levies were confined to defensive action only.

The first such action took place about a week or so later and involved Saw Thet Wa. He was a courageous Karen whom we had dropped into the hills almost a year earlier in order to contact Seagrim. He had been successful in this but had himself been captured by the Japanese and was in Rangoon jail at the time Seagrim was executed, his own fate in the balance. Luckily, however, just then the Japanese began to suspect the loyalty of the Burmese army, and for a short period they tried to cultivate the friendship of the Karens and other hill tribes as alternative allies. Saw Thet Wa was sent to a Kempei unit as interpreter, and it was in this role that he returned to the hills.

He was involved under duress. The Japanese knew when we dropped the first *Character* groups; in fact a Japanese corporal was in charge of the local police force in the village beside which we made the drop and when his police force deserted him to join

234

the levies he hung about disconsolate for a few days before wandering off to report matters to his superiors, who despatched among others Saw Thet Wa's five-man unit into the hills. On arrival at the first Karen village the sergeant, who had a smattering of the language, instructed Saw Thet Wa to ask the headman if he had heard of parachutists landing.

Saw Thet Wa knew the headman spoke English and that none of the Japanese did, so the two Karens began interspersing English messages between the translations and by the time the interview was finished all three were the wiser for the exchange: the sergeant had been told the name of the village where the British parachutists were located, the headman had been told to contact that village and arrange an ambush, and Saw Thet Wa knew he had somehow to detach himself from the Kempei before they reached the ambush area.

He was unable to manage this vital escape however. The Japanese had been watchful of him from the moment they entered Karenni, and maybe that first interview had alerted the Kempei sergeant. Anyway, they kept Saw Thet Wa in the centre of the group on the march and guarded him at the halts. The following day, as they headed towards the ambush and village, must have been an appalling trial for him. Every time they rounded a bend in the track he was expecting a shattering burst of fire, but all the time he had to appear unconcerned in response to the sergeant's questions.

They were about five miles from the target village when they met the ambush. The villagers, hidden in a dense patch of bamboo at the bottom of a steep ridge, opened fire from fifty yards when the Japanese were easing themselves down the slope. Saw Thet Wa was incredibly lucky, for he was in the centre of the five men and wearing Japanese uniform like them; the villagers, assuming he had escaped as planned, blasted away with all their fire power in an attempt to kill every single one of the group. They did kill four, including the sergeant, but one man rolled sideways into the bushes and escaped, and Saw Thet Wa, who was also missed in that opening burst, threw himself behind a tree and began shouting his name.

They heard him finally, stopped shooting, and he emerged

unscathed. The ambush party began congratulating him and themselves on their victory, but he urged them to send off at once after the escapee, for he knew from dreadful experience the savage revenge the Japanese would take on the village nearest the scene of an ambush. The headman then detailed men to contact all the nearby villages and the widespread hunt met with quick success; the sole Japanese survivor was encountered and killed by a group of levies the following day.

Saw Thet Wa subsequently went to join a Karen unit working with *Nation*, a 136 operation with much the same design as *Character* but located west of the valley in the central hills known as the Pegu Yomas. The XIV Army had by mid-March cut the valley road in that cross-country swoop on Meiktila, thereby trapping some ten thousand or so Japanese in the central area, and the purpose of *Nation* was to observe and harass this large enemy force.

Although we dropped only a few dozen men into *Nation*, as compared to more than two hundred for *Character*, they did manage to develop a guerrilla force in the central area almost as large as that across the valley in the Karen Hills. This was because the *Nation* teams worked like the Jedburghs in France, as liaison officers with an organized resistance. When the Burma nationalist groups finally committed themselves not merely to passive cooperation with the allies but to actual offensive operations against the Japanese, Force 136 became responsible for supplying and advising them. Tactically independent and operating in small separated groups, the majority controlled by the Burma National Army, these *Nation* guerrillas lacked the discipline and expertise of the British-led Karens of *Character*.

Even from the air you could notice the difference between the two guerrilla groups. On arrival at a *Character* DZ you would see figures waving and running all about the site, elephants were sometimes visible, people would be streaming along the moonlit tracks from the nearby villages, the whole scene would be lit up by gigantic bonfires. On a *Nation* drop site there were few signs of life; if you looked down closely on the turn you could discern one or two figures skulking about the bordering trees, and like the prey of a hunting spider the parachutes would all be dragged back out of sight into the jungle within minutes of landing. Their fires were often nothing more than glowing sticks, fanned to give flame when you were actually over the site – one group relied on a line of five stubby candles set into old jam tins which we only perceived after identifying the site by moonlight map-reading and making our first run. A *Nation* drop site looked like a secret conspiratorial gathering, a *Character* one like a joyous carnival.

Another difference between the two areas was that when an aircraft crashed in the Karen Hills we would learn about it at once. Everyone was so involved in the struggle against the Japanese that even in the most remote Karenni villages people would hurry to a crash to try and help, and although the crew were invariably all killed we did at least get details back from the field. But if an aircraft crashed in the Pegu Yomas you would have to search for the wreck yourself, unless it happened within the ambit of a *Nation* team or an E Group agent; the local Burmese were not interested, except perhaps to loot the crash, when they would never admit to knowing its location.

Only one Liberator was definitely known to have been shot down on clandestine operations, but one lost that month could also have been from enemy action. It crashed near the DZ, killing all ten crew, and the French team that found it were unable to determine the cause of the disaster. Every plane we lost over Indo-China was acutely felt by the hard-pressed French. After that murderous night when the Japanese had seized control, the French had been unable to stage any organized resistance, and had had to resort to guerrilla warfare. In this they had a far harder time than the clandestines in the rest of South-East Asia, because to the Vietnamese the French were a more important enemy than the Japanese temporary invaders. And the Americans, because of their disapproval of all that pertained to de Gaulle, were not merely supporting the communist partisans under Ho Chi Minh but tried to bar any aid at all reaching the French. The local USAAF commander actually filed an official complaint that we had dropped arms to the French without the approval of the US commander.

It was while this inter-allied sniping was going on that I made a landing in Indo-China, also without the US commander's approval, but on this occasion without being caught in the act. It was Force 136's first Dakota landing behind the lines in Indo-China.

The reason for this flight to Dien Bien Phu was to land 'Passy' (Colonel Dewavrin), who was the head of the Secret Service in de Gaulle's Free French government. Passy, tall and fair-haired, with cold blue eyes, had parachuted twice into France during the Occupation, but on this occasion, when I pointed out a parachute he could use in an emergency, he said he would much prefer to be landed, thanks. It was a daylight flight which was mildly disturbing. That same week five Japanese fighters had strafed a French camp a few miles south of Dien Bien Phu, and there were two Japanese airfields within easy patrol distance of it. The Dakota was not only unarmed and slow, but it had no rear vision whatsoever – however, I still preferred our lot to that of the Liberators which had been stripped of nearly all guns for the long Malayan trips. This meant their crews would have advance notice from the rear turret that they were about to die, whereas we in Dakotas were spared that terrible imminence of death. On this particular day we flew through fighter-free skies.

It was comparatively clear weather, only just a scattering of small cream-puff cumulus casting isolated rafts of shadow over the paddy fields of the plain. You do not really need a map to distinguish the three main ranges of mountains that stretch down the length of Burma; the Chins, nearest to India, are nearly all green-covered in climax jungle, on the far side of the plain the Kachin hills are scarred with patches of taungya, and beyond them in China the rice terraces waver and shiver up the hillsides like the very contour lines marked on a map.

Once over the border we flew into a thick haze which persisted right up to the airstrip itself; so blurred was visibility that we passed directly over Dien Bien Phu without seeing the strip, and had to go on towards Hanoi for a pinpoint that gave a dead-reckoning run back to the elusive airfield. Even then it was not easy to pick out the actual landing area through the haze; Passy had come up to the cockpit and could not accept that the clearing was an airfield until I pointed out the battered old biplane slumped by the perimeter. Dien Bien Phu is in a saucer-shaped plain, low hills undulating all about its horizon, and at that time the red laterite surface of the field was blotched with patches of pallid grass stubble, the strip itself delineated only by four small orange slabs at its rectangular corners.

There were few buildings, just a jumble of white low blocks on the western side and a small olive-green water tower on top of which a windsock hung limp as a burst balloon. We made a low-flying inspection of the strip which was little more than a thousand yards in length and Passy quizzed me with raised eyebrows. I nodded that it was okay, and he went back into the fuselage for the landing. When I put it down we ran to a quick stop on the soggy earth surface and I made a wide turn to avoid the inside wheel becoming bogged; then we trundled back to the touch-down point where a group of people awaited us.

I kept the engines running when Passy and the other passenger descended – this was an RAF navigator from the 136 Calcutta office who had come in for a few days to report on the French resistance. On that first landing I stayed in the aircraft as briefed, whilst they unloaded the medical supplies, but I did go down the fuselage for a glance at the proceedings. The two French generals were there; Sabattier leaning heavily on a walking stick and Alessandri with a cigarette drooling in the Jean Gabin manner from the corner of his mouth, and there were about thirty soldiers in uniform scurrying about from our doorway to a low thatched shed with the containers and packages we had brought. They were moving with an urgency that suggested they were fearful we might depart, or Japanese arrive, before they had collected every precious item of our load.

On a second trip four days later we stopped the engines and went outside to relax and chat with some of the French – those who could speak English, or comprehend my version of their own language. There were two stretcher cases to be taken out, together with another two walking wounded and three women. One of the wounded men was having a fight for his life, so instead of flying directly back to India I decided to break the journey after three hours and land at Myitkyena to have his condition checked. We called up the American base and told them of our medical need.

As we slanted down across the Irrawaddy the sun was setting directly ahead of us, the malachite green hills were slashed with shadows, and high overhead the streaks of cirrus were streaming away softly from the low sun like a woman's golden hair floating in clear blue water. Down on the airstrip an ambulance took the badly wounded man to the hospital for a full examination, and the crew went off with them, but I stayed while the US medical team checked our other wounded. They spent a long careful time on the patients.

I waited outside in the gathering dusk, watching the homing parakeets again as they streamed southwards to the trees. Every time we landed at Myitkyena I would recall that first day when, trudging back in retreat over the paddy fields with our wounded, we had seen and heard the birds streaking past overhead; they had been darkly coloured under grey skies that day, but now the massed flocks were like fluttering bright flags against the primrose sky. Across the Irrawaddy the shadows on the hills dulled from purple to indigo and the last embers of the sunset died away in the western sky and the stars came thronging out in their glittering millions. Then the nurses finished their care and we went up together to join the others at the canteen.

If the US medical services were aware of their government's official attitude towards the French forces they paid no heed to it; the wounded Frenchman could not have received more attention that night at Myitkyena had he been their President. When they did return to the aircraft a couple of hours later with the critically injured man the doctor spoke to me before supervising the loading of the stretcher.

'He should be all right,' he said. 'But I'd worry about him all night here if I stayed at Myitkyena. I have to go with you.'

He did, and stayed with the Frenchman until he was delivered safely to hospital at Calcutta, where he recovered fully in the weeks that followed.

The French were bitter about the refusal of the US administration in nearby China to give any help during their sufferings at that time. That was a political decision emanating from Washington. The US Army Medical Services were above such petty politics; they saw a dying man, and they saved his life.

16

Except that he was only about five feet tall, Colonel 'Pop' Tulloch looked like a parody of a British army officer. A dapper little man with neat waxed-end moustache, he carried a monocle attached to the top button of his bush jacket by a black silk cord; his practical use of this was arbitrary, sometimes he would raise it to his right eye to read or to study a questioner – giving himself time to deal with an awkward probe – and at other times he would glare or read without bothering about the monocle. He was the third of the *Character* triumvirate, in command of *Walrus* section. He was even further into his fifties than the other two but just as fit and tough, the most sharp-witted of them all, and the best company.

Pop's passage to India had solved a delicate problem for his regiment back in England. The military future of Major Tulloch was extremely precarious when the head of 136 Burma section, Ritchie Gardiner, arrived in England on a visit to SOE headquarters. He happened to hear of Pop's problem about a cheque, and also about his bravery in action, and said he would be happy to take him for an operation he had in mind far away in Burma. So, with some relief, they allowed Pop to depart for foreign shores and become a lieutenant-colonel.

His background was not so clearly above board as that of the other two. What Peacock or Turrall told you one day you would hear again when the question was asked the next time; their answers were the same to all men, and the chronology of their careers easy to follow. Not so when you questioned Pop. His past was adjustable, it could be adapted according to the knowledge of the questioner. There were gaps and anachronisms in his history, and his innumerable stories of financial jiggery-pokery carried a wealth of specialist detail surprising in a man who apparently had led such an active outdoor life.

He told me he had flown with Billy Bishop, the famous Canadian ace of the First World War and I believed him for a few minutes. He told Bob Hodges he had driven the first tank into battle on the Somme in 1916 and Bob, who was generous in trust, believed him for an hour or more that first evening. He told the group captain many things that first night he joined us in the mess at Jessore and the station commander actually went off to bed still believing them. Bob and I, however, when walking back past the fragrant heliotrope to our house that evening, decided that Pop was certainly a liar but a fascinating and amusing one, so his harmless stories should be encouraged.

Bob Thornton, the chief parachute instructor, was not so tolerant. He took the group on their first jump the following afternoon, and when they drove past the flight hut I was surprised to see Pop in the truck with the others. He had told me that as he already had his wings he would skip the parachute course; he was actually wearing them that first night, so I had been prepared to believe some of his stories about exhibition jumps made in the 1920s. It appeared, however, that he had been premature in pinning the wings to his bush shirt.

'Never done a jump in his life,' Thornton told me afterwards. 'Biggest bull-shitter I've ever met.'

It was not lack of courage that prompted Pop to try and evade the practice jumps; I think he was just unwilling to admit he was a novice at anything. Anyway, Thornton insisted he went through the full course, including two practice jumps. I took him up on his second practice, avoiding any reference to his unfrocking by Thornton, but he himself raised the matter as an amusing misunderstanding.

'I did all my jumps in America, including a course with the US army,' he said. 'So they're not in British army records.'

There were nearly fifty in the group going in to start *Walrus*. One of them, Tiny Lewes, was a mining engineer who had worked in the remote border areas before the war and knew far more about the country and the people than even Pop dared claim – at least in the presence of Lewes. He was, as the name suggests, a big man; he had to bend his head to go through doorways and the veranda boards rumbled when he approached. The standard parachute was the 28-footer, but there was an outsize for exceptionally big men, and on his practice jumps Lewes used that outsize 32-footer. However, the day we took off on *Walrus* Charles Tyce, who handled the stores, discovered that the last of the size 32 parachutes had been given to a huge Frenchman dropped in Indo-China the previous night, so he marked a 28-footer as being an outsize and gave this to Lewes. When, months later, Lewes reproached him about this deceit his very reasonable answer was:

'You still would have gone in if I told you we only had 28s left, but you would have worried about it all the trip. So for your peace of mind I marked it a 32.'

I had promised Pop to take their operational drop and this resulted in a heavy schedule for us. The sortie with Passy had been flown the previous day, we had been up before dawn and it was past midnight when the van finally dropped us outside the mess where we had arranged a bacon and egg supper; but when we approached the steps and I saw Pop at the bar inside, rocking on his feet and twirling his moustache as he told some story to a delighted audience, I decided to forego the meal. Fortunately, he was so involved that I was able to pull back from the veranda before he saw us. I whispered to the others to count me out, and escaped to sleep.

Moonlight next night was limited to the first few hours of darkness, so our opening drop was set for 7 p.m., with the other Dakotas and a Liberator then dropping to Pop's reception. The early part of our flight was therefore in daylight, and we were about midway to target when a waft of rum signalled the arrival of Pop in the cockpit, with his flask outstretched in offer. I was happy to chat but turned down the rum and advised that he save it for post-landing medical use; alcohol would be a pleasant anaesthetic, I suggested, while they were trying to reset the bones in his broken legs. He said he had broken his back once in a jump in Arizona and had to ride on a donkey twenty miles to hospital where they put a metal joint in his spine. When I asked if it had a hinge to allow him to bend he ignored the question and talked about prospecting in Alaska, then he gave his monocle a twirl and went back to the fuselage for a nap.

The night closed in rapidly over the plain, the patterned squares of paddy fields down below were flooded by the spreading darkness and then gradually emerged again in moonlight with faded colour and fainter lines, a soft tracery reminder of the past. There were flashes of silver from the moonlit waters of the Sittang and its tributaries, then our level horizon began to crumple into the curving ridges of the Karen Hills. Presently, with stars sparkling in the haze-clear night and the moon a lighted porthole in the sky, shades of colour became faintly perceptible again in the scene below . . . the sepia tint of an unfired taungya, a hint of yellow in the cultivated patches by a village from which blue-grey smoke was wreathing up the hillside, the dark copper strip of a laterite road surface, and deep green island ridges set in seas of jet-black valleys.

By the time we arrived over the DZ the team were all prepared for the drop, but it was at once apparent the site was a disaster. It was shorter than the photograph had suggested, and a tree-covered hill at one end would make it impossible to get low enough for the accuracy needed on such a narrow site. Because timing was critical, with the other three aircraft following so closely behind us, I abandoned it at once, likewise another DZ nearby, then flew eastwards while waiting for Pop to take off his parachute and come up for consultation.

Just as he arrived in the cockpit I was circling a prospect, a shallow valley with a mile-long area which was ideal, except that there were two separate villages on the slopes overlooking the clearing. He seized upon it at once, without giving it a monocle check.

'There, Pat! That's all right.'

I pointed out the villages, both of them smoke-misted from dozens of house fires, but he claimed that to be an advantage. They would be Karens, all Karens were committed to our support, which meant a landing among friends. He had the major say in such an area of risk – our unchallenged domain of decision was the topography – so once he had declared for the site I went down to have a close look at it.

245

A low slow run over the valley disclosed that the scattered shadows were not cultivated patches as I had thought but small trees, and so awkwardly placed it was impossible to do a run that would ensure all the string missed them. Pop dismissed this objection with a wave of monocle; they had all been told how to come down in trees, and as the rest would land in the clear there would be immediate help for anyone who did happen to finish in a tree. So I agreed. Pop went back to harness, and I called up the other aircraft to give them bearing and distance of the new site from our briefed DZ.

There was a slight complication caused by the height of the ridge on the opposite side of the valley. I tried a dummy run to see if we could circle inside the valley but the turn was too tight for safe comfort so I decided to make wide circuits and pass behind the high ridge on each run, a decision with a consequence that was of some help later on to the group.

We completed the drop in six circuits around the ridge. All parachutes opened and although one did land in or near a tree, the spread was so close that he had immediate help if needed. So we were content to let the following aircraft rely on ground signals, and we headed back into the setting moon, mind dwelling with admiration on the dapper little man who had jumped out into the Burmese night.

Contentment with the drop was ill-conceived, however. The first setback was not a great surprise. When we arrived home at Jessore that night we learned that the other three aircraft had all returned with their loads. A check with the pilots showed they had certainly found the big clearing, but no sign of a reception party, so we assumed there had been some information from the villagers that made Pop decide to leave the site at once. Agents were naturally edgy immediately on landing, and such a rapid withdrawal was not at all uncommon on a blind drop.

We heard from the field next day that it was indeed security that had led Pop to abandon the site at once, but the drop had been far from a total success anyway. There had been a fatality: a Karen who landed in a tree was dead when they cut him free, and Tiny Lewes had suffered a broken ankle and could only just hobble about with the aid of makeshift crutches.

Pop did render his own account of the landing that night. I never saw the report – it is still on the secret list – and in discussion with him down in Rangoon months later he gave no hint of its damning contents. The official historian has seen it, of course, and his account is based entirely on that Pop-eyed version. He states:

The first wave of *Walrus* – two majors, a second lieutenant, three sergeants, and fourteen Burma Sappers and Miners – under Tulloch took off from Jessore on 24 March 1945. They found their chosen dropping-zone easily, but saw that it had been cleared by burning and was covered in dangerous stumps. Tulloch selected an alternative eight miles south of Loikaw which also proved dangerous because the party dropped from only 400 feet. As a result one Burmese was killed on landing, Major Lewes of the Burma Rifles broke a foot, and most of the others suffered minor injuries, which affected morale. They hastily hid their parachutes and stores in the nearby jungle and set off for the foothills, taking with them only a week's rations.

There is nothing about 'dangerous stumps' in a burnt-off site either in my note book, or in the ORB report; it is possible they existed, of course, and that Pop visited the first site later on and discovered this fact – if it is one. Pop did tell me on return that it was my fault they could not accept the other two aircraft that first night; I had dropped them close to two villages so they had been forced to hide their packages and flee the area. When I pointed out that it was he who had made the decision to land there, despite my reservations about the villages, he said:

'No, Pat, you're wrong. I never went up to the cockpit the whole trip. I kept talking to the men to keep up their spirits.'

I could have produced the navigator and the rest of the crew to prove the truth but by then the wound was an old scar. Anyway Pop was never one to be diverted from a line by mere evidence.

The fatality was a fact however, as was the injury to Tiny Lewes, and naturally I worried about this and tried to discover the cause. Pop's explanation is, of course, a nonsense; it makes no difference if you are dropped from 100 feet or 100,000 feet – you land at the same speed once the parachute has developed. And I dropped from 600 feet. The altimeters, barometric and radio, and my own experience of low flying in the mountains at night, were more reliable authorities on this subject than Pop, who was on the first night drop of his life; even parachutists of great experience admit that height judgement is difficult at night.

It was our parachute expert, Bob Thornton, who correctly guessed the cause of Lewes's accident; a combination of heavy equipment, high altitude, and an undersized parachute put too great a stress on his frame. Lewes himself was in no doubt about that; it was he who later told me Tyce's justification for not disclosing the true size of his parachute. His injury was no great disaster, he said; he had had to hobble about with the aid of sticks for a few weeks but after that he was perfectly all right.

The death of the Karen jemadar had been bad luck. He was the only parachutist of my twenty-one group who finished in one of the trees on the DZ. Precisely what happened was never clear. He was hanging freely with feet almost touching the ground, but his neck was broken and there was a great weal stretching from his ear right around his throat. It could have been caused by a branch but Lewes, who inspected the body, believed he was killed by fouling the static line on exit. Such an accident is not uncommon, even in recent years; it is known as 'rivet inspection', because the foreshortened static line means the parachutist usually hits the side of the aircraft.

The reason for abandoning the stores and rejecting the follow-up aircraft was that the two villages overlooking the site were not both Karen, as Pop had declared; one was a Shan, and they sent off runners at once to the nearby Japanese garrison. Their story was that five planes had dropped about sixty parachutists; this version of the drop arose from our disappearance behind the far ridge on each circuit, and their assumption that five different aircraft had come down in line astern and then dropped in turn.

The fortunate consequence of this was that the Kempei did not rush to the scene. The reported size of the landing force induced a cautious approach, so by the time they did eventually arrive the parachutes and stores had been hidden, and the jemadar buried – by the Karens, not by Pop and the others as he reported. The Karens led the whole group, including Lewes with his walking sticks, to a safe hideout some miles away. Two days later when the fuss had died down the rest of the party were dropped in, and *Walrus* was in effective business.

This was the situation in early April. All three *Character* teams were now in position and recruiting Karen levies, both static and mobile, for the task of gathering intelligence to assist the army advance. But it was mostly arms we dropped in the thirty sorties flown there during that early April moon period; *Character* may have been ordered to concern itself only with intelligence, but they were also making ready for a more aggressive role if ever the XIV Army would allow it.

The timing was perfect.

Picture a capital P. At the top is the Mandalay area whence the elements of two Japanese divisions have been driven out by the allied forces, the midpoint of the P is Toungoo, at the bottom is Rangoon. The Japanese army cannot retreat down the main shaft of the P because it has been blocked above the junction by that cross-country armoured drive in which we were marginally involved with the falsified battle of *Cloak*; so instead, they move around that eastern curve along a motorable road through the mountains which turns back in below the blockage to the Toungoo midpoint. There the Japanese divisions can reform in powerful support of the established garrison, and hold up further allied advance for two vital weeks. Then the monsoon would arrive, and once the rains came the XIV Army, with a mountainous, muddy, river-strewn support line of some five hundred miles behind them, would have no chance against the Japanese defenders with the Rangoon base close at their backs.

That Sittang valley road has been described as 'the longest and narrowest salient' known in warfare. It stretches for two hundred miles – most of that distance only a few hundred yards wide – with road and rail and river down the same slot, and the loop road which joins it at Toungoo its only intermediate entry.

The bottom bend where the loop road of our P turns westward is about a hundred miles from Toungoo. The road winds down jungle slopes and narrow valleys, twisting and turning in search of easy gradients, and along the ridges above it are Karen villages. For this is Karen country, and it was here that the *Character* teams were now lodged.

Mountbatten had decided Toungoo had to be taken by 25 April. The date was critical because of the imminent monsoon rains and the need to synchronize with operation *Dracula*, the seaborne assault on Rangoon for which Fen's USAAF squadron would drop the parachute unit. Slim and Mountbatten were both aware of the crucial importance of this timing; the Japanese were withdrawing in orderly fashion down the mountain road and would undoubtedly put up solid resistance once they had massed their forces in Toungoo. Mountbatten flew down to see the army commander and press upon him that the date was imperative:

> I told him that I would personally take responsibility for his getting anything up to three thousand men killed in an attempt to speed up the advance, and he promised to go down that afternoon to the forward elements of the Fifth Division and stick a sharp spur into them.

General Slim recognized that the key threat to his timetable were those Japanese reinforcements coming down through the Karen Hills. If the two Japanese divisions reached the Toungoo garrison first then the battle was lost. He was at first doubtful if the race could be won:

> It looked as if they might beat us to it. But I still had a shot in my locker for them. As they drew south their way led them through the country of the Karens, a race which had remained staunchly loyal to us even in the bleakest days of Japanese occupation and they had suffered accordingly. Over a long period in preparation for this day we had organized a secret force, the Karen guerrillas, based on ex-soldiers of the Burma Army, for whom British officers and arms had been parachuted into the hills. It was not difficult to

get the Karens to rise against the hated Japanese; the problem was to restrain them from rising too soon. But now the time had come, and I gave the word, 'Up the Karens.'

He gave that order to attack on 13 April. So, according to Mountbatten's timetable, the army had just twelve days in which to win the race for Toungoo. And they had to fight their way 150 miles down the valley road, while the Japanese reinforcements already moving down the mountain road were less than a hundred miles from it.

It was fortunate then that the army's stern order to concentrate on gathering intelligence had been interpreted liberally by Force 136, so that the Karens had guerrilla forces already under training when the surprising call came. For to the men in the field it *was* a surprising call. The restriction imposed by the army had been a source of continuous frustration to the *Character* teams, and many of them had protested against it. Now suddenly, without any warning, they were ordered by headquarters to launch a full-scale offensive against the enemy. What was going on?

We at Jessore were also immediately affected by this sudden change in the nature of *Character*. Up until then all our sorties into Karenni had been night drops, we were dependent on the moon, and now suddenly in mid-April we were flying to some of the sites by daylight. Apart from a rare round or two of light anti-aircraft near Toungoo, we met no opposition from the Japanese. Our enemy was the weather. Isolated structures of cumulonimbus start edging up Burma from mid-March onwards, growing ever more numerous until finally they are no longer individual clouds but just the vast grey turmoil of the monsoon rains. So at this mid-April stage there were days when you had to pick your way carefully over the hills, when if you stayed under the isolated cumulonimbus the air currents over the rugged terrain would have the aircraft bucking and jolting like a fractious beast, and if instead you stayed above then you had to go swaying and sliding through the great white canyons on a track like Chesterton's drunkard: 'a reeling road, a rambling road, that rolls around the shires'.

One of the most demanding sites was Peacock's headquarters at *Otter*. This was on a ridge seven thousand feet high, frequently in cloud or obscured by rain, and almost invariably beset by violent winds. Visiting Otter-on-the-Hill was never a routine flight once the monsoon clouds had started to gather, for thereabouts the ridges were all above normal cloud level, so you were always having to weave a route into the site. It could also be a long Dakota flight, and this had strong attractions for some aircrew, as I learned one morning when four of us were going there on a daylight drop.

You had an option on the *Character* route. You could take an eight-hour direct line over the Chin Hills, or an eleven-hour angular flight avoiding high ground. You had a good chance of staying under cloud all the way by taking the long sea route, which entailed a refuelling stop at Cox's Bazaar on return, but there was another reason for favouring it as I discovered that morning.

The truck had left with most of the aircrew by the time I came outside the ops room. The sun was just about to rise, the sky over the palm trees behind the block was a clear bird-shell blue with just a few streaks of pastel pink altostratus like brush strokes across the zenith. I was still looking up at it when an alert little palm squirrel poked his head over the guttering, only a few feet away; he had as much of a start as I did and made a squeaking scolding noise at me, then jerked about in that stiff clockwork movement they have and disappeared from sight. I went across to my van where two aircrew were waiting. Egerton-Eves was RAF, his navigator Arnold was a Canadian.

'We're having a fight,' Egerton-Eves said.

It was an amicable difference, they were close friends and roomed together. Arnold wanted to take the longer route; he had calculated that he could finish his operational tour with only nine more missions instead of twelve if he could add those three hours plus to each of them. Then he would be home to Canada – sweet, sweet home, and family. Not Egerton-Eves, of course, for he was RAF and would stay on in India on some non-operational job, but he was happy to oblige Arnold if his argument was sound.

Was it? Could they count as operational hours the time from Cox's back to base?

I told them there was no need to split the flight times. Just put down 'Base – Operation *Character* – Cox's – Base' followed by the total flying hours and I would sign it. Good luck to him if he could get home to Canada three trips earlier.

Given this assurance Egerton-Eves settled at once for the longer route and the delighted Arnold rushed to the crew room with the news the moment we reached the flight hut. The consequence was that the other Canadians and Australians all settled down busily to draw new tracks on their charts and make new calculations. We, all RAF, took the short direct route.

Over the Burmese plain the clouds were already piling high by mid-morning, many with grey veils of rain blurring the pattern of forest and fields and flashing water down below. I was fascinated by the exact conformity in the cloud bases; we were flying at 4000 feet, just below the grey base of one clump, and all about us the other cumulus blocks had flattened bases at precisely the same height. Even one that shaded from blinding white crown down to leaden base, which then blurred into a gauze of rain, still had that diffused base at the standard height. The scientific explanation for the phenomenon does not make it any the less fascinating. The clouds were set out above the plain like enormous meringues laid out on a sheet of clear glass.

We reached the Karen Hills without any cloud difficulties and there I disengaged the automatic pilot. You had to man-handle the aircraft in order to reach the *Otter* site. That day a lot of the cumulus blocks were dark with rain, which draped down from the cloud base like diaphanous curtains through which you could glimpse the vague outline of the ridge beyond. We finally picked up the familiar ridge with its two semicircular humps like a camel's back. Cloud was swirling about the tops but the gap was clear except for a thin line of rain that spattered the windscreen for only an instant before we were out over the open hillside. And down there, a few hundred feet below, amid the streaks of rice shoots that glistened like dew-spangled gossamer on a fairway in autumn, was a T laid out in split bamboo and a scattering of dark figures, one waving at us.

It was bumpy down low over the ridge and with the windows open the air was coldly damp; the figures down on the cleared slope moved with glistening splashes towards the fallen parachutes. I tried to pick out which, if any, was Peacock but they were all scurrying about busily the way ants do, clearly under direction yet without any apparent authority; he had probably worked out a drill for this job, and was now himself down on the road concentrating on the primary task, to prevent the Japanese divisions reaching Toungoo before our advancing army.

That morning, the XIV Army had only four more days to meet the deadline set by Mountbatten.

Approaching the Chin Hills on return, we climbed to ensure clearing Mount Victoria's ten thousand feet. There was a long winding avenue of the brightly white cumulus piles stretching ahead roughly on our track and I began to roll the aircraft gently in slight deviation from one block to another, flicking through the swirling edges of the monsters. When you gaze up from the ground at these pre-monsoon piles they look so placid and innocently decorative you can imagine them as actual paintings on the blue canvas of the sky, but fly close and you see they are in violent turmoil, a seething furious mass of dense vapour; they are the white equivalent of great oil fires with their coils of smoke, twisting and turning in awesome power – and they are just as dangerous.

We had a sharp warning from them that day. I had been deliberately flicking the wispy edges of the monsters as we banked a passage through the great white canyons, swaying from one gap to another, and humming 'Sweet Molly Malone' in time to the game with the clouds. Then a curiously shaped pile loomed ahead of us. It outpeaked all the others, probably over 20,000 feet, but instead of being in rough pyramidal shape it had a great chunk out of one side, a gigantic bite. It was too tempting to miss. The centre of the almost circular gap was at our height of 11,000 feet, and as I eased over the control column to fly through it the edges kept closing together, so it was finally almost a complete hole in the cloud.

At the last minute, just as we entered the hole, I had a sudden

254

feeling that it was a trap, but by then it was already too late to escape. An instant later the hole either filled with cloud or it contained an upcurrent so powerful the effect was the same; all I remember seeing was a great swirl of cloud, like an exultant genie, swoop down suddenly to envelop the aircraft. Then two things happened. First, there was a loud sound like a splatter of gravel against the fuselage, then the upcurrent hit us with a thudding jolt. Then there was a 'whomp' sound, like a heavy wave against a ship's hull. I was squashed down into the seat, doubled over with a great force pressing my head down over the control column and dragging at my elbows. The instrument dials toppled and the altimeter needles went spinning like the hands of a clock with a broken hairspring.

Our exit was fortuitous, and possibly our salvation, for I had no control over the behaviour of the aircraft. We were suddenly into daylight, almost on our back, slanting down at an angle that had my head pressed against the side window. I had to brace myself against the seat to get the rudder bars level then use them for leverage to twist the control column central. We came out at last in a gentle dive, the instruments began to settle, artificial horizon wobbling into line and the altimeter unwinding moderately from 18,000 feeet. The violent upthrust of some 8000 feet could have taken only seconds and its relationship to the curious gap in the cloud pile is still a mystery. We descended to a comfortable height, and I never played games like that with the clouds again.

The clattering sound that had immediately preceded the loss of control was probably caused by hailstones – these can be as big as a child's fist, and projected in an upcurrent at a speed of 110 m.p.h. We could think of no other explanation back at Jessore afterwards for the two holes we discovered torn through the lower fabric panel of the elevator and the port aileron. There were no exit holes, and nothing inside to prove any other cause for the damage.

Three other aircraft out on *Character* sorties during that desperate race between the two armies for Toungoo did not escape so luckily from the clutch of the clouds. Their contact with our enemy cost us sixteen lives, and among those that died that month were Egerton-Eves and Arnold – Arnold, who wanted so much those few extra hours to help him get back home to Canada. They were killed on the very flight that would have brought them up to the blessed release figure of three hundred hours.

The men of *Character* whom we had dropped to hold up those Japanese reinforcements were luckier. Not one of them was lost in the battle for Toungoo. The result of that race, in the words of Slim again:

> The Japanese, driving hard through the night down jungle roads for Toungoo, ran into ambush after ambush; bridges were blown ahead of them, their foraging parties massacred, their sentries stalked, their staff cars shot up as they fought their way forward. They fought their way slowly forward, losing men and vehicles, until about Mawchi, about fifty miles east of Toungoo. There they were held up for several days by road blocks, demolitions, and ambuscades. They lost the race for Toungoo.

On 22 April, three days ahead of Mountbatten's deadline, the XIV Army captured Toungoo and the way was open to Rangoon. It was due largely to the men of *Character* that it had cost them less than one per cent of the three thousand lives that Mountbatten was prepared to pay for the prize.

17

When you stood by the cockpit door of a Dakota on a night operation and watched a line of men rushing for the fuselage doorway to hurl themselves out over the moonlit seaweed-green jungle you had a sense of dreadful urgency, as though they were fleeing from some awful threat within the aircraft. The despatcher would be jerking an arm about their shoulders by the doorway and sweeping them out with desperate speed:

'Go! Go! Go!'

They hurtle into the roaring blackness; static lines clatter against doorframe, six humpbacked figures jumble urgently in line as the plane banks, a feverish check of static lines by despatcher, red flash and the first man lurches over to grab doorway, green flash and he disappears on the instant, the next goes and the next, shouts from despatcher as he keeps sweeping them out with that same violent urgency.

There was much the same feeling of desperate haste during the last week of April 1945 when the army were striving to reach Rangoon before the monsoon broke. Slim's top priority signal, calling for 'an immediate all-out effort from the guerrillas', was passed on to us with the same driving urgency of the parachute despatcher – 'Go! Go! Go!' No waiting for moonlight, weather conditions to be ignored, every available aircraft out every single day and black night as the clouds massed denser and higher and darker with the onset of the rains.

The excessive traffic entailed some risk on the actual drop sites. The Liberators could not always get down to normal dropping height – Bob Hodges reported one *Otter* site where he had to drop 3000 feet above the DZ – so anyone flying beneath was in peril. We in the Dakotas could actually circuit inside that valley so it was always dangerous when Liberators were present. This happened frequently during that period of urgency, and the Liberators themselves were not immune from such risk; Lee, the Canadian flight commander, suddenly saw parachutes floating down in front of him one night and had to pull away violently to escape. We do not know for certain if any aircraft was ever destroyed by contact with a parachute load but it was not an unlikely event. Any such contact could be catastrophic. If you fly into a 250-lb container at 125 m.p.h. you, and anyone else up in the cockpit, are dead, and when the aircraft crashes and kills the survivors the evidence of parachute contact is destroyed by fire.

Fear of such a hazard could inhibit a pilot's performance. Dakotas dropping near the Siamese border were at the limit of endurance and could not afford to wait over the target, but Liberator pilots were not always conscious of this and there could be angry recriminations back at base. One Dakota even failed to deliver; he was exactly on time and manoeuvring into the valley when a line of parachutes suddenly came floating down in front of him. He managed to wrench away in time, but when he had staggered up into the clear and called the Liberators he had no response. The big boys, on some frequency deal of their own, went stolidly ahead with their drop in a privately arranged system, but for so long that he reached his PLE (prudent limit of endurance) and so brought his whole load back to base.

You had to muscle in on such occupation. You could go above and drop a signal flare in front of them, or use landing lights to force them to give way; this Dakota pilot performed as briefed, he was new to the squadron. But you had to learn to ignore briefing instructions sometimes and risk an official reprimand; you hoped authority would appreciate the need for, or not discover, the infringement. One pilot who disobeyed instructions was actually put under arrest – even during that pressure period when initiative should surely have been rewarded and we could ill-afford to lose a single crew member.

His name was Jack Blinkhorn, a jovial Canadian who landed his Dakota at Dien Bien Phu just a few days after I had made my trip there with Passy. Blinkhorn was persuaded down by a ground signal to pick up some wounded Frenchmen whom he landed back at Calcutta. There was a slight risk, of course, that the Japanese could have moved into possession and forced the French to inveigle him down, but Bob Hodges and I discussed the matter and felt it could be settled by a warning. The group captain, however, took a sterner line and insisted Blinkhorn be put under arrest, charged with endangering one of His Majesty's aircraft.

Fortunately the charge fizzled out presently – I cannot remember exactly how it was defused – but it had been a damaging decision; if the discretion allowed to people who are operating independently – as most pilots were when on a Special Duty mission – is severely restricted, then common sense will often become a casualty. I had direct evidence of this a week later when out on a dual drop with a Liberator to the *Mongoose* team.

There was a thick haze that night. We had navigation worries even before crossing the Burmese border, and visibility became worse as we approached the area of the DZ. It was late spring, the hills were still streaming smoke from the taungyas being prepared for the monsoon, and the resultant gloom had me with crinkled eyes peering for that roughly square patch on the mountainside seen on the photograph at briefing. The navigator had missed his pinpoint on the Irrawaddy, so when we both sighted a clearing that seemed to tally with the photograph he lacked confidence in positively identifying it, and as a result I was unsettled by the complete absence of reception.

Yet surely that pale brown distorted square was unique? I felt it had to be the briefed DZ, but wanted just a spark of reassurance.

We circled it, then swooped down so low I could pick out the black pillars of stumps left from the fires when the site had been cleared for planting. But nothing moved on the clearing, nor on the tracks seaming the nearby ridge, and there were no grey blobs of wood piles visible. We circled widely but could find no other clearing remotely like it, so I returned and set to work on it; we circled tightly, and low, about the site for ten minutes or so, revving the engines every now and again, flashing lights. Finally we had our reward. Life appeared. We had a reception – of sorts.

It was most definitely not in accord with briefing. We had been told to expect a T of fires, but what we aroused was an L of hand-held torches, just three of them flickering in line, and one offset. After another low circuit the offset one began to flash what could, only by a determined effort of the imagination, be accepted as a dash-dot repetition, the Morse letter C, which we had been briefed to receive. According to orders therefore we should have rejected the invitation as an attempted snitch by villagers or Japanese.

These were only the negatives, however. The positives were: three figures with Gurkha hats were among the dozen or so people now visible among the black tree-stumps; the DZ was undoubtedly the one photographed; torches are an alternative to fires if you arrive breathlessly late on site with no wood piles prepared; if you are short of torches a T might have to become an L; and, finally, a perfectly transmitted Morse signal was a rarity, anyway.

So I made the drop.

The Liberator, due on site after us, did not. Next afternoon I checked his report in the ORB. It read – and still does today:

Unsuccessful – no reception. DR run was made from river Sittang and flew on to area at 0100 hrs and saw 3 lights flashing in line with 4th light offset. Flashing letter was also seen but was unreadable. This was not considered correct reception, after further search sortie was abandoned.

He would have made the drop that night but for the fuss about Blinkhorn's deviation from briefing. The DZ was the correct one.

It was not only the aircrew who suffered as the monsoon approached. The ground crews had an appalling task working on aircraft in temperatures that on occasion were over 120 degrees in the shade – which did not exist in dispersal. On such days when you approached a Dakota shimmering in its pen you kept your hands clear of the ladder and floor, gasped your way through the fuselage oven and, once in the cockpit, you got the plane into the air as quickly as possible with windows open to catch the propeller wash.

Even in the cockpit you were not free from danger. Barlogie, my RAAF deputy, burnt a scar on his arm when it contacted the window runner as he was adjusting his straps, and a corporal fitter had huge blisters raised on his naked back after resting it against the seat during a run-up test. A little later the medical officer issued an order that men were not to work for more than ten minutes at a time in the fuselage; he decided this after tests one afternoon when they had to swab men down as they came out of a Liberator glistening with sweat.

Someone produced a cookery book one day at flight head-quarters in which it stated that the temperature for simmering on a stove was 170 degrees. The flight sergeant and I decided to see how a Dakota floor compared, specifically that flat area just inside the door which you tried to avoid touching when you climbed up the steps. I brought back two eggs from the mess for the experiment and in the early afternoon we took them to a Dakota pen; there, after wiping clear the aluminium floor, we stood outside by the steps and cracked our eggs open on to the metal floor. They sizzled on impact, the albumen turned white in under a minute, and the egg was edible in less than five minutes – the flight sergeant actually ate most of them.

It was a surprise one day during this hectic period to discover that there were people in the world who were not aware of the event then dominating our war, the race for Rangoon. For some forgotten reason the group captain asked me one morning to go down with a Bengali civil servant to examine the dangerous trees south of our runway; it seems the authorities were trying to discover if the trees might be removed without fuss, but the Bengali was convinced this was a pipe-dream and that our visit was a waste of time.

'If it is a bo-tree then the people will not be liking it to be touched in any way,' he declared.

The heat haze had not yet gathered when we left the airstrip early that morning, and as we drove down the narrow track that led to the village I could see a vulture circling for height in a

261

thermal above the open paddy fields west of the village. When we pulled up before the dozen or so brown huts, the big trees towering darkly about them, the people took little notice, just a glance and then they continued with their activities – two men going off to the fields behind a slovenly buffalo, some children returning with bundles of sticks on their heads, a woman slapping magenta cloth on the stones beside a storage tank. The Bengali went off to find the headman in the paddy fields, leaving me to examine the trees.

There were three or four types of ficus in the group; the bo-tree was perhaps a hundred feet high, and there was also a banyan half that size with a dozen or so pillared roots dropping from the spreading branches – an infant compared to the monster in the Calcutta botanical gardens with its six hundred root-props and more than a thousand feet in circumference. The biggest tree, about fifty feet higher than the others, was also a ficus and its great elephant-grey trunk was a writhing mass of embedded roots, as complicated in structure as the entwined serpents and limbs of the statue of Laocoons. The trees, I felt sure, would be there in the village long after the airstrip had vanished. I returned to the van to await the return of the Bengali.

I was still an unseen visitor. There was a charpoy almost in the middle of the dusty quadrangle and two old men hunched up in dhotis were sitting motionless, staring out at the open paddy fields. The roof of the nearest hut was covered in a sprawl of a yellow-flowering gourd through which tendrils of blue smoke were filtering out into the morning air; a woman in a long cherry-red sari emerged, lifted an earthenware pot on her head and swayed like a mesmerized snake as she settled it into position and then started towards the river. She moved so smoothly, and with her feet concealed by the long sari, that you could imagine she was standing still and that it was the background scene rolling past her in unfolding panorama.

The Bengali came back with the headman who pressed his hands and bowed in greeting. We chatted for a moment. The Bengali said there was no possibility the villagers would allow their trees to be touched, then he went over with the headman to pay his respects to the bo-tree. From the grove came the piercing joyous whistle of an oriole, clear, penetrating, melodious, and a mynah started out of the trees and flew low across the huts with flashes of white from its wing patches.

Presently, still ignored by the elders squatting in the charpoy, we bowed goodbye to the headman, and drove off slowly past a little boy who looked startled when I waved but then flashed teeth in a smile and gave a shy little wave in response. I was glad to hear the Bengali confirm their trees would not be touched. A few minutes later we were back at war: aircraft, trucks, uniforms, salutes . . . all so remote from the lives of the people who lived at the end of our airstrip.

On the aerodrome we also had our separate worlds. One night that April when several resident officers of the clandestines were in the mess – we had OSS, Force 136 and ISLD units permanently at Jessore now – I noted quite a heated argument about the separated lives their different organizations seemed to lead. It seemed a pity to many of us, and cause for exasperation at times, that the clandestine groups did not share their ideas and experiences. Practical benefits not only to us but also to themselves would surely have followed.

The Americans in the OSS for example had a good idea with their marked package. Important items, such as mail, cameras, watches, money, radio and specialist instruments, were in this special pack and this was always the last to be dropped, when your marksmanship was at its best after all the previous runs. And their conducting officer would switch a drop if the prime site was blank, an idea I actually suggested to Force 136 about that time. It seemed to me that if you flew seven hundred miles with standard items such as arms and rations it was better to drop them to another group rather than bring them all the way back to India – specific items such as mail and personal indents could be reserved. Even by starlight an experienced pilot could find at least one of the *Character* sites without aid of reception lights, and there offload the standard packages. But Force 136 turned down the idea for some unknown reason.

The OSS were also much more efficient in disposing their small groups about South-East Asia. They would send us out with several teams in the one aircraft, each to be dropped on a different site. We did a triple one that month of April for example, taking out in one Dakota the teams of *Wineglass*, *Acrobat* and *Workhouse*, part of whose jobs was to check on prisoners of war held by the Japanese down in the Tenasserim area of lower Burma. The brief for that particular multiple sortie could with profit have been copied by ISLD, for the DZs were not precise fields but huge areas in which any suitable site could be utilized. Exact positioning did not seem important to the Americans; as shown in that *Cairngorm* group in Malaya they were quite prepared to drop their teams blind and forget them, confident they could survive by their own wits once on the ground.

Another useful OSS practice which the others could have copied was to send out carrier pigeons with their teams. Very often radios were damaged in the drop, or the team had to rush away from the site for some reason or other, so back at base they had no idea what had happened. The OSS leaders always carried pigeons in a small box, attached to their knees when they jumped, and these were released immediately the men reached the ground safely and had checked the radio. On one occasion at least the pigeon landed back at base before the returning aircraft – which had to make a refuelling stop.

There was little contact between senior staff officers of the clandestine groups. Tremlett of 136 Malayan section and Hembry of ISLD did exchange information occasionally down in Ceylon but this was unusual, and there was no 136-ISLD contact in Calcutta. Cooperation was supposed, in principle, to be ensured through P Division, but in practice the clandestines tended to keep to themselves what they intended, what they did, and what they had learned. Secrecy, particularly privileged secrecy, is powerfully addictive.

The RAF could also have opened lines of communication with the Special Duty squadrons in other commands. We in the squadron were given no information whatsoever about Special Duty units in other commands, about their problems and how they had solved them. A USAAF study of long-range Dakota flights never reached us despite several direct requests – I only heard about it from a friend in the OSS. And in Australia they carried out extensive trials of different types of chutes for dropping bodies from Liberators, but we knew nothing about this when we were adapting our aircraft on an experimental basis at Jessore. All this information should have come to us automatically.

Lack of cooperation was sometimes deliberate, sometimes accidental. The OSS had difficulty getting a unit into Siam originally and they had asked Force 136 for help; this had been readily forthcoming but there had been a misunderstanding about a detail and the OSS concluded, unjustly as it happened, that Force 136 was not genuine in the offer. They decided to go their own way, bypassing the P Division set-up that was supposed to check all sorties, and going secretly to Stilwell; they told him their attempt to drop two agents into Siam was being frustrated by the British and he, of course, reacted as expected to such a story. The deceit is described by the official historian of the OSS in more respectable terms:

> The need for secrecy was considered so great that it was considered inadvisable to clear this operation with the British . . . Authorization was accordingly obtained from Stilwell to make a secret personnel drop in northern Siam from American aircraft.

There is a little mystery here. The Americans seemed to have been most successful in concealing their Siam operations from Force 136 after that imagined rebuff. The Siamese expert of Force 136, Andrew Gilchrist, details operations of the OSS in Siam, as does the official OSS historian, and both of them imply by omission that there were no Americans parachuted into Siam by our aircraft. But there were. It was at about this time that we flew the OSS *Siren* operation, landing a team who set up a chain of informants, twelve in all, who were soon passing back a wide range of military, political and commercial information to OSS headquarters. All without a word of their presence noted in British intelligence reports – or by Harris Smith in his history of the OSS in our Eastern war.

Another group of Americans, less fortunate, were also

involved in an ISLD Malayan operation which we carried out that month. This was *Mint*, which had been conceived by Boris Hembry, who commanded the Malay Country Section of ISLD. About that time the allied naval intelligence reported that although the Force 136 operation *Carpenter* was filing useful reports about Japanese shipping movements through the Straits of Johore, there was a serious lack of information about the use the enemy were making of the naval base in Singapore itself, and when Hembry heard this he recalled a trip once made with an anthropologist to a dig site in Johore and the remarkably clear view of the naval base they had enjoyed from the jungle hilltop.

That was the origin of *Mint*. Hembry selected for the job John Hart, who was fluent in English, Dutch and Malay. He was landed by submarine in early 1945 and by this time in April was established in the Hembry lookout and was sending out full reports on dockyard activity – showing, incidentally, that ISLD could also provide tactical information when required, and making one wonder why we needed teams from two different clandestine groups to do the same spying job.

The American involvement with *Mint* occurred in April. Bob Hodges went out one night on a special drop to *Mint* after a call from Hart for extra rations and clothing; these were needed for a group who had just arrived at his camp, among them the surviving crew of a B29 which had been shot down when bombing Singapore docks. Six of the Americans had been killed but the five who managed to bale out safely had been gathered into shelter by the ubiquitous AJUF, the well-disciplined and highly efficient communist resistance force. Unfortunately two of the Americans, unaware of the dedicated anti-Japanese attitude of the AJUF, became suspicious one day when the communists signalled them to stay in hiding while they went ahead to reconnoitre, and they followed to check. A Japanese patrol caught them, paraded them naked in front of the villagers, then cut off their heads.

The remaining three Americans were duly delivered by the communist group to Hart in his *Mint* eyrie overlooking Singapore docks; they also brought John Cross, an ISLD agent

266

who had been in the jungle working with the AJUF for three years since the fall of Singapore. Cross was udder-heavy with intelligence which ISLD wished to milk as quickly as possible, so when Hart signalled that the group were ready for departure they arranged at once for a submarine to collect them.

These long trips to Malaya proved to be a poisoned sweet for those aircrew trying to get home quickly, for some mean-spirited staff officer suddenly declared that the operational tour for Liberator crews would be lengthened by twenty-five per cent to four hundred hours to compensate for the occasional lengthy sortie. It was cruelly wrong to impose such a sentence without notice. And this at a time when the European war was practically finished and thousands of aircrew were available for transfer.

The ruling must have been catastrophic for those few men who had just managed to hold on to reason by ticking off the hours to their final trip and return home or, if RAF, to a quiet base job. There were two cases of LMF – Lack of Moral Fibre – noted that month, the last two out of the four recorded at Jessore; their collapse was almost certainly a direct consequence of that miserable decision to extract extra hours as compensation for a few long Malaya sorties. The new ruling did not affect us on the Dakotas; we still had a three-hundred-hour stint, which meant our crews flew five or six more missions than the Liberator men, but then we had far safer aircraft.

A number of us in the Dakota flight were then nearing completion of the operational tour. I was ahead, having started first, and had reached the total in early May; three others completed their stint later that month, the Canadians and Australians left for home and the RAF members went to staff posts. We were therefore already putting in requests for replacement crews in April, and I was lucky enough to discover an experienced pilot purely by chance one day in Calcutta. I had flown in for a conference on DZ photographs at our group and had gone on to Force 136 afterwards, ostensibly to examine a photograph there but mainly in the hope of finding my favourite FANY on duty.

Unhappily she was not. But the RAF liaison officer in whose

office she worked had a French pilot with him who spoke perfect English and was on a visit from Mountbatten's headquarters. This was Marcel Langer. He was one of the original de Gaullists, having come out of France in 1940. Subsequently he had flown with the Lorraine squadron under British command in Africa, then later under allied command in Europe – he had been decorated with both the British and the American DFC. After the liberation of France he was in the Military Cabinet of Charles Tillon, de Gaulle's Air Minister, and had asked to be posted to South-East Asia. De Gaulle agreed, and sent him out as liaison officer to Mountbatten's headquarters where one of his tasks was to prepare for the arrival of a French squadron which would be employed on Special Duties in collaboration with us.

It was this which had brought him to Calcutta just then. There had been a clash between him and the commander designate of the new squadron, the future General Jouhaud. Jouhaud had no particular fondness for either the British or the Americans, and was not interested in seeking local advice from them or Langer. He and Langer had been at the same school in their youth but the two of them were now at loggerheads over the equipping of the new squadron. Jouhaud wanted to use Fiesler Torches, small single-engine aircraft used for communication by the Germans from whom the French had acquired a large number. Langer had been advised that the aircraft was totally unsuitable for such a role in our command, a fact he recognized himself within a week or two of arrival, so he had reported this back to France. Jouhaud spurned the advice and declared he would be bringing out these aircraft.

That was the position when I first met Langer that day in Calcutta. He told me he did not intend to let the matter rest. He had discussed it with air command and learned that neither the RAF nor the USAAF could, or would, give logistical support to such a mal-equipped squadron, and Langer intended to report that back to Paris. He said his severely critical report would probably mean he would lose his liaison job, and when I asked what he would do in that case he said:

'I'd like to join your Dakota flight.'

I told him we would be delighted to have him but that, as we had just told his countryman, a decision of that sort did not rest with me. He realized this, he knew RAF service procedures from long experience. All he wanted to know at that stage was if he would be welcome. Once I assured him of this he said he felt certain he could work the mechanics himself – he had staff experience and friends in the right place. His self-confidence was justified. A few weeks later, his report having had the expected effect on Jouhaud, Langer arrived out at Jessore to join us. I arranged a crew, gave him an introductory flight or two as second-pilot on some *Character* jobs, and thereafter he slotted in perfectly.

We then had representatives of five national air forces on the squadron: British RAF, Canadian RCAF, Australian RAAF, New Zealand RNZAF and the Free French. And with us also on the station was an American USAAF officer attached to the OSS.

We needed every one of those national aircrews presently when the monsoon broke earlier than usual, on 2 May, and the rains came sheeting down over the hills and plains of Burma.

18

Jack Masters was sitting sideways in a jeep, feet over the open doorway, writing in a signal pad which was on his lap. Only when our Dakota came clattering over the PSP (pierced steel planking) taxi-strip directly opposite did he look up; he raised his hand high in the air like a fascist salute in response to my wave, then bent his head and resumed writing. I taxied the aircraft off the metal planking on to the silent sodden earth and into a dispersal bay which was nothing more than a rectangle delineated by an oil line on the brown surface. When we opened the door to put down the steps the hot sodden air of the monsoon came flooding past us into the fuselage. The first sound I heard when we stepped on to the ground at Toungoo airstrip was a Burmese cuckoo, that sad reverse call of oo-cuck, oo-cuck, remembered so well from those three long months slogging through the hills along the Chinese border.

'Never seen your knees before,' Masters said in greeting.

The last time we had met we had been in jungle green slacks and carrying monstrous packs on our backs. He was a lieutenant-colonel now, and working with a general whom he admired rather more than he had Wingate; he had some staff job on 19 Division which was trying to drive up the hill road into Karenni where the guerrillas were under such pressure. I had come to arrange details for a temporary detachment of three Dakotas to service *Character* in the nearby Karen Hills.

When the XIV Army tanks forced their way down the valley road in that race against the monsoon, moving over fifty miles a day at times, the effect had been like that of a gigantic snow-plough hurtling into the Japanese army, thrusting them away into great piles on either side of the Sittang valley. They had left behind nearly twenty thousand enemy troops on the west of their cleaved passage, and about forty thousand on the east of it. This huge eastern army which the men of *Character* had blocked from reaching Toungoo was still a formidable force, equipped with tanks and trucks and in full control of the roads through the Karen Hills, so the guerrillas were now caged with the tiger they had so successfully frustrated. Our aircraft remained their lifeline until 19 Division cleared the road, and when I asked Masters what progress they were making he said:

'Half a mile on a good day.'

I had brought a scratch crew and they piled into the jeep with us on the drive over to the RAF mess tent. The station adjutant was not around so I left a message for him about discussing our detachment, then went off with Masters into the battered town, bounding over the rutted road, splashing and being splashed by jeeps passing in the opposite direction. Masters kept waving at other drivers, and stopping once to give an instruction to a flustered young lieutenant.

We had lunch with three other staff officers in a tent set up in the grounds of a bombed house. Between the house and the tent was a huge straggling frangipanni tree, and the fragrance as we passed underneath brought an instant vivid memory of the Solomon Islands, of a frangipanni tree beside our bungalow and that same delicious scent on the veranda when the trade wind was blowing in the evenings. The lunch was a bad curry with strips of tough goat meat, but there were roasted pumpkin slices with raisins which were delicious. By the salad stage, green mango and cucumber, we had settled details about our detachment and were beginning to chat about Chindit days when I discovered there was another old army acquaintance in Masters's division.

This was Brigadier Morris. He had been in command of the Gurkha battalion to which I was attached and I had shared many a K ration and many an argument with him during our three-month trek behind the lines. He was now back again in a conventional army job, in charge of a brigade within the normal command structure, and with all normal army regulations and procedures in operation. Above all, with a normal general in command. That must have been a wondrous relief. Morris was a regular Indian Army officer of thirty years seniority and his time with the aberrant genius that was Wingate had been a nightmare – never sure of his position, no regular command structure about him, and having to make decisions without a staff to consult and to blame. When I asked how happy Morris was now with his work Masters said:

'We're going up to his HQ. You can ask him yourself.'

We set off after lunch. The road into the Karen Hills had been badly cut up by tank tracks and we had to pull off when we met a squadron coming back from their week-long stint against the Japanese blocks. They clanked and clattered past us, splashing water out of the pot holes and wafting heat waves and the stink of exhaust, with turrets open and men waving to Masters who stood up in the jeep to hail them.

Over the far side of a temporary bridge we passed a wild cherry in flower, clusters of carmine blossom hung like glowing embers from the branches, then the jungle began to close in on us as we climbed in gear-whining turns, scarcely ever more than a hundred yards of visibility ahead, mostly in shadow from overhanging branches. We set jungle fowl in squawking flight, and even above the noise of the jeep and the thud of distant artillery I could hear that regular sighing sound from two hornbills when they planed low down across us before banking away out of sight behind a huge dark sprawling fig tree.

Masters, as always, was good company in a strange country. He could tell you the geography of the place, the history of the local people, and produce a fact for nearly every observation made on the road: a crippled Burmese led him to announce that there were more lepers *per capita* in Burma than anywhere else in the world; when we passed a roadside cross he gave me the number of Italian nuns in the area; he told me how to skin a porcupine (you boil it first); and why a falconet was swooping in attack on a vulture four times its size (territorial aggression). He was good on animals but not so good on trees and plants, good on birds but not so good on insects. I caught one of a swirl of butterflies through which we had passed – it was like an ordinary cabbage white but had orange hairstreaks radiating towards the wingtips, and he could identify it only as a butterfly.

The road was clogged with jungle, mile after mile pressing close on both sides, and often overhead, as if only held back by a glass arcade from smothering us and the vehicle. After the recent rains the scent was like that of a watered hot-house, damp earth and vegetation, stealthy surging growth. Close beside the road the ferns and trailing mosses hid sight of actual tree trunks, but when you looked up a valley towards the ridge you could see grey trunks thrusting clear of the frothy turmoil, with branches trailing aerial roots and epiphytic growths, as if after forcing a way through the strangling vegetation they had emerged still dripping with torn and ruptured basal growth.

We passed several of the Japanese bunkers plugged into the dark shadows of valley turns. They were the same type we had met in our attacks against the Irrawaddy ferry point, roofed with tree trunks and rail lines, a thick layer of earth above; their strength was evidenced by the sight of two burnt-out tanks which had not yet been collected by the engineers. When you saw the structure and situation of these bunkers you realized why aerial bombing, even shellfire, had been so ineffective, for they were packed around and above with tree shelter. Men had to go in there, on foot, and blast out the enemy.

It was that dense tree shelter on the narrow winding road that had enabled a few hundred brave Karens led by the *Character* men of Force 136 to hold up an entire Japanese army for those vital ten days during which the XIV Army was striving to win the race to Toungoo. The parallel with Horatius did not appeal to Masters; he said it represented his men in 19 Division, which had been leading the attack down the road, as little more than base staff driving down to a new office that had been fully prepared for them. He had a different picture; the dash by 19 Division was the Charge of the Light Brigade, the guerrillas were a few infantrymen up on the ridge taking occasional potshots at the enemy gunners. He knew too much military history for me to win any arguments on the theme.

We failed in the object of our search. Brigadier Morris was back in Toungoo somewhere. While we sat by a Japanese bunker talking to one of his battalion commanders we heard heavy firing from a 75 mm tank gun (Masters's identification) a little further up the road. He asked if I wanted to go up closer and have a look at the action.

'I'd much rather go back to my aeroplane, thanks,' I told him.

So he took me back down through the jungle, now steaming after a five-minute deluge which just missed us. In Toungoo we still failed to find the brigadier, so Masters returned me to the airfield where I settled arrangements for our detachment, recovered the aircrew and then set off westwards across the darkening plain for India. I never met Masters again in the flesh – only in his books.

The fall of Rangoon on 2 May was of no benefit to the *Character* guerrillas nor to us in the squadron. It did not overrun a single one of the clandestine groups we were servicing, and in the next few weeks we were actually dropping new parties in to help the levies in the Karen Hills, as well as groups into the southern area to garner intelligence about the new Japanese concentrations around Moulmein.

One of these new groups was another OSS mission planned to cover the extreme southern area down on the border between Siam and Malaya; I think the operation was called *Cicero*, its purpose to collect intelligence and check the possibility of raising a guerrilla force. As the area was thick jungle the drop was at first light to ensure the men landed in the clear, but there was a Japanese air base just across the Malayan border and when nearing the site just after daybreak they ran into nine Oscars, Japanese fighters, circling high overhead in formation. There was not the faintest puff of a cloud in the whole of the bright dawn sky to hide their big fat Liberator aircraft.

There could be only one outcome. Within seconds the fighter cannon shells were exploding throughout the fuselage, petrol in one of the packages was hit and the whole interior was aflame, with oxygen bottles exploding and three of the crew already dead. With the port wing ablaze and the aircraft barely under control, the pilot somehow managed to miss a dense patch of jungle in the final crash, steering the Liberator between two trees. A wing was torn off, which fortunately opened the fuselage so the survivors were either hurled out into the clear or managed to scramble free of the blazing wreck.

They carried the wounded further away into the shelter of some trees and there waited for sense to return. During this interval one of the gunners, badly burned and only half-conscious, wandered about abstractedly collecting the ping pong balls which were being fanned towards them from the blazing wreck – the wings of the Liberator were filled with these to help flotation in case of ditching. Six aircrew and one of the OSS team had been killed, and all the survivors were injured to some degree or other. Local Siamese took them into hiding and care, and subsequently the Royal Thai Air Force flew them to a remote country strip up north where we picked them up in a Dakota.

Crashes behind the lines had an interest for D Division, as I discovered late that May when we were asked to include in a sortie an urgent drop for them. I was at HQ in Calcutta when a captain from D Division called with a request. He drove me to his office near the end of the maidan, a commercial block with a Victorian classic façade, doric columns to a portico that was deep enough only for a pigeon roost. In his office two floors up he asked me to wait a few minutes while he went to fetch his precious package – from a locked safe.

I waited, unimpressed. The office had a splendid view of the river and maidan. To the north you could see the red brick Victorian pile of Howrah Station and the black skeleton of the bridge beyond. It was literally alive with people; from a mile away the mass of pedestrians rippled like a multicoloured caterpillar along the footway. In the opposite direction across the maidan the trams along Chowringhee were moving all aflutter with crammed overflows of white-clad figures.

The captain came back, shutting the door behind him, and then, as reverentially as though handling a ming vase, he placed a perfectly ordinary haversack on the desk between us. He allowed me, as a very special privilege, to see the important contents. They were ordinary blue airgrammes, about fifty in all, elastic-banded into several packets each with a slip giving a

275

unit address. They were English stamped and postmarked, and all of them, so he assured me in a hushed voice, were from different hands and different typewriters.

The purpose of the mail was to reinforce a story that an army force was being assembled to strike at Moulmein, and the haversack was to be dropped close to a P38 of the US 10th Air Force that had crashed in the Karen Hills, as though it had been carried aboard. It seemed to me an extraordinary amount of effort to put into a deception that could have been of only limited interest to Japanese intelligence at that stage of the Burma campaign. Perhaps they had a large stock of these letters, with dozens of clerks back in England writing them every day and posting them off for assembling in India with unit labels to await the next crashed aircraft.

Still, the cost of delivery was small. We took his revered bogus correspondence as a trivial addition to a proper job, just as with dead pigeons, brigadier's caps, and other D Division props. In our case we were on a drop to *Hyena* and after finishing it we flew east, luckily finding a cloud gap that enabled us to map-read to the crash site. It was in a paddy field, a black splattered circle out of which the tailplane skeleton was rising like a monument; there was a large bamboo grove at one end so I dropped the package well away at the far end, just in case there were Japanese sheltering there who might see the fall of a haversack, and so see also through D Division's trick.

The day after the fall of Rangoon our Lysander flight at last became operational. The pilots had had a frustrating ten weeks waiting for the crated aircraft to be unloaded and then assembled in Karachi, and even when they were flown to Jessore they had further delay when one crashed on landing. Worse was to follow. Just a few days after they flew into Burma to start operations, a sudden violent storm hit the airfield and three aircraft were completely wrecked. The flight commander, George Turner, a London policeman before and after the war, and normally stolid against fate, was stricken by this blow.

He was even gloomier when I saw him down at Mingaladon airfield about a week afterwards, for his stock by then had fallen to five. He had damaged one slightly on landing at a strip the

Mongoose people had prepared, and before a repair party could be flown in the Japanese arrived, so Turner had to withdraw to the group headquarters while the enemy destroyed his aircraft. He and several of the guerrillas were lifted out presently by the Americans who sent in four of their little L5s; these had been used extensively in pick-up operations for both the British and American forces ever since the Wingate days.

The Lysanders not only landed within the *Character* area, they also made free drops of rations and mail. Their main purpose was to bring out wounded and other passengers, acting as courier aircraft, but they were equally invaluable taking in liaison or specialized officers who were untrained, or too old, to be dropped by parachute. Though they lost half their aircraft in that gale and by accidents on the ground, they were luckier than the Liberator and Dakota flights in one vital respect – not a single life was lost in the Lysander flight.

Not all men behind the lines appreciated the difficulties we faced sometimes in reaching their DZs once the monsoon had broken. One group signalled back to Force 136:

WHAT WENT WRONG? ONLY ONE OF THE
THREE PLANES ARRIVED LAST NIGHT AND
THE WEATHER WAS PERFECT.

What went wrong was the weather between them and Jessore. The monsoon broke a fortnight early that year, and it had a disastrous effect on our performance. Only half the operations launched from Jessore in May were successful, and twenty-five aircrew were killed in crashes that month. Our success rate was better than 358 Squadron – we in the Dakota flight could often get through under cloud by utilizing valleys where space was much too tight for a Liberator to manoeuvre – but we too had our share of failures as the grey skies of the monsoon enveloped the hills and plains of Burma.

Often it was a matter of luck in timing. One pilot could find a site obscured by cloud, another come minutes later to find it clear; one could find an easy track to the target, another be blocked by a violent storm. Such a variation in performance occurred in a *Character* operation four of us made one night just after the rains had started. We took off that night at half-hourly intervals, knowing there were violent storms awaiting us all about the hills and plains down south.

We were the second aircraft away. It was two hours to dawn, a moonless night with the mist so high and solid over Jessore that when we sheared through it into the splendour of starlight the vast expanse of pearly grey landscape below showed not a single dark blotch as far as the horizon. The mist thinned and began to shiver away as we neared the sea, and then we were over the black featureless void of the Bay of Bengal. An hour or so later however, just when dawn light was beginning to soak up the stars, broken grey clouds started to stream about us and then presently we had joined the monsoon; after that it was cloud, cloud, cloud, all the way and all the day.

When the unseen sunrise gave light enough to show a black storm ahead of us over the Chin Hills I made a wrong decision. We turned north instead of south – the choice had to be arbitrary – and after fifteen minutes the menacing blue-grey mass still barred our way. I then tried the direct track, flying straight into the dark turmoil, but after a few minutes met such violent turbulence that when we did manage to fight a way out again it was with the conviction that there was no way through the storm. So we tried the southern route, and for the next hour as we flew down the bay we kept bounding against the cloud mass again and again in probes for a gap, then at last, far down near the level of Rangoon, we discovered a passage through to the plain. Once there we flew through broken cloud across to the Karen Hills, where again we had to probe up and down for half an hour before finding a clear valley that gave passage to our DZ.

It had taken us six and a half hours to reach the target. My original deputy, the Australian Barlogie, had finished his tour and was on his way home by then, and the new deputy was the Canadian Ben Hewson. He was out with us on that operation, went south at once when cut off by the storm, quickly found a gap and reached the DZ in an hour less than me. The third pilot left earlier than both of us, took the direct route without meeting any trouble, and in less than five hours was making his drop. The fourth man took off just before us, probed at the storm for nearly an hour without being able to break through, and so he returned to base with his load.

That was a comparatively good day; three out of four had got through to the DZ. Had the fourth man been more experienced it could well have been total success. An older hand would have landed at Cox's or Akyab on the coast, refuelled, then tried again an hour or so later, but when your only experience of monsoon weather is what you have heard in the flight room and mess during the few weeks since arrival from England you are understandably apprehensive at first sight of a tropical storm. Neither Bob Hodges nor I was ever critical of a weather failure; on the contrary, it was often cause for compliment. A criticized pilot might try to force a way through the storm next time, then your words would have caused the deaths of eight or nine men.

Occasionally during the monsoon the Chin Hills became impassable for transport aircraft. The advance of a very active frontal system was reported on 15 May and such was the tenor of the reports, followed by confirmation of the danger from a high-level photographic reconnaissance next morning, that all flights into Burma were cancelled for that day. Then in mid-morning a signal was received at 136 HQ in Calcutta saying that blood plasma was needed urgently for a wounded man at the *Otter* site over in Karenni.

Bob Hodges was away ill in hospital and I was in command of the squadron just then, so it was with me that the station commander checked for a reaction to the signal from group. It seemed to me a simple matter of trial – one could always turn back if the weather was violent; but it did not make sense to take just the one tiny package of plasma all that way, so they added a full load for the nearby *Ferret* team who were very short of food at the time.

The plasma was brought out by an army doctor, and an off-duty nurse in a sarong-type skirt of bougainvillea purple and banana yellow blouse who was the stunning highlight of that day. She was an Anglo-Indian girl, with skin the colour and smoothness of honey, fine-boned hands and features as delicate as a porcelain statuette. It was no wonder the doctor guarded

279

her with precious caution, made no introduction and whisked her away from us as soon as he delivered the plasma.

The earliest we could become airborne was just before two that afternoon, which meant we were being harassed by time right from take-off; once darkness fell we would be finished, for the site could never be found within the black storm, so when we arrived at a dark menacing cloud mass we had no alternative but to strap down and fly into the monster's throat. We had three or four minutes of calm flight, so dark I had to light up the instrument panel, then we were struck by a violent downdraft that had me floating above the seat with shoulders hard against the straps. Two of our parachutes were lifted clear out of the locker on to the gangway, and the despatcher, just about to go through the cockpit door to check the lashings of our load, was for a moment suspended in mid-air as he hung on to the door handle.

After that the turbulence was continuous. It was like driving at speed over a pot-holed road, jolt after jolt, up and down, hundreds of feet at times, with your body structure braced against the seat but its contents loose to follow. We bounced and swayed and slammed about, the airframe creaked, wing-tips fluttered, and the instruments were all aflicker in the swirling grayness.

In the midst of this mayhem we plunged into an electrical storm. The turbulence eased during this period but the tension within the aircraft did not, for it was a terrifying phenomenon. And yet fascinating. There was a brief warning, a crackle of blue sparks from the nose to the port engine nacelle, and then suddenly it was all about us, flashing and sparking and splintering from the fuselage and along both wings. There would be a flash against the nose, as if we had struck something, and a brilliant white light would shatter into streaky fragments; they would elongate out to the wings or along the fuselage, snaking out in jagged white-and-electric-blue lines, many of them to the prop where they went flashing around for a moment like a fairground wheel before splintering into disappearance.

One of the electrical discharges was a unit, a sparkling globule that wobbled in unsteady mass like a jellied chandelier;

it bounced off the fuselage into the prop and was smashed to pieces, splatting into a shimmering flashing screen that covered the wing. Another discharge on the port propeller did not splinter, it whirled about for a moment then seemed to be hurled across to the Rebecca aerial just outside my window where it flashed and flickered for a second or two like a firework sparkler. I cannot remember any sound at all apart from that first crackle of impact, but there was a very strong scent of ozone even though the windows were all shut. And no lightning.

Ben Hewson also had an encounter one day with such a phenomenon. He said of his electrified aircraft:

'It was like it was all dolled up for the First of May.'

We emerged into murky daylight over the Burma plain but, although in the clear under a mass of high cloud, the turbulence was still severe. So it continued right up to the *Otter* DZ. By this time it was already dusk–gloomy under the cloud mass but we found the smoke-marked site without difficulty, a darkly wet square of taungya on the side of a hill with nearby secondary jungle a solid bulging mass, like a monstrous clump of broccoli. The panel T was at the head of the line of smoking fires, beside it a man flashing the code letter, and there were about a dozen other green-clad figures scattered down the dark slope of the site.

Strips of cloud came fleeting about us as we flew over the site, and I had a sudden fear the DZ would be obscured before we could get the plasma down. So I sent the navigator back to tell them the plasma was to go at once, to skip the marker package. In a matter of seconds, turning so tightly we were still banked over the first fire, I flashed a quick green and then dipped the port wing steeply, anxious to see where the parachute would land. To my dismay it floated across the square clearing through a swirl of cloud and landed just beyond in some trees. We turned in at once and swooped down over the spot but the men just stayed in their scatter on the site, waving at us. Cloud must have hidden the drop from them. The parachute was out of their sight down a narrow gulley. I decided to use our marker to direct them to the spot.

This did the trick. It was a lucky shot, and floated down almost on top of the plasma parachute, with them running towards it as it fell. As the following drop was not vital we stayed circling low over the treetops in the gathering gloom for five minutes or so, flittering cloud breaking up our view, until we saw them finally in secure contact with both parachutes. Then we left for the secondary.

By this time there was very little daylight left down under the cloud layer, so the *Ferret* job was done quickly. And not very well. Four of their twenty packages fell over a cliff to the east of the site. In the bouncing buffeting wind it was difficult to get close to the ground, and visibility was confused by strips of cloud whipping across the hillside during our five tight runs, but at least they saw the ones that missed the DZ and could perhaps recover them.

It was cloud dark when we finished the drop but then we climbed up through the overcast and came out clear at eight thousand feet into a beautiful sunset; the sun must have gone down just a moment before, and ahead of us in the west there were black clouds bordering the bottom edge of an ember-red sky, a deep warm orange that faded with height through apricot to gold, and in the zenith a pale, pale yellow. The colours were so lovely I was glad at first to climb as we approached the cloud mass, because the climb prolonged the sunset and you could brighten the orange glow by climbing more steeply – I saw two sunrises by change of altitude one morning on return from Indo-China.

The next few minutes were among the worst moments of that plasma flight. As we neared the cloud mass we ran out of climb, the aircraft was beginning to wallow, and we had to drop down. We had no oxygen, we could never clear the black wall anyway for it went up well over our ceiling, so all we could do was to plane down to mountain-safe height and head into the sinister dark mass. And as I disconnected the autopilot, and checked the seat straps tight, I felt cold and clammy. The bastard had been waiting all the time for us to come back!

But nothing happened. We plunged in, hands sweating rigid on the stick – the others too must have been tense after my shouted warning – but she just flew on, steady as stillness. We could have been running a test on the ground, an engine check before leaving the pen, poised there within a solidity of blackness, the aircraft gently throbbing under mid-power, gentle glow of phosphorescent lighting, all needles rigid in position. And so it continued all the way back to Cox's Bazaar, where we refuelled in the clear, and then across the calm starlit Bay of Bengal to Jessore. There we were set free from the operations room within a few minutes, nothing unusual to report, and by ten were back in the mess, talking and drinking and laughing with friends.

They recovered the plasma without any difficulty apparently, not even mentioning that it had landed in a tree. The clandestines did not seem distressed when loads landed in trees, probably because they had expert local climbers to help in recovery, and they could use explosives if necessary. On the Wingate campaign we had often been forced to leave loads in the trees, but I never recollect seeing an abandoned parachute on any of the clandestine's sites. Peacock cut a system of tracks into the surrounding jungle on his *Otter* site, had a man charting the fall of each parachute, and claimed he never lost a single one that was sighted in fall.

Masters told me of a mystery parachute in a tree that was found by a tank crew in his division. It was on the road up which we had driven together, and he had pointed out to me a huge tree that was scarred with shellfire high up the trunk. The tank crew had seen the parachute dangling from a branch about eighty feet above the ground and had managed to shoot down the branch; it was then they discovered that a harness was attached, not just a sling, so presumably it must have held a body. But there was no body on the ground, nor any bones, and the Karens in the nearest village a few miles away knew nothing of a parachutist. I asked Masters to see if he could track down the parachute and give me its number, for we could possibly trace the user, but I assume it must have been disposed of by then for, as already mentioned, I never heard from him again after that day.

By this time many of the agents were taking a safety line with

283

them. This idea seemed to have originated with Derek Headly whom we dropped in Malaya on *Multiple*, a code name that was particularly apt for his mission. He was sent in with a question-naire that covered a wide range of political and technical matters such as train services, transport regulations, rubber production, the local education arrangements, the organization of the opium monopoly, broadcasting details, coalmining activities – a whole magpie collection of subjects which were rather more the province of an ISLD agent than of Force 136.

Almost certainly it was Headly who, by illustrating its value on his own entry, had started the practice of carrying a rope. The night before his take-off he heard in our mess about Richardson landing in a tree and being rescued by good luck, and the ingenuity of an aboriginal, and it occurred to Headly that fate might not always provide both these agents of salva-tion. He took his team down to Jessore town that same night and bought in the bazaar a 60-foot hank of rope for each of them. His plan was to attach one end firmly to the parachute harness and have the rope coiled ready to be dropped should it be needed.

The next night when he went down the slide over the Malayan jungle he alone of the seven-man team finished in a tree. He was wise, and lucky, for he bunched up his body and landed without breaking a bone or even his skin. But there he was, parachute firmly caught, gently swinging from the bough high above the ground and nothing within reach of his waving arms. And no sound from the others.

In the darkness under the trees he had no idea how far he was from the ground, and felt he had no alternative but to make the descent. So he let drop the rope, having first made certain of its attachment to his harness. Once it had gone whispering down into the blackness he swung it rapidly backwards and forwards but was unable to feel if the far end had actually reached the ground, so he had to set off down in hope. Unclipping the harness he lowered himself from harness to rope and then started off, hand under hand, down and down and down the full sixty-foot extent of the rope. And there, right on his tiptoes, just sixty-seven feet six inches below his discarded harness, was solid ground. He stayed on it, firmly, transmitting information twice daily on regular schedules until the end of the war.

Headly had been dropped from the Liberator that night by Art Coy, one of our Canadian pilots who that same week took Smiley into Siam on *Candle*, to train and organize the Siamese resistance force for a possible uprising against the Japanese. Smiley already had a bucket-load of adventures working for SOE behind the lines in Abyssinia, Albania and Greece before he came out to us in India.

When they arrived over the DZ that night Coy found the correct V signal laid out in panels on site and arranged with Smiley that if he landed safely he would change the panels into an X. There was a snag on the run-in because the man immediately behind Smiley, who went out first, started to go down askew and the despatcher had to grab him and disentangle the static line from his legs. So the rest were retained on the slide and only Smiley reached the ground. The others went out next time, and on the following run with the containers Coy saw the signal panel had been changed to an X so he knew all was well.

A week later however, we had to land a Dakota one night to bring Smiley out again. He had taken with him a special Secret Service briefcase, one that had an explosive charge which went off to destroy the contents if opened in any but the correct way. Unfortunately, of course, it was opened incorrectly – these intricate spy gadgets always carry an 'unfortunately' story. Smiley was wounded in the arm, so we had to make a moonlight landing and pluck him out to a hospital in India. Later, after the surrender, we took him back again when he was instrumental in saving perhaps a hundred lives in a prison camp by arranging food supplies and medical treatment without waiting for the official RAPWI teams to arrive.

Coy was one of those who was caught so harshly by the sudden extension of the operational tour from 300 to 400 hours before he would be given that wondrous flight back home. In Coy's case it was a particularly bitter disappointment. He was actually out on that Headly Malayan trip which would put him over the 300-hour figure, and so back home to Canada, when the signal came through about the change. He landed back at Jessore to be told that his dream was a mirage. Instead of going home within a few days he was condemned to a hundred more hours of operational flying – so decreed an accountant-minded staff officer somewhere remote from war. Coy survived the imposition, despite him.

19

This chapter is an insert. None of it was in the original account of my war experiences written up in 1946 from my notebooks.

Forty years later, when preparing that old manuscript for publication of this book, I discovered by chance that the Captain Tony Bennett whom I dropped one night on the Nutshell *operation was living within a few miles of me in Sussex. When we met he produced an equally old manuscript of his own, written in Burma just after the armistice in 1945, with much of the material being copied directly from his notes in the field. Included among his records were two pieces of particular interest to me: the description of the flight on which I dropped him and his group on the night of 6 May 1945; and the supply drop I made to them three weeks later.*

With his permission I have included these in this chapter which deals with the Nutshell *operation. From a friend who wishes to remain anonymous I have received a document dealing with the origin of* Nutshell *and part of this is quoted. The official custodian of SOE documents in the Foreign Office has kindly provided a copy of the* Nutshell *mention in the post-hostilities final report on Force 136 operations in Burma.*

Here then are the records of operation Nutshell.

* * *

This is an extract from a report sent by the Burma Country Section in Calcutta to 136 HQ in Ceylon in early 1945:

> . . . nothing now mounted in the Moulmein area. The enemy is concentrating large forces in that sector so it is important the teams for *Nutshell* be sent in at the earliest possible opportunity.

The first priority of the operation will be to set up observation posts on the Japanese escape route from Moulmein into Siam . . . and keeping the Army informed about the enemy's movements and intentions.

The listed aircraft requirement includes support for a levy force. Each group will raise a force of approximately 200 levies. These will be available for guerrilla action at the behest of the army commander, but it is recognized that the primary objective of the operation is to provide the army with intelligence. All officers will be made fully cognisant of this commitment.

[Details of liaison with XIV Army follow, and then among the other organizations mentioned are PWD, and . . .]

There is also E Group. We understand they are preparing a team under Major D. Ferguson to infiltrate the area further south along the Burma–Siam railway. This is in connection with normal E Group POW activities. We have arranged that this party be dropped in due course to *Nutshell*. They will arrange guides and contacts to help E Group teams to their ultimate destination.

*   *   *

Here is an extract from the post-hostilities report on *Nutshell* (showing that an adjustment of the levy plan was forced upon Force 136).

. . . was launched in April and May, to organize levies and send intelligence on the escape routes into Siam. Owing, however, to shortage of air lift the parties were instructed not to build up a large levy force but to concentrate on intelligence . . . much valuable information was received from the Kawkareik and Moulmein areas.

*   *   *

The following is a copy of the entries in my Pilot's Flying Log Book dealing with the two operations. The first is the landing of Bennett and his group. The second is the landing of the E Group team on 28 May. This is the full extract from the log book; I never entered any comments about my flights:

Date	Aircraft	No.	Pilot	Others	Duty	Day	Night
6 May	Dakota	KJ 913	Self	Crew	Base–op. Nutshell–Base	9.40	2.00
					(Total flying hours: 11.40)		
28 May	Dakota	KJ 921	Self	Crew	Base–Cox's Bazaar	1.35	
					Cox's–Akyab	1.30	
					Akyab–Op. Nutshell–		
					Cox's Bazaar	8.00	
					Cox's Bazaar–Base	1.25	
					(Total flying hours: 12.30)		

★   ★   ★

In the operations room after landing, the Intelligence Officer questioned the crews and then immediately recorded the information in the RAF Operations Record Book. These are now available for study in the Public Records Office at Kew in London. Here are the ORB reports on the two *Nutshell* operations:

A'C Type No.	Crew	Duty	Time Up	Time Down	Remarks
Dak 'A'	S'Ldr T. P. O'Brien	Nutshell	6 May		Successful. DZ was reached
	W'O J. H. Middleton	Antelope	0322	1408	at 0944 & correct reception
	F'Sgt. R. T. Wright	5			of T of panels was recog-
	Sgt F. H. Burley	1725N			nized. 4 agents, 6 con-
	Sgt A. S. Osmaston	9754E			tainers, 13 packages, were
					dropped in 7 runs – 3-500
					ASL. 10 packs nickels
					dropped posn 1725N 9744E
					at 1004 hrs. Weather en
					route – 8 – 10'10 S Cu
					mainly over Chins. At DZ –
					10'10, 800' base – vis 4
					miles.
Dak 'H'	S'Ldr T. P. O'Brien	Nutshell	28 May		Successful. A'C was over
	F'O F. S. Stevens	Antelope	2110		DZ at 0031 hrs where T of
	W'O G. Middleton	12	Akyab		lights & flashing A was
	F'Sgt R. T. Wright	1623N			seen. 6 agents, 2 containers
	F'Sgt F. H. Burley	9758E	29 May		& 15 packages were
			0450		dropped in 6 runs from
			Cox's		5000' ASL & all fell on
					area. S'C base 0052 hrs, 24
					packs nickels dropped
					1650N 9728E – 0109 hrs –
					8500'. Weather en route
					10'10 AS 14000' – patches
					of Cu and Cb 5'10 S Cu
					base 3–4000' – vis 5 miles.

Here are copies of Bennett's account of the two drops, written in August 1945. I felt obliged to cut his references to me.

ENTRY INTO BURMA

We were given lots of advice before we left, most of it useless, some bad. The worst was 'Get tight before you leave, take a bottle of rum in the plane, and when you jump you don't give a damn.' I ought to have known that I could never keep drinking as long as that, but foolishly we all tried it.

We sat in the mess, Basil and I, with the rest who were 'going in', and I stuck to gin and ginger (there wasn't much choice) from seven to nearly eleven. Then I went to dinner. I have no idea what I ate, but doubtless it wasn't much. From half past eleven until one thirty I lay down to sleep. When they woke me I felt awful – head, mouth and stomach. The mere thought of drinking in the plane was enough to make me ill.

We drove to the dispersal area; Franklin from HQ was with us and we took a good view of his getting up to see us off. We hung around for the crew, and the pilot turned out to be Pat O'Brien. We were considerably cheered because . . .

As soon as we took off I lay down on the floor and, with my chute for a pillow, tried to sleep off my nausea. By five I was fully awake, and ate some of the sandwiches provided. They were so awful I left them even though I was hungry. The coffee was worse. I was cold and the continual roar, the swaying, bumping and vibrating of the plane, made me wish I was anywhere but there. I hoped to see a glorious sunrise but it just came up through the mist in a red ball. I looked below: mist, sea, islands and jungle crept by.

We were due over the target at eight, so at seven thirty we started getting ready. I bandaged my ankles with crepe, put heel pads in my boots, and tucked a spine pad in my trousers.

They were official precautions; unofficially I bandaged my knees as well. We had overalls on. Underneath we wore normal uniform, skeleton webbing and had a lot of odds and ends around our necks and resting on our chests. I also stuffed my bush hat in my belt and by the time my chute was buckled on tightly I was so cumbersome I could hardly move, and sitting down was very difficult. I tied my helmet and tucked in the loose ends well, as in the slipstream they can give a nasty slap.

We looked out; a sea of white cloud. It was eight o'clock. The plane circled in vain to find a break; it daren't go down as there were hills below. But Pat . . .

We prayed for luck. To go back and wait for days more in the concentration camp would have been heartbreaking. We found the edge of the clouds and came down low over the plains. We flew south for an hour and a half I thought, but when we landed I found we had turned and been flying north for some time.

What a flight it was! We were on thorns all the time that the navigator would come through and say 'Wash out', as petrol was not unlimited. We entered a valley. Clouds still covered the hill tops on either side. It got very narrow, and from my stiff uncomfortable position I could see trees flashing by the wing-tips, and trees well above us too. We were about two hundred feet up. We banked steeply at every turn and heaven alone knew what was round the corner. I'm sure Pat didn't. We cleared a ridge by inches and dropped down the other side. We were flying in a small box of trees and cloud.

Basil said afterwards that he was scared. I don't think I was. I was interested and I was aware that it seemed dangerous; but I'd have flown anywhere to find the DZ. The thought of a five-hour flight back again terrified me. I loathe flying; and things were changing so quickly that if we went back we might never have another chance.

We swung round a big conical peak and suddenly the despatcher tugged my arm. I looked out his side and saw a paddy field with a big bamboo T, fires, and people and some cows nearby. My heart leaped and thumped. This was it! The navigator came through all smiles, and helped remove the door. We expected to jump first, after what Pat called his 'sighter' package, but the DZ looked so small and the run-in so awkward that he decided to let all the stores go first for practice. It gave us more time to work up into a panic.

We climbed to dropping height, about five hundred feet, which is a bit low for jumping, and banked around the peak again. A short run and out went some packages. Next time we felt a lift as the containers went from underneath. Two or three more circuits and the plane was cleared.

My stomach went tight, my knees went loose, and my mouth went dry. There wasn't much time left. They whipped out our static lines and hooked them up. I gave mine a good tug and held it in my left hand. I was jumping first, then the two signallers, then Basil. I stood in the door, left foot forward, hands on a girder overhead. They teach you not to look down but as we swung around that peak I could see nothing but ground. I was stiff with fear. I knew I'd jump; I had faith in parachutes and I always landed safely. It was just stepping through that door. I remember saying, 'Thank the pilot' to the despatcher on my left. His hand was in the centre of my back (to help me out and to stop the next man jumping too soon) and he was watching the two lights. I was not supposed to look at them and the door hypnotized me anyway. I felt sure I was paralysed and unable to move. Suddenly it came!

'Action stations, number one,' snapped out the sergeant.

I slapped my hands on to the fuselage just outside the door. My mind went blank; for a second I was just a spring.

'Go!'

There was a roar, a slight crack, and I saw my chute opening over me. I had a few twists and had jumped so low that by the time they had gone I was almost down. Voices shouted the old training instructions, 'Pull down', and I looked to see where I was heading for. I'd no time to enjoy any of it before I was sitting down – I never do a proper roll – having just missed a paddy bund. I looked around for Basil and found there had only been time for two to jump on that run. A fellow came up to me and said:

'How do you do. My name's Briant. All okay?' I was in Burma.

PS After unpacking and distributing all the stores we had brought we decided to stay for a day in the hope that the other planes which had set out with us, but not found the DZ owing to cloud, would return. We were disappointed however, and, leaving a rear party to wait for another day or so, we moved off south.

★　★　★

The following is his account of our drop of the E Group team.

ON THE DZ

'HOPE DROP 2230 HOURS 28 STOP SIX MEN TWO CONTAINERS 15 PACKAGES. . . .'
So had read the signal received two days ago. Now it was the night of the 28th, well past eleven, and still no sound of an aircraft. We had set off at nine o'clock, cursed the mosquitos that were whining all about us, and walked down the muddy slippery track to the DZ. The clouds kept drifting across the rising moon, threatening the chance of a successful drop, and then any possibility at all was wiped out completely when we reached the disused paddy field and it started to pour with rain.

Nevertheless we had to get it ready. Working in the rain, with just a single fire to guide us about the site, we laid out the fires in the pattern ordered in the signal. We also spread large strips of opened bamboo, white-inside uppermost, as recognition signals though there seemed little chance that they would be seen in the blackness of the wet night. But we had finished the job well before ten and then, just when we moved in to shelter from the rain, it stopped. Not that we minded. Getting wet again did not matter so long as we got the drop. All we could do once the fires were ready was to sit down and wait, hopefully.

But now it is nearly midnight and we are still waiting, not so hopefully. For the last hour or so a successful drop has been possible; there have been intermittent breaks in the low cloud and a pilot can get in his runs between cloud if he – and we too – are lucky. At the moment it is too clear, brilliant moonlight, the Japs over at Kya-in could probably see the drop; we don't like an audience for these shows, particularly at night when they could come in close without any warning from our friends the villagers. However, clouds are piling up in the southwest and blocking out the stars in that quarter. Soon it will pour with rain again – just as it did yesterday, and last night, and all this month.

'I expect she's hit a bad patch and turned back,' says Basil disgustedly, throwing away his 'cigarette' – it's made with local tobacco wrapped in a message form. We have been out of Woodbines for ten days now.

'Well, if they come in this clear moonlight,' I answer, 'the Japs will have a grandstand view. We'll have to be away like a dose of salts.' I never have been keen on meeting the Japs.

'Listen!'

The silence is broken by a faint drone. A plane!

'Sounds like a Dakota.'

'Get those fires burning. Flame! We want flame, so he can see it.'

The levies fan the smouldering fires into flame, and we throw precious dry wood on to the pile. (You use wet scrub in daylight to make lots of smoke but flame is important at night as a guiding light.)

'She seems to be to the east.'

'Pretty high, too.'

Nobody listens to what anyone else has to say. We are all too busy with our own hopes and prayers. Mail, tea, milk and sugar, cigarettes, socks – oh, everything we have been waiting for!

'There she is!' Basil has spotted her passing across the moon.

'What is it, Tony?' Having been in AA previously I am considered an expert on aircraft recognition.

'Can't tell. Too high. But sounds like a Lib – and it's going away, anyway.'

'_____' in chorus.

'Well, if she can get through, maybe the Dak will be along soon' – Ian the optimist again.

It is fortunate we never have to worry about the Jap air force, by day or night. The pattern of fires would have given us away at once if the Liberator had been hostile. We settle down to glum silence, broken only by slaps and scratches as we are attacked by every conceivable insect in turn. The heavy cloud in the southwest seems to be sliding more westwards, maybe it will miss us. But patches of low cloud now keep blotting out the moon. Cigarettes glow in the dark as we wait in growing despondency.

'It did say the 28th I suppose?' someone asks at last.

'Well, you deciphered the message, old chap.'

'Yes, but it was a bit corrupt.'

'Not as much as that, though.'

'And today's the 28th all right.'

No chance of us making a music hall comedy out of it with us all waiting on the wrong day. Damn the monsoon; only once has one of our sorties been able to get through on time. We ought to be used to disappointment by now but it is just like jumping – it's the same each time, but worse. And now the clouds seem to be thickening, you can't see the figures near the fires. Soon we will have to go back to another meal of rice, chillies and salt, and wait for the inevitable message: 'Sorry chaps, try again 31st.'

Suddenly we hear a sound. It's a Dakota sound I'm sure, but I dare not say it. Then I see it low against a moonlit cloud, crossing below us. We flash the signal light and yell for more flame on the fires.

'She's turning. She's seen us.'

We keep flashing the signal lamp, and the air is suddenly full of smoke.

'Boy oh boy, doesn't she look good.' You can see her clearly now against the low white cloud.

'She must be ours. She must be.'

'Damn good navigation.'

A girl's school after the Christmas holidays is nothing to the excited pandemonium as the plane flies in and out of the low cloud and blocks out the stars. The moon is fully clear as the Dak comes in on her first run, swaying slightly like a lady on a tightrope. We can see the red warning-light glow in the open doorway of the fuselage, then as she comes overhead we see it change to green. A pale balloon-shape suddenly appears below, a single parachute. It falls slowly to earth near the trees on the far side of the DZ.

'It's Pat O'Brien. He always lets go a single marker. I'm sure it is.'

(I was right. The E group chaps told me after they landed that Pat was the pilot.)

'Bit more wind than he allowed for; he'll be okay next time,' says John wisely – as if we all didn't know.

Two containers drop from under the fuselage as she slides across against the stars; right in the centre they fall. Then I'm sure it's Pat; he always lets the load out first as he did with us. He says he wants to make sure he has the range perfectly by the time he drops the 'bods'. Round again she comes and we see the despatcher in the green-lit doorway flinging out packages, five of them come down, and she goes turning away through a scudding cloud. We picture the despatcher and the navigator, who usually assists him, piling up packages for the next run and hurriedly tying the static lines to the roof cable.

Another five on the next circuit. Good. Next run should finish the packages. Already the bullock carts are creaking over to the edge of the site to be loaded, the site is busy as a market with fire and smoke and blobs of fallen parachutes and hurrying figures. Another run and the last five come out, two of them so close together the chutes get tangled, fail to open properly and the load goes flying out of the paddy clearing, and the packages crash down together in some trees to the right.

'Hell,' says Basil. 'I bet one of those was the Luxury.'

The 'Luxury' contains a bottle of whisky or rum each, Penguin books, soap, and odds and ends, all of which help to make us comfortable. And most important of all, mail.

'One of the men will have the mail.'

They always sent it that way when dropping a man, it was

safer. (They did it this time too, and we got our 'Luxury' safely also.)

The men came out in two runs, three each time, and landed perfectly except for one who almost crashed into the centre fire. He hurt his knee twisting away, but he was all right next morning.

We go over to meet the men who have landed and then a cloud comes over just as the Dak is making her farewell run. But she comes in very low, under the cloud. We frantically wave and flash our torches and acknowledge the 'thumbs up' from the despatcher at the lighted doorway. As she flashes by with a swoosh out comes a small bundle which lands at our feet. The last week's papers, collected by the despatcher from the table in the Sergeants' Mess and dropped as his personal gift to us. To him and to every supply-dropping crew in SEAC we say:

'Thanks a lot.'

* * *

I did not include details of all operational flights in my notebooks; from time to time, sometimes on consecutive days and sometimes not for weeks, I would put down an interesting trip or thought or memory or observation, dreams and hopes and fears, and for this reason it is sometimes difficult to be certain which particular trip out of three or four is associated with the written note. What follows is a selection of the entries, including all references to Nutshell, *that I made in May 1945 (I usually recorded the month, only rarely the date).*

Two Libs out with us on *Nutshell*. We got in finally but the Libs had to bring their loads back to base, they never had a hope of getting under the weather, bloody silly waste of petrol and risk of lives sending Libs down there on the off-chance they will get through. There should be reports from a weather aircraft, coming in every hour, so you could decide if it would be worthwhile sending off the big boys. I got through in the end by flying under cloud up the estuary but Libs can't do that because they could never make some of the tight turns in the estuary. Dropped leaflets afterwards near Bilin, dropped from 5000 feet then dived down to fly through them – sent them swirling over a far wider area than simple drop. More fun, too.

She was a Burmese nurse who had worked with Seagrave, the American missionary doctor. Sin-Ti – it sounded like – her name. Wearing a navy skirt, and over a white bodice a daffodil blouse of such fine silk you only saw the colour where it creased. We passed under a beautiful tree covered in tiny white conical flowers and I asked her if she knew it. Her answer was like a catechism response:

'That is an eleocarpus. The eleocarpus, a native in Burma, is akin to the lime tree so common in northern climes.' Then she laughed and said: 'I've never seen a lime tree. That's what our schoolbook said.'

At Akyab we sat under a grape vine and watched the sunset as we drank. The sea was flat as glass. As the sun descended a maroon glow arose in the eastern sky and the water of the bay took on this strange colour. Near shore the water was a shrill green and these beautiful strips of maroon lay between us and the far shore. The moon came up, flat at first and pale rose in colour. As it climbed the colour changed from rose to yellow, finally to silver white and the dark water of the bay was divided by the silvery yellow beam when a boat crossed; the little boat drew its own moonlit trail behind as the men pulled it towards the shore. . . . I had this sudden vivid memory that seemed to have nothing to do with the scene: my sister Mary at the piano playing a favourite of mine, the 'Norwegian Bridal March', her slender fingers not so much striking the notes as dancing on the keys to the music of Grieg, and then playing it again for me as I lay on the floor, eyes closed, watching a Norwegian bride in white emerging from a tiny church on the narrow shore of a beautiful blue-water fiord. . . . What has this got to do with a sunset at Akyab? Maybe someone said something that struck the chord, or was the sun setting through the grape vine back at home in Maitland when she played it once?

He said it was a Punjabi sweet their family used to make in Lahore. It was thick cream to which you added saffron and cardamon, and it was kept on ice for four or five hours so that it became vaguely solid, like a junket. Then you added a thick layer of crushed almonds before serving. It was delicious.

We come out of the operations room in mid-morning, and the palm squirrels go skeetering away over the roof into hiding. Coppersmith ponking away in the sal tree by station HQ. I wait by the three-tonner for the crew to join me. Bonnet probably already too hot to touch. I say to the navigator of that day something like:

'We'll take the direct route. Usual height.'

And I know what he'll say. The sense, anyway, if not actual words. It will go like this. . . .

From navigator S. 'I'll stay here with the others and work it out now.' He'll go back inside. When we arrive at the plane that night he'll tell me the course and either of us will set it on the magnetic compass. He sits by me most of the trip and likes to chat, mostly about flying matters – he has done a tour on bombers. We discuss pinpoints as they come up and he makes rough adjustments in his head.

From navigator W. 'Okay, sir.'

Nothing more. He'll get into the back of the truck. When we arrive at the aircraft that night the ring on the magnetic compass is already set on his course, and he gives me a little slip of paper with course, estimated time over target, and time of landing at base. He stays back in his navigation cubby-hole most of the trip, just coming up occasionally for a specific pinpoint or giving me a new ETA and then returning at once to his desk, never stopping for idle chatter.

From navigator M. 'What about the coast route, sir? Weather looks ropey over the Chins.'

I stick to decision, also overrule his suggestion about a different height, and adjusted time to take-off. When we arrive at plane that night he asks if I want to stick to the original decision, then has to go back to his table to give me 'that other course'. He sets his preferred course on the magnetic ring, apologizes and changes it. He spends most of trip wandering from cockpit to fuselage giving everyone opinions about their jobs. He disagrees with my estimate of the actual moment we are over that Irrawaddy bend we use as a major pinpoint. And when I agree with his disagreement he disagrees with me again.

From C-1. 'What cruising speed, sir? Will you climb straight from base or when we get to the hills? Should I work out the coast route alternative course? Any idea how long the drop itself will take?' When we arrive at the aircraft he has some more questions, and when he finally gives me the course in the cockpit at my direct request says it is 'just to go on' till he checks it. Has not touched the compass, spends all the trip drawing new course lines and making calculations, rushing backwards and forwards from me to his cubby-hole with tiny little alterations in course (which I simply pretend to follow) and checking the ground anxiously to confirm we are exactly on track.

From C-2. 'Oh! Left my maps in the ops room. Won't be a tic, sir.' When he comes back, peering at them as if unsure what they cover, asks me to repeat what I told him, and when we arrive at the aircraft that night says, 'I wasn't too sure if you said coast route or over the Chins. I'll just give you a course to steer while I work on it.' He has not touched the magnetic compass. He spends the trip in his cubby-hole, asleep probably, no mid-course check, only when within about half an hour of the DZ or base does he start coming up to look at the ground. The others always have to call him back for his share of despatching.

We took off at about 3.30 a.m. *En route* just south of Jessore we passed by a train that was rushing northwards, the smoke was a beautiful silvered-grey. I closed my eyes and tried to remember it and I had a picture of a girl with silvery-grey hair streaming away behind her in a wind. That was the shape of the smoke trail as I remember it.

When you take off from Delhi and climb through the moisty mist you can see the jagged white line of the Himalayas over a hundred miles away to the north. It's clearer in outline, whiter and more sharper-edged against the blue than any horizon cloud would be. On the ground in Old Delhi you pass by the Red Fort and perhaps a temple or two and might assume there is nothing more to the place, but from the air you can see that the old city is embossed with dozens of palaces and temples and mausoleums, gilded cupolas and marbled minarets, gleaming white, rose red, sandy yellow, many of them hemmed in by shanty dwellings, or within close-encircling roads. They look like jewels thrown on a rubbish dump, these legacies of empires long passed and princes long forgotten by the streaming crowds. A few miles away, aloof from this jungle growth over the past, is New Delhi with the pink Lutyens blocks of severe symmetry, confined by wide straight avenues decorated around the edge by little white houses each of them garlanded with a circlet of green containing tiny coloured gems of flowering shrubs and exotic trees.

In dispersal tonight . . . a nightjar chok-choking all the time Chiefie was talking to me . . . jackals howling over towards the village . . . a crow gives a sleepy wail . . . that brain-fever bird down near the flight hut . . . scuffly noise from long grass behind the pen. The petrol bowser always stinks worse at night; at least in H dispersal pen you can go over the top of the mound and catch the scent from the four-season lemon tree. Maybe I should plant one behind each dispersal pen? [I did later.]

Out on the practice DZ watching a drop (Bob Thornton wanted me to fly out and jump with him, but I've done one now and that's enough). He came out first and alone, then halfway down he began to yell at the sergeant who was standing beside me at the fire.

'Why the hell did you –' and we lost the rest.

'What did you say, sir?' the sergeant called.

'I said –', then Bob paused, attending suddenly to the ground that was fast approaching, flexed his knees and landed perfectly, still upright, released his parachute which he left on the ground about twenty yards from us, and continued his complaint as he waddled over: 'Why did you bring the jeep?'

'I thought you said you wanted it, sir.'

'No, I just meant the bloody truck, man. Collect my parachute,' he said and went on grumbling for a minute or so, then forgot his troubles as the first stick of eight came popping out of the Dakota doorway above us and began yelling at the descending parachutists:

'Legs together, number four. Legs together. Bloody fool. Check that swing, number two. Grab your lines. Pull, man! Pull!'

I told Marcel Langer that the cloud was thin and broken as we flew up a valley, that it was as if the fragments were being flung at us. He said he had made a two-line poem about clouds, and wrote it down for me.

Sweet stratus sheets like wedding veils
And mellow slanting light through liquid air.

I could not get the last line out of my head – particularly when I discovered it went perfectly with that marvellous Don Giovanni 'Il mio tesoro' – the Gigli record I used to love playing in the Solomons.

At Akyab the little white blocks of houses among the scattered coconut palms remind me vividly of the Solomons, but a difference is that the sea is a uniform ultramarine because there are no corals to give off those shoreline greens and yellows you see in a Pacific Island surround. And although Akyab has this special characteristic of a white lighthouse stuck up like a figure atop a wedding cake, the spirit of the place with its little collection of expatriates and the security of its club life is reminiscent of Tulagi back in the Solomons. When you fly low over the Bay of Bengal you see flying fish too; well, you don't actually see them, you get that occasional flash of silvery reflection and then are over the spot before you have time to focus. Like the pastel shades of jellyfish in the sea, you see them only in memory after they've shot beneath the fuselage, merged in colour like a coral reef.

It took a lot of time to get into *Nutshell* – nearly 24 hours on the job, with three landings. Back to Cox's first time, wait two hours and then take off again but still no soap, back to Akyab and wait again, then got through third time at midnight. You go up and down the coast looking for gaps to get you inland, like the mosquito jabbing about the net trying to find a hole through to that tantalizing blood-meal. Even when you get inland it's not always the end, sometimes you have to go scooting up the valleys to reach their bloody DZs. Trouble is that the Joes are not pilots, so don't know the sort of location to make a good DZ – no, that's rubbish, when down there myself I picked a DZ where I could find a clearing that was reasonably safe from Japs, and of course they do the same. As would anyone with any sense. So we just have to accept the stinkers with the great big open spacious ones you get in Indo-China.

Two little Bengali boys sitting close together in a tonga, both holding slates against their chests, passing me as I stood by the lakeside – going home from mission school, in a tonga, clearly thrilled by the drive, and the world, and life to come . . . My brother Frank and I coming home for holidays from our convent school, catching a cab from the station, settling down into the dark interior as the horse went clopping down the slope and on past the lucerne fields, chattering excitedly about the endless holiday and all the delights of Christmas to come.

Sometimes like tonight flying high over the Bay with a prairie of flat cloud down below and the stars filling the moonless sky you long to know what is out there beyond the universe. You pray for an answer, really pray from deep down inside you, please tell me, tell me! Maybe it's a deep human urge and this is why the religions appeal so much, they give the answer and so you don't have this longing to know. I knew the answer when I was a boy back in Maitland and we would say the rosary every night; when we were kneeling down by the brass bedstead, with each of us saying our decade, and the red lamp glowing before the statue of the Virgin Mary on the altar, and the picture of the Sacred Heart on the wall, I knew with absolute certainty about heaven and hell and purgatory and limbo and God and how the world began, and why, and where it would all end. Now I have shed that belief and I'm ignorant, and when I'm up amongst the stars I feel this passionate desire to know, before it's too late.

We have only one short life, terrible to think we might finish without ever discovering the answer. So I pray to the stars, in the cockpit sometimes, that poem of Housman's about it, whispering it in prayer:

> From far, from eve and morning
> And yon twelve-winded sky,
> The stuff of life to knit me
> Blew hither: here am I.
> Now – for a breath I tarry
> Nor yet disperse apart –
> Take my hand quick and tell me:
> What have you in your heart?
> Speak now, and I will answer.
> How shall I help you, say;
> Ere to the wind's twelve quarters
> I take my endless way.

from 'A Shropshire Lad'

I drank too much last night. But it was a pleasant session with the OSS and *Nutshell* crowd. A few of the crews, including pilots, have a drink if they're flying that night, I rarely do and Bob never did, yet there's no rule about it. Perhaps there should be. But what happens then if an emergency flight comes up on your night off, when you have had a few beers? I remember Thomas taking off quite sozzled one night we were on a Brest raid in filthy weather and he was the only one of us who found the docks.

I asked one of the E Group Joes what he did in peacetime and he said he'd been a jail warder. Now that's exactly the sort of bloke you want to send out into the jungle to chase up prisoners of war; he knows the job.

20

Shortly after the war I talked to Colonel Wilson, who was in charge of the Calcutta office of D Division, and suggested that although their double-agent radio links might have achieved something the artistic work put into their other deception stunts had all been wasted effort. He did not agree of course, and showed me a report by Fleming which mentioned two possible successes.

There were reservations in Fleming's claim but Wilson said he himself was convinced that *Sceptical* had achieved its purpose. This operation was designed to suggest we were planning a pincer attack on Bangkok, by sea up the Gulf of Siam and by land down the Burma-Siam railway. The story was set flowing through the usual D Division channels, via Japanese agents in India and China, and we added to the flood with documents dropped near Moulmein. Fleming suggested that the Japanese division moved to the threatened area from Indo-China might have been a reaction to this fictitious intent, and Wilson said he had seen a Japanese order to withdraw allied prisoners from the railway area 'which is under threat by the enemy'. As none of the postwar studies mentions *Sceptical* it is difficult to check these claims.

The other was *Stultify* (there is some confusion about this code name, but let it serve for this brief notice). Its purpose was to persuade the Japanese that we were planning in the spring of 1945 to launch a sea and airborne landing against Moulmein, thereby isolating their Rangoon forces. Here again they used their normal methods of disseminating the fiction, including a contribution from us in that package we dropped beside the burnt-out aircraft.

Fleming in his report was dubious about the effect of *Stultify* but Wilson again was confident. He claimed that it had been an important factor in the Japanese decision to withdraw from Rangoon, so allowing our troops to enter without opposition, for the garrison would have been cut off by such a landing – one can see a sound military reason for the withdrawal however, without any D Division influence. Again, no military historian that I have read even mentions *Stultify*, let alone supports Wilson's claim.

Wilson himself was dubious about the effect of *Conclave*, an operation which Fleming did not even mention in his report. The purpose of this D Division effort, in which we participated that June, was to divert Japanese forces in what has been described as the 'great epic of guerrilla war' in our command. Southeast of Mandalay there is a road through the mountains which was a possible escape route into Siam for the 10,000 Japanese trapped in the north; opposing this army of seasoned veterans well equipped with tanks and artillery and motor transport were 3000 guerrillas of 101 OSS under Colonel Peers, without artillery or armoured support, and dependent entirely on the US 10th Air Force for supplies.

Peers was undoubtedly the most experienced guerrilla leader in South-East Asia. For nearly three years he had been fighting behind the lines in northern Burma, he knew the country and the people, above all he knew how to use his irregular forces to maximum effect. The tactics employed were the same as at *Character*; the superior Japanese force was ambushed at every move, night after night their posts were attacked, they were given no peace and no opportunity to engage in pitched battle against guerrilla groups that simply dispersed to reassemble elsewhere when threatened by concentrated attack.

The result of these tactics was complete success. In the space of five weeks the men of 101 OSS had killed more than twelve hundred Japanese at a cost of forty of their own men, and the road was clear. I do not know what effect the contribution from D Division *Conclave* had on the campaign, but suspect it had little. The success of that northern campaign was entirely due to the fighting efforts of the multinational force of Americans,

Kachins, Shans, British and Chinese that made up the 101 OSS Detachment.

My involvement with *Conclave* was to deliver the D Division fake-battle artifacts for their stunt, which was to be operated by Force 136 *Squirrel* group working with the OSS unit. We had taken off in the early hours of the morning and arrived over the hills as the sun was shrivelling away the mist and the bulges of forest beginning to emerge clear, like fluffy green shaving cream spread over the ridges. The DZ was a narrow clearing along a valley, with reception fires streaming white smoke, but about five miles away was an airstrip marked out on the open hillside with bamboo laid out to form the word:

LAND

By taking wide circuits as we made our drop we kept passing over the airstrip, so enabling us to study its surface and check out the twenty or so green-uniformed men among the turbanned locals who went on waving us down. Everything looked right, particularly when in a final very low pass one man opened his bush shirt and gave two-handed strokes up his chest in what was meant to be seductive appeal. So I landed. We began to settle the moment we stopped and I taxied about for several minutes feeling for sogginess in testing pauses before finally discovering a patch where we needed brakes to stop instead of being pulled up by mud.

The first man to greet me was Tom Leonard, an OSS Texan who had been at a Chinese village called Sima'pa when I had delivered a Japanese prisoner up there the previous year, and who after a rum or two had shown me a picture of a lovely laughing Evelyn whom he had married just before leaving home. He was with an American army captain who explained why he had called us down. About a dozen British troops had been trapped there when the Japanese closed the road, and they wished to get back to their unit. There was also a French priest who wanted to get back to his base at the Leper Hospital in Mandalay, and when I told the captain that the field there was temporarily out of action he asked me to land at Myitkyena, for they would ensure his return when it was possible. So we set him down there on the return flight.

There was a major disturbance in the squadron that month. Air Command decided that our Liberator flight should concentrate on the Malayan operations, flying from Ceylon which was three hundred miles closer to the peninsula. Bob Hodges would go with the detachment, leaving me with squadron headquarters and the Dakotas at Jessore. I had finished my tour of operations by this time and was well into another, but Bob had not disclosed this because he hoped that I would be able to take over command of the squadron when his own tour ended and he went off to staff college as an instructor. He insisted I take ten days' leave before he departed with the Liberators because, as he put it, there was little likelihood another opportunity would ever occur once I was on my own.

So I went up to Darjeeling for ten days, travelling up by that little narrow-gauge railway on a track with such sharp bends that at times you could look out of the front carriage window and just below see the back half of the train passing you in the opposite direction. My only note, and memory, about that leave is my performance of the statutory duty of those who visit Darjeeling: all must observe the spectacle of sunrise on Everest. I had three mist-ridden failures but on the fourth attempt all went well. With about a dozen others I stumbled up in the cold darkness to the top of Tiger Hill and there we had our reward.

Looking across the dark purple valleys you see first of all in the Eastern sky that jade-green lightening of the false dawn, then shortly afterwards the mountain tip suddenly appears a hundred miles away, like a parachute flare hanging in the sky, a blaze of fire; it changes quickly from flame red to pink, then another flare is sighted, and another, until presently a whole series have joined together like a vivid rose-pink wave caught into stillness against the deep blue of the skyline. It lasts perhaps for a couple of minutes and then the sun blazes away the last touch of pink to leave a blinding and snow-white jagged line, a vast border of flawless white stretching for hundreds of miles, while the nearby hills remain darkly conifer green, and the valleys still steeped in deep purple shadows. Then, back to the hotel in warming sunlight, to lime-splashed pawpaw and crisp brown toast.

The last trip Bob Hodges made before going off to Ceylon with the Liberators was a flight to Siam. For some unfathomable, and surely misguided, reason he flew almost all his operations on Liberators but this particular sortie appealed to him and so he took a Dakota into Siam to pick up Nicky Varanand. Varanand was a prince of the Siam royal household, who had joined the RAF in England and had completed an operational tour on fighters in the Normandy campaign. He came out to India to join our planned Lysander flight but because he had invaluable contacts in Siam he was asked if he would go in there for Force 136 while we waited for the aircraft to arrive, and he grabbed at the opportunity.

His mission was to check airstrips suitable for Dakota landings, discover the sentiment and utility of the Siamese Air Force, and to report on the location and strength of the Japanese air force operations in Siam. The job was expected to take several weeks but he had completed the task munificently in less than a fortnight because he had not only the eager sympathy of the government and all its officers but was actually provided with transport facilities by the Royal Thai Air Force. They had flown him on a tour of inspection to eight different airstrips, landed at an operational Japanese airfield to show him the defences, and provided him with a complete record of the disposition and strength of the Japanese air force. So, literally with a suitcase of information, he was ready for return to India. The Dakota duly picked him up from one of his approved strips and that was the last sortie that Bob made from Jessore. A week later he departed with the Liberator flight to Ceylon.

There was a typical gaffe due to lack of liaison between the clandestines following Varanand's return. One of the strips he examined seemed perfect for its condition and seclusion, but in discussion with the caretaker he discovered it was so badly drained it could be totally unserviceable after heavy rain. He happened to know the Siamese liaison officer with the OSS and told him about this, but he chose not to pay any attention to this unofficial notice, and later on that June the OSS sent in a Dakota from China one night for pick up. It had rained the day before, the aircraft sank into the ground up to the engine nacelles and was still bogged solid when day dawned. They had to burn it lest it be spotted by the Japanese.

The day we brought back the French priest was another one of those occasions when I personally saw a contact between the Americans and French that was completely at variance with their relationship over the border in Indo-China. When the priest boarded the plane the American officer had come up into the fuselage to see him into place, and at our Myitkyena stop the American duty officer took him into care with an assurance that they would fly him to Mandalay. It was difficult to reconcile this sort of friendly personal contact with American state policy, and with actual events in Indo-China.

There was no doubt, however, about the chilly political relationship between them. It made life complicated for all who had to deal with both parties, even in SEAC command as well as in China. I had no personal contact with General Browning in the war – as Mountbatten's Chief of Staff he was loftily remote from the flight commander in one of the ninety-eight RAF squadrons in SEAC – but shortly after the war we did meet two or three times through a mutual friend in quite level circumstances and we chatted then about Burmese days. Although he was vague, or reticently discreet, in answering many questions, there was one aspect of our Eastern war on which his memory was clear and his vehemence outspoken. This was the disastrous relationship between the Americans and the French.

'Those were the two at war in Indo-China,' he said. 'The Japs were not in it.'

There is ample support in the record for this view. It was in Indo-China that the differences between Roosevelt and de Gaulle found their most concentrated expression. After the murderous Japanese take-over in March that year the French might have managed sustained resistance had they had support from the Americans at their back across the border in China, but little was forthcoming. The American commander in China, General Wedemeyer, was an enthusiastic supporter of the official policy, and in conversation with Mountbatten's political adviser he openly expressed his contempt for the French. The 14th USAAF actually bombed some French supply dumps, probably by mistake, but the French were not to know this and there was apparently no apology. On the contrary it was made quite clear to the French that American policy was one of positive encouragement for the nascent communist group controlled by Ho Chi Minh.

There was an official complaint from Wedemeyer about the activities of our squadron; he heard we were dropping arms to the French – which they might use against the Japanese! – and he demanded that it be stopped. Mountbatten managed to avoid compliance by referring to a clause in some agreement somewhere, and we continued to support the French resistance. It was very limited, just whatever sorties from other clandestine duties our two squadrons could spare, but it was all the French had at that time and we did at least deliver some supplies and medicines and bring out some of their wounded.

These were bitter in their condemnation of the American attitude. One of our pilots brought back to India a badly wounded man whom I myself would have landed at Myitkyena for treatment; there the Americans would always give help, you only had to signal your need and they would have doctors and ambulances waiting for you at the end of the strip. When I reminded the pilot of this he said he did consider it but the wounded Frenchman would have none of it.

'He said he'd rather die than have any American touch him. So I came straight on back to Cal.'

You could understand the French bitterness when you heard some of their stories. At Dien Bien Phu there were over a hundred wounded Frenchmen awaiting medical attention and supplies at one time, a US aircraft landed from Kunming empty and lifted out just four OSS officers who had been in on a liaison mission to the communist forces. They could have taken out thirty of the wounded, but they took none, despite the pleas of the French doctor.

They were fully aware therefore of the urgent need for medical supplies, but when they came in again a few days later to pick up six American airmen they brought nothing with them; the men were from a crashed plane, the French had protected them from the Japanese and brought them to the strip

311

for evacuation, but nonetheless the pilot refused to carry out any French wounded despite the pleas and even threats from his own countrymen, who were outraged and humiliated by his action. But the pilot was adamant. He said he had strict and precise orders to this effect. And these were casualties sustained against the common enemy, the Japanese, whom the French were fighting far more fatally than were the Viet Minh. But they were damned by official policy.

Peter Kemp, of Force 136, was involved in another incident when on a mission with Captain Klotz, a French officer, in Laos. They came across an OSS officer with a group of the Viet Minh communists who having discovered Klotz was French turned their guns towards him. Kemp stood between them and the intended victim and appealed to the OSS officer to hold back his Viet Minh group. The American said:

'I guess I am now a neutral.'

Two of the Viet Minh then darted around Kemp and shot Klotz dead with their US carbines. Mountbatten was outraged by the report and filed a complaint with Wedemeyer which had no sympathetic response.

Colin Mackenzie, the head of Force 136, was in the forefront of the fight to change Wedemeyer's policy towards the desperate French forces; he felt that if the US General Sultan in Burma could interpret Washington policy in a manner that evoked positive gratitude from the French then Americans in China could at least adopt a humanitarian attitude and not provoke a hatred that would take years to heal. In urging a modification of the policy, Mackenzie wrote of the damage it was doing to the American image, with particular reference to that aircraft landing to collect American airmen whose lives the French had probably saved.

'The American name is mud, repeat mud, with French and British about this whole episode.'

Unfortunately Mackenzie's appeal achieved nothing. The US command in Kunming remained sternly anti-French, with only rare exceptions – General Chennault did order the 14th USAAF at one time to machine gun a Japanese column that was attacking a small unit of French. Wedemeyer refused to permit the French CIL (Corps Leger d'Intervention) to enter the theatre of operations, and although he had not managed to stop the small amount of help we were giving the French, he did make our work as arduous and expensive as possible. We were still banned from using USAAF bases in China which would have enabled us to give significant, instead of trivial, assistance to the beleagured and battered French.

There was one tiny islet of harmony in this sea of discord. The chain of Force 136 coastwatchers which had been in contact with the US fleet had been wiped out in the Japanese takeover, but we dropped in French replacements presently and they continued again to provide valuable information about shipping movements to the US Pacific Fleet – who must have been out of touch with Washington.

In the Burma theatre we had little evidence of the Washington policy; there too the American command in the north, like the Pacific Fleet, was not only willing to accept French help but was also most generous in offering it. If the French, or any other ally, wanted medical aid, food, shelter, ammunition, fuel or repairs, they had it without question throughout Sultan's command. Even the distinction in battle areas which Stilwell had utilized to remove our clandestines no longer applied. The British had an E Group team and at least one ISLD team in the northern area, and several of the old *Dilwyn* groups, including *Squirrel*, were actually fighting under 101 OSS control in that major struggle to take over the road into Indo-China.

I heard something of that French-American friction from an old friend in 101 OSS one day in June when we landed at Bhamo. There was a long bamboo hut at one end of the field and we went over there for shade while they refuelled the aircraft. It was a hot still day and I stood listless by a roof support as we waited. Merged into the tawny windowsill a gecko was panting for cool, hornets were drifting aimlessly above the long trestle table with their legs dangling from dumb-bell bodies, and the hammer-on-anvil beats from a coppersmith bird outside were like thuds of heat that set your head nodding. Then a voice called:

'Anyone here from Sima'pa?'

The name started me into life again. The voice was familiar too, and even before he moved out of the doorway glare into shaded vision I knew it was Oscar Milton. Sima'pa was a village just over the Chinese border where Tom Leonard had been with Oscar when we met the previous year. Oscar had been with 101 OSS since the unit started operations, and had a remarkable record and reputation in his intelligence activities behind the lines. He was British, had worked with a timber company before the war, made the long walk into China when the country was invaded and then walked back along much the same track on his work with the OSS. Even Stilwell recorded admiration for Oscar, who told me about the final battle of 101 OSS on the Japanese escape road, now nearing its end. He told me too about the French encounter.

His story illustrates the difference the technical border made to the Franco-American relationship. A party of twelve French soldiers, having been cut off from Dien Bien Phu by a large Japanese force, had set off on the two-hundred-mile trek to Burma. They had a bad time of it; two of their wounded died on the trail, then they thought they were lucky when they came upon a partisan unit, two American officers and some Viet Minh. By this time, about half the journey completed, they were weak with hunger and carrying a man who had been wounded in the leg. They asked for food and help for the wounded man but the American officers turned their backs and allowed the Viet Minh to make not a response to their appeal but a threat to their lives. Such was the conviction of the threat that the French felt themselves lucky to escape without having to fight their way clear.

A week or so later, by then across the border, they had a clash with the Japanese when six of the party were killed, but the action was fortunate for those that survived however, for the sound of the firing had been heard by some Kachins of 101 OSS. They gave the French group food and shelter, then took them to Oscar. The fact that the four survivors were French meant nothing to Oscar and the other OSS Americans who welcomed them into the camp, sent a call to Myitkyena and presently two L5s of the USAAF landed in the hills to pluck them out. After treatment at the American hospital in Myit-kyena they were flown out by the USAAF to Calcutta.

Oscar found it difficult to believe the story they told him of the encounter with the US army officers in China command. He had never heard of any order forbidding assistance to be given to the French, nor had any of his colleagues at Myitkyena.

'I don't understand it,' he said. 'It's not like that in 101 OSS.'

We were suddenly much more involved with the OSS. The Pentagon had issued an instruction that all activities of 404 OSS, the group that operated from Mandalay southwards, were to be under the aegis of Force 136. This policy decision, inspired perhaps by the enthusiastic welcome and assistance Colin Mackenzie had given to the OSS on their arrival in the theatre, was accepted happily by all concerned and worked well in practice. We had a permanent OSS section with us at Jessore, final parachute training was done by us, we flew them in on their operations and supplied them in the field.

The 404 OSS had a photographer, Corporal McFarlane, who, while waiting at Jessore for a Liberator drop he had to cover, came out with me on a *Character* sortie. He had little light for his photographs that day. The fuselage was roaring with rain when we took off in the black dawn, and though it cleared temporarily when we crossed the delta area, where the monsoon-flooded Ganges was bleeding brown into the Bay of Bengal, the black clouds were piled against us on the Chin Hills so we took the long route south over the Bay.

It was now late June. Over the Burmese plain there was shattered evidence of the monsoon in the mirrored fragments that littered the countryside, a blue and white mosaic of reflected sky and cloud occasionally flashing in the shafts of sunlight that slanted down through the gaps in the overcast. As we crossed the plain, however, the cloud gaps became less frequent until at the Karen Hills the sky above us was once more covered in a thick layer of stratocumulus; we were flying in a band of gloomy daylight, dark green ridges below and dark grey clouds above. Here and there were misty blocks of rain joining earth and cloud, some of them so sharply defined you could fly one wing wet and one wing dry. As the glistening dark green ridges rose closer and closer beneath us the scent of damp vegetation came seeping into the cockpit.

Visibility was good between the rain drapes, about six miles clear, and we could see our pinpoint kink in the Salween well before arrival. McFarlane had been up with me in the cockpit when we arrived over the hills but once we had our pinpoint he went back to record the action as the others began to remove the door panel, line up the packages, and clip on the static lines ready for the drop.

We had been briefed for two separate sites belonging to *Mongoose*, the most southerly *Character* group. The first was a clearing on the brow of a hill about 5000 feet high; it was a pallid grassy rectangle laid like a strip of plaster across the smooth curve of the ridge, and you could skim over the top low enough to set the grass shivering. We did so, but our passage went unmarked. The line of black circles told of old reception fires, but there was no wood piled on them that day, no upturned faces, and the tracks nearby were also devoid of life. I gave it only a few minutes then map-read on to the second site.

There we had reception galore. It was an emergency landing strip and a Lysander was parked on it when we arrived. Two split-bamboo letters were laid on the ground, one for their own DZ and the other for the nearby deserted site. Gurkha-hatted levies were drifting about on the surface, and the Lysander pilot waved from near the plane as we manoeuvred for the drop. A moment later he was scurrying for his aircraft when one of the parachutes went swaying down within a few yards of it, and by the time we made our next run he already had the engine started and was taxying rapidly towards the shelter of the trees on the far side of the strip. We gave them the double load, finishing just in time to miss a wide curtain of rain that came sweeping up the valley, straddling the ridges on both sides.

McFarlane had photographed every stage of the drop and was delighted with his day's work. I never saw the pictures, however. A day or two afterwards he went out in the Liberator drop to one of the OSS sites and the aircraft crashed *en route*, killing the ten crew and McFarlane, who was the only passenger.

The Liberators had a bad month. Twenty-nine more men of Jessore lost their lives in three fatal crashes that June, all of them on operations. Peter Farr, the commander of 358 Squadron, carried out a stricter regime of in-flight training than we did but, as he said one night when discussing the latest loss, you cannot train a crew to overcome weather conditions that are beyond the structural limits of the actual aircraft. Every sane pilot tried to avoid dangerously turbulent conditions but you were bound to blunder into them from time to time when flying through cloud, and then you needed luck as well as skill to escape. Some, inevitably, missed out on the luck.

There should have been yet another fatal crash that month. The aircraft was out on a very rare mission, one in which the Americans and French worked amicably together. The cooperative group were after prisoner-of-war intelligence, six Indo-Chinese were being dropped into Laos, and it is indicative of the difference between Wedemeyer's and Mountbatten's commands that such a rational flight would have been impossible to stage from Kunming but was settled without question from Jessore. The mission itself however was not so free of trouble.

The pilot was Flight Sergeant McCulloch, who had what he later described as 'take-off trouble' after a stop at Akyab to top up his tanks. The Liberator was grossly overweight, as usual, so he expected to graze the grass at the end of the strip, but the pitch control on one engine went haywire just after passing the critical point of take-off, and the grass-grazing became grass-bouncing. With both pilots engaged in the struggle they managed to get the aircraft into the air but even a four-feet fence was too high a barrier; they crashed through it at 110 m.p.h., and that cost them a precious fraction of an impetus already inadequate for climb. And there was still ahead of them a little grove of trees on the far side of the road before they could reach the shoreline.

They crossed the road with wheels still down, one smashing into a telephone pole and snapping it clean away. The trees on the far side of the road were about the same height and the aircraft tore through them trailing telegraph wires, and with the

317

propellers chopping off branches that beat against the fuselage. They emerged with further loss of airspeed but luckily, for even a clear stretch of level ground was no longer good enough, the shoreline was just ahead and there they were able at last to put the nose down in gentle incline for twenty precious feet to sea level, so gaining enough speed to survive.

However, the aircraft was severely damaged and difficult to control but McCulloch decided nonetheless to continue the operation. It was a rugged ten hours to their DZ over near the Pacific coast and they were caught in two thunderstorms on the way, but they finally managed to drop the OSS-French team safely to the DZ and get themselves back to Jessore. He received awards from both governments, the American Silver Star and the French Croix de Guerre.

We had a personal call from Fleming, of D Division, shortly after Bob Hodges left. He wanted us to do a simple job, to drop a haversack on a road down near Moulmein; this was easy enough to arrange because we were servicing three OSS teams and the 136 *Nutshell* group down there. I suspect Fleming had not passed this operation through P Division, nor even through our group headquarters. D Division worked a lot of private deals; they had our old Hudson pilot Jimmy King on their staff and he spent most of his time wangling lifts for Fleming and others. And Fleming seemed to be his own master anyway.

On this occasion he arrived by car, and came striding into the squadron office where I was signing log books. He was carrying a haversack and asked if we could deliver it. He did it so genially, and he was such a pleasant character, that I did not quibble. The job was no effort anyway, an official sortie would cover it. I told him we could do it on a *Nutshell* due out a few nights later.

There was a slight complication in that he wanted the haversack to finish near an opened parachute. He hoped the Japanese would find the parachute next morning, with the haversack nearby, and assume the agent had either dropped it accidentally or had had to bolt for his life on landing. The documents in it were 'the usual thing', he said, fake orders to a non-existent agent to contact spurious units purporting to be in the vicinity, or presently to arrive there; and there were also a couple of love letters written by a girl in his office to an imaginary boyfriend in some forward unit. He did have a suggestion as to how we might arrange for the parachute to open convincingly without body weight, and finish with the haversack nearby.

'What about ice?' he asked.

It was clever, but there were practical problems I did not like. His idea was to weight the parachute harness with a block of ice, which would have dissolved by morning when the chute was found. But we would have to find the ice locally, to pack it in the harness would be a tricky business, and the stuff would melt during the six-hour flight, giving a slippery surface to the floor where the despatcher had to work when we were bounding around over the DZ.

The simple answer was to open the parachute in the aircraft and then toss it out as a bundle just after the haversack so that they would then finish close together on the ground. I was sure it would open enough to convince anyone. Fleming was happy enough to leave the problem with me, and stayed for a few minutes chatting about our joint experiences in the gliders on the Chindit operation. I have never heard anyone speak with such felicity of language as Fleming. His travel books must have cost him little writing effort; he could, I feel sure, dictate the finished version without a note in front of him. Just talk his books on to paper.

I tested my method that afternoon, not at the practice DZ but alongside the strip at Jessore itself. We used both objects, the actual haversack and a rolled-up opened parachute; it worked perfectly from about fifty feet, with the parachute opening well enough and looking as it might have done had an agent shed it hurriedly, and the haversack was only a few yards away. There was an awkward moment when I saw the group captain's car pause at the runway crossing while we were bundling up the parachute again, but he drove on after a moment, and by the time he spoke to me that evening I had a story ready about using parachutes as markers on a DZ. It was dull enough to kill off any interest in pursuing the subject.

319

We delivered the package in the prosaic method we had tested. The drop worked slightly better than in the test because the parachute finished draped over what looked like a banana plant, and at least from the air that night it presented a most convincing picture. The haversack was clearly visible on the road itself nearby.

Although I met Fleming again a few weeks later down at Rangoon that was the last stunt we worked with D Division – as far as I know at the moment. But if any pilot from Jessore were to tell me now that he had subsequently had a visit one day from a charming colonel who had asked them to drop a dead goat wearing a collar with a regimental badge, I could well believe him. Contact with D Division could permanently unsettle a sceptical nature.

21

It was only rarely that the men down in the jungle blamed us on the squadron for failure to arrive on a planned drop. Most of them appreciated we might have difficulties with the aircraft or with weather, so they tended to curse fate if we did not arrive when expected. A few of the staff, however, both those of RAF headquarters and of the clandestines, were not so understanding, and could at times be quite insensitive to the stress that monsoon flying could create. Charles O'Brien came into the office one afternoon in July to point to a failure on an ISLD site the previous night.

'That's the second time your chaps didn't find the place,' he grumbled. And Charles was himself a pilot – long ago.

He had not been out as conducting officer on the mission. From about May onwards he scarcely made another trip, but he always visited the operations room to check crew reports on ISLD sorties. The weather had been atrocious and this was stated in the report, but he suggested it had been a navigation fault that had caused the failure.

'Then go and read the ORB report again,' I told him.

It is possible that the casual attitude of some conducting officers towards dangerous flight conditions sprang from a confidence gained on flight experience with us. That is, it was we who encouraged them to belittle the danger. If an aircraft is being hurled about in a black storm, with all your Joes being sick and terrified, and you make a jerky stumbling way up to the cockpit to discover the crew carrying on with apparent calm at their separate jobs then you begin to reassess the situation. You feel it cannot be so dangerous after all.

Just a bit of cloud . . . bumping around a bit . . . obviously nothing serious . . . a fairground ride for these RAF chaps.

There was an OSS conducting officer on a sortie that July who had acquired that typical case-hardened attitude towards our occasional trials. The operation was *Cutter*, two Americans and two Burmese to be landed down the coast, south of Tavoy. We had already introduced a 404 Detachment team in the area and they were to provide a reception for our party. The task of *Cutter* was to observe and report on Japanese activity down that coastal road towards the Malayan border.

For some reason or other the OSS decided not to stage the operation through Rangoon but to go direct from Jessore. This meant we had to fly a thousand miles direct to the DZ rather than a mere four hundred from Rangoon. I argued against this stupid brief but to no avail; the order had come from OSS headquarters down in Ceylon and the conducting officer, though sympathetic, dared not query them. So it was from Jessore that we took off one black sodden night, heading south towards the Isthmus of Kra in the Andaman Sea.

We started off above scattered cloud, a brilliantly clear moonless night with the sky covered by a glittering diamond dust of stars. There was a display of falling stars, thousands of them streaking across one another like silvered tracer bullets from outer space. But for us the spectacle only lasted ten minutes or so, just until we reached the coast where the cloud mass was banked solid, then we had to descend through a gap, down and down until we could discern the wraiths of foam on the dark sea, and presently even that glimpse of the world disappeared when we plunged into the impenetrable blackness of the rains.

We were now at the height of the monsoon, and in this period there are times when the rain belt over the Bay of Bengal can be hundreds of miles in depth. This was such a night. We flew for six hours through a tremendous mass of water pouring from cloud to sea, like cleaving through a seemingly endless Niagara. At little more than two hundred feet above sea level, just under cloud base, we were in a solid blackness of water. The windscreen was a grey trembling sheet across which the wiper blades slid continuously without leaving mark of passage, water squeezed an entry through the side window, the sodden air condensed on every smooth surface, it splattered the throttle box and pulped the maps, and my fingers became wrinkled and clammy as the belly of a plaice.

Earlier on that torrential night, just after losing sight of the falling stars and plunging into the rain mass, I thought of Housman's beautiful poem and kept on repeating the lines as I peered down through the side window, with an occasional flick of landing lights to ensure we remained well clear of the ruffled grey sheet of the sea:

> Stars, I have seen them fall,
> But when they drop and die
> No star is lost at all
> From out the star-sown sky.
> The toil of all that be
> Helps not the primal fault;
> It rains into the sea,
> And still the sea is salt.

There are numerous islets strewn about the Tenasserim coast so we had flown a course designed to take us to a point just fifty miles out to sea from our DZ; we finished much further out than that, however, for we were flying so low that I had for safety kept nudging right rudder as we neared the turning point. We were still in rain then, all was black outside, the windows showed only a cockpit reflection, but by switching on the landing lights we could still discern the white-flecked sea two hundred feet below, giving us a rough check on the altimeter. I had no intention, under those conditions, of turning in towards those rocky islets, hundreds of feet high, which guard the coast, so I called up the OSS conducting officer to tell him this.

'That's okay,' he said. 'They'll wait for us on the site.'

He stayed in the cockpit for a few minutes, looking out into the void and shaking his head gloomily, then went back to his charges. Then, for an hour or so, we circled in the blackness waiting for the cloud-delayed dawn.

It came at last. Slowly the solid blackness dissolved and a

grey world began to emerge – leaden-grey clouds, battleship-grey sea, and pearly-grey curtains of rain scattered about the horizon. We turned east towards the coast and in less than ten minutes the first islands emerged from the gloom ahead, two tree-covered wedges of sombre green land with peaks plunged into the cloud layer three hundred feet above, a layer that showed not a single tiny ray of sunlight offering a break. A spatter of rain veiled the scene as we flew between the two islets, but apart from such occasional blurs the visibility was good, two to three miles perhaps, so we had warning to avoid the increasing number of islets nearer the coast.

The shoreline came up as a sandy beach, amber-coloured in the rain, with dunes giving on to level ground where squares of paddy fields were set out as neatly as on a sheet of graph paper. We turned south along the shoreline, a calculated choice, and flew low for a few minutes until we came to the mouth of the river that had been our objective. The DZ was only a few miles up the inlet at a river junction, and as we flew over the flat surface of the sheltered water breaks appeared in the overcast and I began to feel hopeful about completing the drop.

On arrival at the confluence we found the photographed DZ. It was a flat clearing with spectral lines of old paddy bunds visible fleetingly as we changed the angle of view. Beyond the far end a tree-covered slope rose into the low cloud, but there was room to turn before reaching it, and sufficient breaks in the cloud to allow us to climb up to six hundred feet for the drop itself. All was set. Except for one important factor. *Cutter* was not at home. And we had to have a reception, that was the order.

There was a night during the Wingate campaign when I was crouching under a damp blanket on a mountainside away to the east of Bhamo, six thousand feet up in the cold insinuating mist, shivering, hungry, miserable, huddled by the wood pile with matches and brush ready as I prayed for the sound of the approaching planes that would relieve our hunger. But they never came. So I knew what it was like for men down on the ground to wait in a hope that dwindled away in the darkness to anguish, and finally to despair; and I could feel sympathy with

324

those who came back from the field and told of the pain on those nights when they had waited vainly for our arrival.

But now I had learned that aircrew too had their times of bitter disappointment. You fly tensely low for eight hours through dank blackness, trying to keep close to mother earth without actually contacting her, you turn and bank through squalls and valleys, squeeze over a saddleback, and then finally get through to your DZ only to find it devoid of life. No explanation for absence. No apology. Nothing to tell you that down there the men are in desperate peril, or rushing with all speed to the site, or just blissfully asleep in a cosy bamboo shelter somewhere in the jungle. What to do? Go away at once lest your noisy presence increase their danger? Or fly about for a time to give them a chance to reach the site?

Almost invariably I would wait, as I did that July morning. I called up the conducting officer again and he stood beside me in the cockpit as we circled the clearing, flew up and down the estuary, and roamed inland over dark trees and glistening green paddy fields as far as rising ground would allow. He remained as gloomy as the sky, but did not argue when I suggested we gave them another half an hour. So we continued meandering about in the same locality, but when presently the dark skies began to drape blankets of rain all about, threatening to envelop us, I decided to escape before the trap closed, and went skittering out low over the rain-dashed surface of the estuary to sea safety. The OSS chap gave a shrug and said airily:

'That's okay. We'll try again tonight.'

Just like that! Not with me, I told him. Nor with anyone else in the squadron. We would try again only when he was certain the *Cutter* team were still alive down there, and had an assurance from them that they would be in position next time. So after refuelling at Rangoon we flew back to base and waited until OSS had sorted out the problem with their field party. It was resolved after an exchange or two. There had been a misunderstanding about time, regret was expressed, and three days later the reception party was on hand when we dropped the team without a hitch.

One consequence of the fall of Rangoon was that we now had

a good staging post for southerly operations. It was little more than half an hour from Mingaladon airfield to the *Character* area, so I was now discouraging crews from trying to break through bad weather over Karenni, advising them instead to fly on down to Rangoon and wait on the ground for a break, then have another try. You could make three or four attempts in a day from there. This scheme was greeted with enthusiasm by our RAF group headquarters, who promptly issued an order stating that aircraft on *Character* drops should in future stay at Rangoon until a sortie was completed.

It is a common stupidity of lesser, officious staff officers to create a binding regulation where only a suggestion is required. Discretion is anathema to them. The absurdity of the rule was manifest at once. One pilot kept an aircraft at Rangoon for three days while he made eight determined efforts to reach an impenetrable site being used by *Hyena*; he might have wasted away there until the end of the monsoon, except I landed to discover him still there and stopped the nonsense at once. A call to 136 allowed the load to be dropped to another *Hyena* site, I condemned the high one as too dangerous, and it was abandoned.

The order from our command had been promulgated, of course – you have to follow the system – but I told the pilots to ignore it where they felt there was little profit in waiting at Rangoon. I said they should return to base and blame me, or serviceability, for the disobedience. An English warrant officer, Milne, was one of those who was unhappy about deliberate defiance of an official order. I found him one day down at Mingaladon about to make a further attempt at the *Wolf* site which was obliterated by a vast cloud mass covering hundreds of square miles; even the most experienced pilots would have had difficulty getting through at that time. Monsoon flying had put great stress on Milne, and the flight deputy, Ben Hewson, had suggested we try to get him relieved from operations. I had been working on this with the station commander and in the meantime was using him only for close-range daylight operations.

When I told Milne that day to abandon the *Wolf* job and go

back to base he reminded me about the instruction from group headquarters. What would he say at debriefing? As he was not the type to tell a convincing lie about an aircraft problem, such as a mysterious loss of power in an engine, I told him to put the blame on me, to tell operations room I had ordered him back. He did so. It was duly recorded in the ORB and is still there today: Instructed to return to base by flight commander.

When I signed that completed ORB entry at the end of the month Milne and his four crew were already dead. They died because he tried to complete an operation when he should have abandoned it. Another pilot out with him that day decided the weather was far too dangerous for the attempt, cloud base was well below the high ground and there was violent turbulence in the hills, so he sensibly returned to Jessore. Milne kept on to his death.

I took off at first light next morning in a search for the crash site; the air–sea rescue unit was supposed to search for all crashes but you tried to make some effort yourself, just in case anyone might still be alive at the crash. Conditions were still violent below cloud level on the hills. At one stage, when leaning over to reset the gyro compass, we were struck by a powerful upcurrent that jerked the 'spectacles' with such force they split the skin open against my jawbone and knocked me silly for a moment. By the time we could get organized again my clothing was a bloody mess, and the navigator had to raid the first-aid kit to staunch the flow. Lucky perhaps that my head had been in the way when we hit the turbulence; at least it prevented the 'spectacles' turning and the aircraft rolling on its back to plunge into the trees. We found nothing in our eight-hour search, nor did the air–sea rescue plane. They located the wreckage a week later, smashed into a jungle-clad mountainside.

The Liberators of 358 continued their run of bad luck in July when eight more aircrew were killed in a crash near Jessore. Another machine should have crashed and killed all on board, but again the pilot managed to keep it flying after contact with the ground. This was an even more destructive contact than the earlier one. Large chunks of the aircraft were torn off, and it had no aerodynamic justification whatsoever for remaining in the air subsequently.

The aircraft was out on a *Walrus* site which was located just below the saddle of a ridge that was hidden around a valley bend. I knew the site well. It was not too difficult for a Dakota because we could turn within the valley short of the bend, but there was far too little room for a Liberator to do this, so if they did try to get down to our dropping height they had to start a full throttle instant climb after each run, in order to clear the saddle around the bend.

This pilot, new to the site, went in too low over the DZ. Because of some extraordinary lapse at briefing he had not been warned about the deceptive cross-ridge. It seemed no great hazard from on high, and he only realized the danger when he turned the bend in the valley and saw the jungle wall close in front of him. He pulled back sharply but had insufficient speed to climb above the trees and the aircraft just went blundering through the tops of them like a monstrous self-propelled hedge cutter. Bits of the aircraft fell away below with the chopped branches, but somehow or other the Liberator crashed through into the clear, ripped and battered but still in flight of a kind.

They wobbled across the Burmese plain and the Chin Hills to the air above Jessore and there the two pilots, having been hard at work on the control yoke ever since the tree contact, stayed in the aircraft while all the others baled out safely on to the airfield. Then the pilots landed the aircraft in a diving rush that kept it just above stalling speed until thump-down, when it shortly swung off the runway and slewed to a stop on the grass outside our flight hut. I studied it that afternoon in wonderment. It should never have flown. A four-foot length of the starboard wing had been ripped off, half the tailplane was gone, and the belly looked as if it had been raked by the steely claws of a tyrannosaurus rex. It never did fly again.

I had a disappointment that month. Bob Hodges finished his tour of operations, came back to Jessore to say goodbye, and told me I was not to get command. A new man was coming out from England to take over. The Wingate business had been a promotional disaster for me. In 1942 I had been in command of the RAF station in Bombay and two other separate units, but to get into the Wingate force I had to drop rank to the flight-lieutenant vacancy. During the eighteen months with the army there could be no promotion so it was only when we got back from behind the lines and I rejoined the air force that I could return to pre-volunteer rank as squadron leader. Seniority only started from the return date, all the earlier and Wingate time did not count; in the records I was therefore too junior to take over a squadron, despite Bob's recommendation. Hence they appointed someone from England.

I was, however, still left with the job of running the squadron headquarters at Jessore, as well as the flight split between base and Rangoon, because the new commander went down to join the Liberator detachment. No one apart from Bob Hodges seemed to be aware that I had long ago completed the operational tour and was now nearly through another, and my name seemed to have slipped the notice of the repatriation section – by this time all the other survivors of those who had flown out with me to Singapore in 1941 had returned to England. My name had been lost somewhere in the system. I made no noise about either of these administrative lapses, I liked my job too much. So I managed to stay on unnoticed at Jessore.

The RAF were not the only service now with officers in plenty to take up posts in India; the army too had all sorts of people in England who were anxious to come out and join our Eastern war now that theirs was ended. Popski, who achieved fame with his 'private army', suggested he could operate such a force in our command, pointing out that as a Belgian he would be particularly useful in Indo-China; the commander of the LRDG (Long Range Desert Group) wrote to urge his unit be employed in the jungle; and the SAARF commander (Special Airborne Allied Recce Force) suggested the presence of his group could make a major difference to our war. They were all told that Force 136 had such matters well in hand, thank you. Individuals could apply there for consideration if they wished.

After the fall of Rangoon, ISLD, like Force 136 and the OSS, continued at much the same pace as before. I suspect that the senior officers were on holiday that July for it is difficult to believe that the professionals in the Secret Service would attach such mysteries to simple tasks as Charles O'Brien did that month. One which I flew for ISLD was quite bizarre in its complications.

This drop was to *Blast*, a three-man team of theirs which was reporting particularly on the political activity of the opposing nationalist groups. Although the Japanese were still in complete control of that southeastern section where they were working, and one would therefore expect some precautions to be taken, the ISLD instructions as delivered to me by Charles struck me as nothing more than theatrical effects. Here is the list that I jotted down the next day:

a. Aircraft will arrive at DZ at 1650 hours precisely.

b. There may be no reception, no fires nor signals. (May be?) In any case the aircraft will pass over the DZ on course without showing any sign of interest in it, and continue straight on course over the DZ in a southerly direction.

c. It will stay on this course for seven minutes and then return directly to the DZ.

d. The reception triangle of fires will be lit temporarily only when the aircraft comes into sight on the return journey.

e. The recognition letter K will be flashed twice only.

f. Fires will be doused immediately aircraft completes first run.

g. Aircraft to leave immediately last run completed, no circling of site.

h. It will go direct to Bilin and circle the town widely just twice then return to base.

Bilin was about twenty miles south of the DZ. Charles would not tell me why we should circle it twice, nor give any explanation for all the rest of the rigmarole; when questioned he just looked mysterious and said he could not divulge the reason. It is possible he had not been told, but far more likely he created all this complexity himself – he liked to make a mystery of every ISLD drop.

He did not come with us but I did nevertheless plan the sortie to follow his brief. There was a break in the monsoon and we flew down through great sunlit swatches of sea with cloud shadows like dark stains on the ultramarine surface. Now that Rangoon port was open convoys could be seen in the Bay of Bengal; we passed one that afternoon, steamers with attached smoke clouds and wakes like stubby white hamster-tails, all looking as permanently set as models when we flew past some four thousand feet above in the clear still air – cautiously clear of them, for on three occasions during the war in Europe the navy had fired at me.

Nearing Rangoon we discovered we were about ten minutes ahead of Charles's timetable, which pleased me because we could circle the Shwe Dagon. The pagoda was a glorious sight in the setting sun, a warm rich gold on the shaded side that brightened through yellows to a sudden flashing brilliance in the west, so bright it lit the cockpit for an instant like a searchlight when we banked in turn. Around the base of the golden pinnacle were glittering gems of shrines and chapels and small pagodas, amber and copper and topaz, piled-up offerings to the temple that is the heart and soul of Rangoon and the centre of the Buddhist world. I never minded having to circle for clearance at Mingaladon airfield; the Shwe Dagon was always there waiting in wondrous view.

We approached the mysterious ISLD site exactly on schedule and in the gathering dusk could identify it positively from three or four miles away; it was open paddy fields with a semicircular patch of lucerne-green bamboo curving around the northern end. Despite Charles's briefing there was a lamp already flashing dah-di-dah, the letter K, as we approached. The triangular pile of firewood was clearly visible, so also were a dozen or more white-clad figures jumping about and waving their arms, including three standing by a rickshaw at one side of the clearing.

Then, while we were still on the approach, the fires burst into life – literally – like a stage magician's display, a flash of fire and then smoke. They must have doused the wood with petrol, the smoke piled up so quickly that as we passed over there was a single great white blob covering the whole triangular layout. And up near the bamboo the signal lamp flashed Ks continuously, still at it after we had banked in turn to look back at the whole riotous reception.

So much for all Charles's nonsense. It was ridiculous to go away for seven minutes as he ordained (why not 6.53, I had suggested), so I gave the despatcher a red as we descended in a turn for the drop. When we completed the first run and came in the second time the lamp was still flashing but the fires had been extinguished, just dying trails of smoke rising from the piles. This was the only gesture made to the complex briefing instructions, but could have occurred simply because the wood was wet. They made no attempt to rush the collection; some of the people went on waving to us on each run, and the ground was still blotched with parachutes when we made our last pass over the area.

Such was the ostentation of the reception, as opposed to Charles's furtive scenario, that I wondered if the group might have been surprised by the enemy and were in the bag, but the set-up looked too casually innocent for a studied Japanese copy. We did circle Bilin twice as requested then came home, skimming over a scattering of drowsy cloud in the Bay, to learn that the field had already signalled receipt of a 'perfect drop'. Charles refused to give any explanation for the discrepancy between his briefing of mysteries and the carefree spectacle actually offered to us on site.

A few days later we visited Bilin again, on a leaflet drop when returning from a pick-up operation in Siam. It was an odd situation in Siam at that time; the Japanese were military masters of the country but the Siamese government was working actively with US and British clandestines to arm and train a huge guerrilla force. We dropped supplies on one DZ that was within actual sight of a Japanese garrison. Inevitably the Japanese became aware of all this unfriendly activity, resulting in a sudden panic order one night in July to cancel all our operations immediately. A fortnight later, however, we began working Siam again and I flew in to pick up two men of Force 136; it seems the Japanese decided it was better not to strike against the Siamese – nor the Malayan MPAJA either – because similar action in Burma had proved disastrous for them.

We landed at Phukeo, the field where that US Dakota had to be burned, and I made a very close inspection of the surface before putting down on the earthen strip. A Junkers aircraft and two small biplanes of the Siamese air force were already parked at the edge. Once on the ground, where they covered our markings with tarpaulin sheets, I learned that the Siamese planes were available to transport allied agents about the country. The Force 136 men drove across to us in an open Packard tourer, with them some Thais – including an elderly woman in slim fig-purple skirt who must have been responsible for the wisps of delicious perfume I noted when greeting them by the car. They had flown out from the Japanese air base at Don Muang, which is just outside Bangkok, having been delivered there by Colonel Jacques, the head of the 136 mission in Siam. Jacques had his headquarters in town close by the Japanese military barracks, travelled freely around the city in his car and always wore his British military uniform.

The OSS had an even more luxurious Bangkok set-up. They were based in genuinely regal splendour, at the Palace of Roses, and they moved about the city in a limousine carrying the royal badge and driven by a chauffeur. The intelligence reports coming in from their agents scattered about the country were collated in the Palace headquarters then transmitted to Ceylon. They had close contact with Jacques and other 136 agents, both by personal meetings within the capital, as well as by telephone. It was a very civilized way to run a spy network. The Palace even organized a huge ball one evening for the underground, with three hundred American, British and French present in uniform and evening dress, while outside in the street the Japanese soldiers were carrying out their normal patrols.

We sighted a massive storm on return from that Siam trip. Just after dropping the Bilin leaflets, when flying at a cool ten thousand feet and above scattered cumulus, I noticed a large cloud formation ahead of us on the horizon; it seemed to be about fifty miles away, a huge threatening mass, and after discussing it with the navigator I decided to continue on course until we came close and could discover if it was as dangerous as it looked. We could then divert if need be. So we continued steadily across Burma, clear above the separate clumps of glittering cumulus which kept flashing their white reflections in the glassy sheets of paddy fields down on the plain.

The ominous cloud mass on the horizon grew slowly higher as we approached, but still when we came to the wide flood of the Irrawaddy more than fifty miles after the first notice we seemed as far away as ever. Even when we arrived at the jade-green ridges of the Arakan Yomas the cloud mass was still ahead but by then we could distinguish a typical anvil jutting from the peak and knew it for a massive cumulonimbus storm-cloud. It was still too far ahead to bother with a change of course, and not until we could see the flat sea beyond the hills did we finally turn east to avoid the monster. By then the sun was setting behind it, the rays splashing out in a golden shower from the glittering edges of the tumbling mass, and the line of the mountain ridge below was engulfed by the huge dark base.

The height of the anvil peak was miles above us, maybe as much as eight miles higher, and we calculated that we must have been over two hundred miles away when first we saw it. You might think that the curvature of the earth would make such a visual distance impossible, but we both saw it from near Bilin; and if you argue that it may have moved as much as thirty miles towards us you must bear in mind we made our reckoning only from the time we noticed the cloud on the horizon, and it had certainly been visible before that notice. So we must have seen it from at least two hundred miles – and it could well have been further away than that.

Back at Jessore there was a message waiting for me from group headquarters. They wanted a detachment of three aircraft to be sent urgently to Toungoo to deal with the needs of *Nation*, the 136 unit operating in the central area of Burma. The *Nation* guerrillas were the first to be affected by what has been called 'the break-out'. Most of the Japanese division that had been frustrated by *Character* from reaching Toungoo in time to stop our army's southward drive had now reached Moulmein, and the other group was about to try and rejoin the main enemy force down there. This was the army of 20,000 Japanese which had been caught in the Pegu Yomas where *Nation* was located, and they had to cross the Sittang valley and then fight their way south through the Karen Hills to reach Moulmein.

Army intelligence knew about the attempt. Rubenstein, who was with the *Nation* team in the Pegu Yomas, showed me later on a document he had captured which set down the plan of the break-out. It is a document which tells a great deal about the nature of the Japanese soldier.

54 Division Plan for Movement

1. Aim. The main body . . . will cross the Mandalay Road on the evening of the 20th July and advance to the fording point. Thereafter without any further delay will cross the Sittang River and concentrate at . . . [a map reference] . . . the other side.

Separately the KOBA detachment will cross the Toungoo road on the night of the 20th and advance to Bilin.

The whole movement will be employed secretly, but in case of enemy hindrance the enemy will be destroyed.

[It then gives map references of meeting points]

That was all. Except for the implication that any opposition encountered would be trivial, there is no mention of the problems facing the division in this movement. There were in fact three formidable obstacles.

The first of these was the British army. The main road and rail-line down the valley were firmly held and a full army division was waiting for the Japanese to try and cross the open flooded paddy fields on each side of these transport routes. The army had tanks and artillery lining the tracks, and aircraft standing by, all waiting like a shooting party at the butts for the drive to begin.

The brief instruction to cross the Sittang and assemble on the other side could also have come with a warning. The Sittang was in full monsoon spate; it was several hundred yards wide at the selected crossing point, a tumbling brown torrent impossible to swim and difficult even to traverse by boat. And the army had been scrupulous in the removal of all river craft from the area.

335

The third obstacle was waiting on the other side of the river; the Karen levies of *Character*, now a battle-hardened force of guerrillas, armed and led by the men of Force 136 whom we had landed two months earlier. The Karens, with bitter memories of friends and families who had been wiped out in Japanese punitive expeditions over the past three years, had machine-gun posts set up on the far bank of the river and in the foothills beyond the flooded paddy fields over on that side of the river. Now it was their turn to be executioners.

The Koba detachment, numbering about two thousand men, were told simply to cross the road and advance to Bilin. There is no mention of the river, nor the fact that Bilin was nearly two hundred miles south of it, along tracks that crossed two monsoon-flooded rivers, and all through the country of a people who were waiting with guns in hand and hatred in their hearts.

The last sentence of that Japanese army order could not have been written by a sane man.

Of the force that set off to follow these battle orders thirteen thousand were killed in the senseless attempt. Day after day the Japanese soldiers streamed like lemmings towards the river and met their death. I wonder how many thousands more might have lived had they behaved differently towards the Karen people during the time they had occupied the country?

22

The rain was pouring down the stem of the banana plant on to the purple ovoid flower, gushing from the tip as though from an open tap. Despite the low cloud and the solid rain, however, you could still hear aircraft landing and taking off from Mingaladon airstrip about a mile away. I was about to go back inside to my bedroom office when a jeep came slewing in off the Rangoon road. It swished through the puddles under the flamboyant trees and pulled up almost touching the railing. Fleming stepped out directly on to the veranda steps.

'You should get a portico,' he said.

Not a drop of rain had touched him. He looked elegant, wearing long khaki slacks and polished brown shoes as if off to a conference. He wanted a lift back to India. This was easy enough, we had an aircraft leaving that afternoon and I was also going back next morning; he chose the first and followed me into the office alcove beside my bed. After I had given him the aircraft number and take-off time we chatted about the operation D Division had mounted up north with 101 OSS; this somehow led on to game shooting and I mentioned an incident that he seized upon excitedly.

The previous day I had been talking to a Karen about the massacre of the Japanese striving to cross the river, and he said that in between shooting the enemy they had been using some of the generous supply of ammunition to vary their diet. He had listed the bag of his group as two buffalo, three sambhur, seven wild pigs, twelve barking deer, and 'many dozens' of birds.

'Where is he now? Could he take me there?' Fleming asked.

The Karen could not. I had flown him back that morning to Toungoo, nearly two hundred miles away. It appeared that

Fleming was a keen shot who delighted in killing birds and animals – not for food like the Karens, but for sport. Such was his interest in the game potential of Karenni that for a few minutes that afternoon he thought seriously of abandoning the return to India. When I told him the situation in the area, however – the only means of access still being by parachute – he accepted that even with his contacts and influence, which were considerable, it would be difficult to get into Karenni just for a game hunt. He drove off sadly over the sodden and trodden blossom towards the airstrip. I never saw him again.

This was the beginning of August. The break-out of the Japanese central army had passed its first stage but the survivors of the Sittang crossing were still far from the end of their trials. They had yet to cross two more rivers, the Kyauk-kyi and the Shwegyn, both of them also in monsoon spate. Along a twenty-mile length of the rivers the guerrillas of *Character* had dug-in positions at roughly hundred-yard intervals, each with communicating trenches and protected runs. From these butts they killed many thousands of Japanese who were driven past blindly obedient to their orders.

Deprived of boats the Japanese cut down huge quantities of bamboo; each man had to carry two poles to the river, there to construct rafts and paddle across. It was a murderous plan. The rafts were almost impossible to direct in the flooded rivers, and the men sitting on them were easy targets for the Karens in their trenches lining the far bank. A thousand or more men must have died before they abandoned this scheme.

In the adjusted plan they stayed in the water for the crossing. Their rafts were covered with plaintain and other broad leaves, and the whole assembly was camouflaged to look like debris being carried down the flooded river. The men entered the water carrying short bamboo pipes, and immersed themselves both under and around the structure with just the breathing tube protruding up into the leaves. Then they swam their raft-cover over to the far side. They had some success with this scheme for a while, but inevitably the Karens discovered what was happening and began to use mortars to drop shells on any bulky debris that passed their trenches.

The unequal battle was still going on when we had an incident that week as we set off to drop them more ammunition. Shortly after the pre-dawn take-off, the night black with low cloud, there was a muffled explosion from the starboard engine. Afterwards, for a few moments, all seemed well but then the temperature gauge began to show a steady inexorable rise, despite reduced throttle setting. I realized we would have to turn back. It seemed serious, for although we had throttled back the engine temperature continued to rise so I shut it down and feathered the propeller. We had a full load, but this was of no concern; the Dakota could fly perfectly well with double the maximum recommended load, and on the single engine that night it maintained height with much the same throttle setting as on the climb.

It was only after we had landed that we found out what had happened. We had hit a huge owl. The bird had passed almost completely through the propeller and was rammed into the intake; there was enough left for us to identify it later as a fully grown Indian Great Horned Owl, well over two feet in length. It was, as far as I know, the only time anyone at Jessore had a collision with an owl, but we had had three with kite-hawks and vultures previously, in one of which a Liberator gunner was wounded. Shortly afterwards a more serious incident occurred when a vulture collided with a Dakota.

It took the ground crew half an hour to clean our intake. I stayed with them out at dispersal, sitting on the grass mound and chatting as the sun rose behind the control tower and sleepy warblings of small birds from the jalpitri tree livened into longer separate songs. There was a line of low cloud on the horizon, which was like a foaming pink surf as the sun was edging into sight, but then a minute or so later it glared white in definition against a primrose sky. Crows went cawing past in languid flight towards the village, and an Indian workman in a drab dhoti walking from the airstrip cleared his throat in the ratcheting crescendo of a bull-frog croak.

It was 6 August 1945. The atom bomb was dropped on Hiroshima that morning, killing a third of its population.

I doubt if any Kachins shed a tear when they heard – certainly not the villagers in Sinthe, where half the population were beheaded because that group of Chindits passed by one day in April. And I doubt if many Karens wept for the dead of Hiroshima – certainly none in the village near Kawkareik where the Japanese slaughtered everyone who was able to speak English, simply because such people might be spies. And I would feel more sympathy for the people of Hiroshima if they did not persist in hugging their horror as a unique experience, if on 6 August every year they were not so exclusively selfish in remembrance but spared a thought also on that day for the other innocents who were slaughtered by their countrymen in the hills of eastern Burma, and on the streets of Nanking.

Japan's surrender the following week brought no relief to us. We still had to contend with our main enemy, the weather – we lost three more aircraft and twenty-four more lives before August ended – and the clandestines were still in the field, many of them actually fighting, all of them still relying upon us for supplies. There was a burst of activity in the parachute school at Jessore, and even a month later we were still taking people up for practice drops preparatory to landing them throughout South-East Asia.

These were mostly E Group people. We were immediately involved in the work of RAPWI (Repatriation of Allied Prisoners of War and Internees), dropping in special E Group teams, also a few of the OSS. The prison camps of Siam were the main objective. The teams, each including a doctor, started immediate medical care and listed not only the names of the survivors but also those known to have perished. Meanwhile four bomber squadrons were dropping medical supplies, food, and clothing. The actual lift-out did not begin until mid-September and then, with all transport aircraft committed to the task, retrieval was swift; it took only a fortnight, for example, to fly out all of the 35,000 men who had been in the notorious camps in Siam.

Meanwhile the fighting continued in the Karen Hills. It was a frustrating period for the men of *Character* and *Nutshell*. They knew Japan had surrendered, that the war was officially over, yet still the Japanese were fighting their way southwards to a headquarters vainly trying to contact them with orders not to fight. The Karens could not lay down their arms, they still had to kill the enemy or risk being killed, so naturally they continued firing. Inevitably there were some Force 136 men who lost patience and tried to insist the killing must stop.

Tiny Lewes, who had jumped with that undersized parachute a few months earlier with Pop Tulloch, was one of them. I was dropping supplies to him three weeks after the surrender when, so he told me later, he heard sounds of fierce action in the distance. He waited until we had finished the drop, waved the usual goodbye, then went off to investigate the noisy action. A mile away he came to a wide valley where there was a huge area of open paddy field with a wooded knoll in the centre. His Karen guerrillas were all firing at the knoll and their fire was being returned by a party of Japanese trapped there.

'It was such a silly business,' he said. 'The war was over. I had to stop them.'

He put up a white flag, approached the hill, and a Japanese lieutenant came out of the trees to meet him. They had no language in common but Lewes managed to make him understand they should await an interpreter, and he sent off one of the Karens to the village to fetch an Italian nun who spoke Japanese. The two of them waited in the paddy field, the Japanese accepting a cigarette, until she arrived. When she did, and told the lieutenant that there had been a general surrender, he refused to believe such a story.

They were manifestly lying. The Japanese Imperial Army would never surrender. Lewis was trying to capture his group by deceit.

So he went back to the knoll, and presently the shooting started again. Next morning when Lewes checked the knoll the Japanese had gone, leaving just one dead man under the trees.

Down in *Nutshell* Tony Bennett also became impatient at the delay, and finally walked into the town of Kawkareik where there was an enemy garrison of some three thousand men. He accosted a surprised Japanese soldier on traffic control who took him to the commanding colonel; he had a radio, had heard about the surrender and had noted an absence of bombers recently – this was a fortnight after the armistice – so he was inclined to credit the incredible. Consequently Bennett was able to move into town and live in a house, fêted by Karens, until early September when he grew tired of waiting and made his way down to Moulmein where he contacted the British army.

Colonel Turrall, the leader of *Hyena*, was another who decided to impress the facts upon the Japanese. Just a few days after the declaration he crossed the Kyaukkyi river with a white flag and went to the Japanese garrison to take the surrender. He was lucky to escape with his life. They kept him imprisoned for a week, beat him up from time to time, refusing to believe his preposterous story that the Japanese army had surrendered; slight doubts arose when they saw leaflets being dropped by allied planes and they let him go. But he had to find his own way back to his headquarters, evading other parties of Japanese who were equally committed to continuing the war.

It was not only the clandestine parties in the field who were confused by the stillness that followed the surrender. The Japanese were even more bewildered. They finally came to believe that their army had indeed surrendered, but in many areas they had no evidence that the allies intended to act upon this stunning truth. Throughout South-East Asia Japanese units were suddenly deprived of creed and purpose; no one came to tell them whether they should still keep order in the locality or not, to whom they should yield their arms, where they should go, what they were supposed to do. A month after the surrender I had to make a check on the landing possibilities of a number of airfields in Indo-China and at two of them the Japanese officers approached us hopefully for orders.

We had one post-surrender crash. The relief of prisoners was of such priority for all squadrons that no aircraft could be spared for normal transport duties, and that any aircraft going back to India for maintenance was ordered to be fully loaded. So one of our Dakotas going back to Jessore finished up loaded with some urgent supplies for *Character* as well as ten Indian Army passengers. It never reached India. We learned from the field that the aircraft had circled the DZ but it had begun to rain just as it was turning into position for the drop and they never saw it again.

I took off on a search just after daybreak, certain in my mind that all fourteen aboard were now dead. To my surprise we were able to reach the actual site of the DZ but visibility during our search was only intermittent; as we flew low alongside the ridge, a strong wind was funnelled through the valley, the trees were flailing wildly, and shreds of clouds were swirling and wreathing up the mountainside like flurries of smoke from a bushfire. We found no sign of a crash nearby but we could see so little between the flitting clouds that we may have missed it from only fifty feet above the trees. We searched the hills for another nine hours without a single instant of hope.

It was a week before the crash was discovered ten miles away. The aircraft had flown into a hillside about a thousand feet above the level of the DZ and everyone on board had apparently been killed on impact. On hearing the news the same question was immediately asked:

Had it been carrying prisoners of war?

It had not. This was greeted with expressions of relief. It is curious that we all feel more acutely the subsequent loss of a life that has just been saved. The previous year we had come across a man left behind in the jungle from the first Wingate expedition; he died a fortnight later, before I could find a site for a possible airstrip to lift him out, and there was scarcely a man in our column who did not feel touched by the tragedy. Yet he was only one of hundreds who perished on our campaign, and we scarcely knew him.

In September I was suddenly left in command of 357 Squadron, without being appointed or promoted; the Liberator flight was simply swept away from us and I was left with the remnants. We still had the Dakotas and Lysanders operating at full stretch, and at Jessore we had squadron headquarters and maintenance, and were still busy training parachutists for Force 136 – some were dropped into lower Burma and Laos as late as the first week in October, nearly two months after the end of the war. And three French aircrews had joined us.

The French crews arrived at Jessore complete with aircraft.

They came out from Europe and were put under my command to help clear the prison camps, particularly in Indo-China. Interned there, in addition to the French soldiers recently disarmed, were about three thousand American, British and Dutch civilians, and we were already flying them out when the French trio joined us at Jessore. They dropped E Group teams into Laos first, then military teams to take over a civil administration already being appropriated by the Viet Minh.

The French teams were from the DGER, the French Secret Service, and came to us fully equipped and trained for the drop. They introduced one of the rare instances of friction between Force 136 and the French. It sprang from the differences between the old French liaison officers and the new men now arriving in India. The old group such as de Langlade and Marcel Langer had been Gaullists right from the fall of France in 1940, but the late arrivals, including the French aircrews and the DGER teams, had mostly spent the war in France.

The DGER came to India complete with its own command structure. They set up a separate office in Calcutta and made it clear that they would run things their way, thereby antagonizing the old French section of Force 136 right from the start. We on the squadron were not involved in this internecine struggle but Force 136 parachute training school under Thornton did receive strict instructions to avoid all contact with the new French group. He was told he should not offer them advice or equipment; they had cut themselves off from Force 136.

Disobedience of this injunction, not by Thornton but by Captain McCarthy, his second-in-command, had a tragic outcome. Thornton went on leave towards the end of September and McCarthy at once began to help Grandvoynet, the senior pilot of the French group, particularly in the preparation of the DGER teams. Now that the prison camps had been cleared these teams were going in as military administrators, and encountering fierce resistance from the Viet Minh.

One or two of the men had not had parachute training and when I took them up for a practice jump McCarthy came as despatcher. As Grandvoynet's trio were under my command, and we had no orders about non-cooperation, Langer and I gave them all the normal help they might expect from allies. And I had no authority to stop the activities of McCarthy; he was a Canadian on attachment to Thornton's parachute training school, and if he gave help to the French or flew with them it had nothing to do with me.

Grandvoynet himself decided to take the first fifteen DGER men to be dropped, and McCarthy offered to accompany him as despatcher, an offer that was accepted gratefully, for Grandvoynet had no experience in dropping parachutists. For that reason also I raised no objection about Langer, who by now was experienced in dropping both men and supplies, going with him as adviser.

The drop itself was successful, though the men did not survive long afterwards; that first group, led by Captain Guilloux, were all killed by the Viet Minh within a few days of landing, as were most of the other DGER teams that followed. The aircrew of course knew only that the drop had been successful and they flew back that afternoon to India content with their work. McCarthy went up to sit in the co-pilot seat as they neared Jessore, and then, with only about thirty miles to go, they had a collision with a vulture.

It smashed through the starboard window directly into McCarthy's face, inflicting horrendous damage to his skull. Grandvoynet was badly cut by splinters of perspex but luckily his injuries were only superficial and he was able to keep the aircraft on an even keel. Langer managed to crawl up the floor against the hyper-hurricane wind that was screaming through the smashed window, and reach the co-pilot's seat. He dragged McCarthy down to the floor, pulled the tongue back out of his throat and applied artificial respiration. Due to his efforts McCarthy was still alive, but only just, when they made an emergency landing at Dum-Dum, the nearest airfield at the time.

Had McCarthy had a tracheotomy at once he might have survived, but he was not wearing a jacket at the time of the impact and that proved to be fatal. The men in the ambulance did not know if he was a serviceman or not and there was a long delay while the babus fussed about which hospital was correct for him. They finally sent him to the military hospital in Calcutta but he was dead on arrival.

When I saw the aircraft later I felt the rest of them were fortunate to be alive. Had the bird hit the centre of the windscreen Grandvoynet would have lost control and Langer would probably never have been able to reach the cockpit. Curiously enough there was much bird activity just south of the airfield while I was standing there by the damaged plane that afternoon; kite hawks were wheeling high above the trees, gliding, dipping, soaring, in excited flight, and stiff-winged vultures were planing down purposefully from all quarters towards a probable scene of death. It made me wonder how many crashes had been blamed on the dead pilot – an easy victim for the investigators once fire had destroyed the evidence of a fatal contact with vultures, great owls or even kite hawks.

We did have a crash investigation that month. Air Command decided that a court of enquiry should be held about the loss of our Dakota that had flown into a hillside, and the outcome was that I was found negligent in not ensuring a dinghy was carried on the fatal journey. The track of the aircraft from the drop site to Jessore crossed the corner of the Bay of Bengal, and though the plane never reached the Bay and the absence of a dinghy was irrelevant to the loss, King's Regulations stated that a dinghy should always be carried on water crossings and the court's verdict was that I be officially reprimanded.

So I now had two reprimands on my RAF record. The first one had been recorded during training as a cadet in Cambridge in 1940. I had stayed in bed one night when the siren wailed an air raid warning, instead of going to the shelter as ordained, and when I heard the Duty Officer coming up the stairs to check the rooms I had dived under the bed. But he had a suspicious mind. And a torch. So he flashed me out. Brought up on a charge next day I was reprimanded far more severely and at greater length than for, officially, contributing towards the deaths of sixteen men in a Dakota crash.

Despite the reprimand, I was still in command of the dying squadron. It was now the end of October, the prisoners had been brought out of Siam, and we were once more making drops to *Character* sites. The war had been over for six weeks by then but there were still occasional skirmishes with Japanese groups in the Karen Hills, and we completed more than seventy sorties to various groups in the hills up to mid-November when 357 Squadron was officially disbanded.

When a unit was disbanded it was usual for a senior officer to send a valedictory signal. Down in Ceylon the Liberators were in close contact with Command, and on dissolution the air marshal sent them a signal praising their achievements; a number of awards were granted. Also down there, in SEAC headquarters, was a staff wing commander who had made his name in Europe on Lysander flights, and had always shown special interest in our Lysanders; so it was no surprise when they too had an air marshal signal congratulating them on their record in Burma. Both of these notices were sent to me in Jessore to be included in Daily Routine Orders (DROs), so that all should know that the sterling work of these two flights had been noticed on high.

No one noticed the demise of the Dakota flight, however. We received no message from anyone. I decided that this had been a slip of memory on Mountbatten's part, so I wrote a fine valedictory signal from him. It was couched in much the same words as that received by the other two flights, perhaps a trifle more fulsome. It spoke of 'the outstanding contribution to clandestine operations made by the crews of the flight', and re-marked upon the 'respect and gratitude of the clandestine organ-izations which had been served with such distinction by the Dakota flight of 357 Squadron'. The ground crews also came in for commendation. It was altogether a fine tribute to our work.

There was no great difficulty promulgating the signal. We had two sets of daily Routine Orders, one for the Rangoon detachment and one for Jessore, and I told each of the adjutants that the signal had been received in the other's office. So the message from on high was quoted in both DROs and enshrined in the record. It was a source of considerable pride to many in the squadron, both air and ground crews. Had Lord Louis himself seen the result of its promulgation I am sure he would have given it his belated blessing.

When the squadron was disbanded all the air and ground crews, except those due for repatriation, were transferred to a Rangoon unit and I came back with the remnants to Jessore to finalize the closure. This procedure included the final recommendations for awards, and I wrote five citations for officer and sergeant aircrews. Unfortunately these had to be filed in Rangoon, and no one there knew anything about our work on Special Duties. None of the five got a medal.

There was still a little activity. We had three Dakotas being serviced on disbandment day and these took some time to come up for flight test and despatch, and some ground crew remained to service the French trio under Grandvoynet, for they were still flying to Indo-China on DGER work. By the end of November, however, the parachute school had been shut down and the last of Force 136 had left Jessore; all their offices in India were closed shortly afterwards, the lovely FANYs had all gone home, and the records were all sent back to the parent organization, SOE, in England. There, it would seem, everything relating to the organization was being bundled away to obscurity by the Foreign Office permanent intelligence unit, MI6, delighted to be rid at last of the wartime interloper in its domain.

I was left waiting at Jessore. Just twelve months earlier I had been waiting there for action to begin, and though my circumstances now could not have been more different the weather was still the beautiful same – crisp-cool autumn mornings with the mist lingering over the paddy fields and placid roadside lakes, the sun still gently warm under the clean blue haze-free sky, and still the same tingling coolness at the end of the day as the twilight thickened and the bee-eaters went flighting homeward over the lawn in flashes of green like the fuselage signal light for action on a drop.

As 1945 drew to a close my command had shrunk to eight men. By then I had completed more than four years overseas; four months more than the stipulated time, and I sent a signal to our group pointing out this fact. After two weeks without a response I sent a signal to Rangoon command asking them to pursue the matter. They did not reply.

Christmas came . . . three of my four men left . . . the French trio left . . . the group captain and all his staff left. In January 1946 I was still there with about a dozen others, mostly Indian, all of us now living as a single unit in the old station headquarters mess.

By January only one Dakota remained. It had been awaiting an aileron and I finally took it up on flight test late one afternoon at the end of the month. There was no crew, just the fitter came with me for the ride. We flew over the practice DZ where now the grass had grown high enough to hide the old ploughing lines, and over the lake where I had often watched the duck flying in to the shoreline reeds in the evenings, and low over the margosa trees where, back in the spring, I had stopped the van to stand under the light graceful foliage and breathe in the fragrance of the creamy white flowers. Then we circled the mess, deserted except for a pi-dog skulking about the heliotrope bush from which the mynah would sing for his evening crumbs, giving that rich melodious whistling attempt at the opening four notes of Brahm's Lullaby.

For the last time I lowered the undercarriage as we flew over Thornton's deserted quarters by the little stream, let down half flap as we passed over the hut where Peacock and Turrall had argued about duck, made the final turn over the village with its sacred cursed peepul tree, put full flap down over the cemetery where the flickering fireflies set the villagers off in panic flight, and then smoothed back the throttles for the last time to touch down on the tyre-scarred concrete and let it run easily past the empty control tower to a stop outside the silent flight huts at the end of the strip.

It was the last time I ever flew a Dakota.

By the end of January in 1946 the last airman had gone and there was no one left of the squadron in Jessore except me. For two months by then I had been listed as 'Commanding Officer, 357 Squadron (Disbanding)' but now there was nothing more to disband but me. I had joined the squadron in September 1944, the month it started to operate from Jessore. I had served it under three commanding officers and for longer than anyone else in air or ground crew, and I was still serving it two months after it had been pronounced dead.

It was a curious, dazed existence. I would go down to squadron headquarters, now attached to the maintenance unit, and deal with mail still coming in addressed to 'The Commanding Officer, 357 Squadron (Disbanding)', although the unit no longer existed. I signed a form or two . . . typed an occasional letter . . . wrote up my note book . . . went on pointlessly from day to day, like that watch in Thomson's 'The City of Dreadful Night':

> As whom his one intense thought overpowers,
> He answered coldly, Take a watch, erase
> The signs and figures of the circling hours,
> Detach the hands, remove the dial face;
> The works proceed till run down; although
> Bereft of purpose, void of use, still go.

On the first day of February 1946, in a lonely mood and seeking contact, I drove down to the old operations room. Two palm squirrels went darting away from the actual doorway as I drove up, and when I climbed down from the van the red dust settled slowly. A coppersmith bird was pinging away in the sal tree at the back of the building but there was no other sound – no voices, cars nor trucks, no aircraft running up engines nor in the circuit overhead. I stood for a moment by the bamboo at the corner, my cheek against the smooth green stem which had stripes of bronze like brush-strokes of paint too drily applied, and listened acutely. The only human sound I could hear was my ear pulse throbbing against the cool bamboo; no other human being was within sight or sound of the whole operations room block.

Inside the silent dusty room the blackboard was still up on the stage but the maps had gone, and the chairs and benches that used to be in rows up the length of the room were stacked untidily against the back wall. There had always been a smell of tobacco in the ops room, a blue haze would be swirling a little above head height as the crews assembled in a jostling noisy throng for briefing, but now the smell was of musty dryness. A thin glitter of dust raised by my entry hung in the still air and the only sounds were from the coppersmith bird, and the creaking bamboo close outside by the open doorway.

But in there I could hear voices when I tried, and I could almost see faces too. Then suddenly, as often happens when emotion threatens to overwhelm you, I escaped into anger. What was I doing stuck there in the Bengal countryside? What in hell was going on?

I drove back in fury to the mess and wrote a letter.

Officers in the RAF have a final resort if they feel they have a grievance; they can apply for a personal interview with the Senior Officer in their command. In my case it was the Air Marshal of South-East Asia Command down in Singapore. This is the letter I wrote:

Sir,
I have the honour to request I be granted an interview in connection with the delay in my repatriation.

In December 1941 I left England by air for the Far East. I was then successively in Singapore, Sumatra and Java as flight commander of a light bomber squadron, until we lost all our aircraft and the majority of our crews. The remnants of the squadron, including myself, escaped by boat to India.

My sense of grievance is based on the four following facts – and the one conviction:

1 Every single surviving officer of that Far Eastern squadron has now been repatriated.
2 I am convinced there can be few, if any, Air Force personnel in this command who were in the original Malayan campaign and have remained here since without a break.
3 The overseas tour is supposed to be three years and nine months, and is to be further reduced 'shortly'. I have completed over four years.
4 Air Command were signalled on this subject early in December in the hope that I might avoid spending the Christmas period overseas for the fifth successive year. They did not reply. Nor have they replied to a signal sent subsequently from AHQ, Burma.

351

5 I have recently seen a list of officers for repatriation. There were over a hundred in the list and every single one had left England the year after I flew out to Singapore.

I feel the more aggrieved in that I have spent most of my time on operations; some of these, such as bombing in Malaya and operating behind the lines with the Chindits, have been particularly hazardous. Before I left England for Singapore I had already finished a tour of bomber operations and was well into a second tour; I had almost completed two further tours of operations here in this Special Duty squadron when the war ended.

There is no reason therefore, as far as I am aware, why I should not be accorded the same treatment as any other officer or airman in your command. If there had been any hope of being given leave in Australia, as requested in September, I could understand this delay, but as there was never a response to that request I feel I am entitled to an explanation for a punishment being uniquely awarded to me.

I await your convenience for the requested interview.

I have the honour to be,

Sir,

Your obedient servant,

T. P. O'Brien, S'Ldr.

That uncovered me. Within just a few days a signal arrived to say I was to report immediately to Air Command in Singapore. At Singapore I was interviewed by a group captain who said the delay had been caused by Air Ministry bungling my application for leave in Australia. A priority air passage had been arranged for me to Sydney in two days' time, and I had been granted a minimum of three months' leave.

Did I still wish to pursue that request for interview with the Air Marshal?

I let it go. The war was over. I was going home.

BIBLIOGRAPHY

Allen, Louis, *End of the War in Asia* (Hart Davis, 1976).
  Sittang – The Last Battle (Macdonald, 1973).
  Burma – The Longest War 1941–5 (Dent 1984).
Beamish, John, *Burma Drop* (Elek Books, 1958).
Beevor, J. G., *SOE: Recollections and Reflections 1940–45* (Bodley Head, 1981).
Bowen, John, *Undercover in the Jungle* (Kimber, 1978).
Chennault, Claire, *Way of a Fighter* (New York: Putnam, 1949).
Cross, J., *Red Jungle* (Robert Hale, 1957).
Cruikshank, Charles, *SOE in the Far East* (Oxford University Press, 1983).
Donnison, F. S., *British Military Administration in the Far East 1943–46* (HMSO, 1956).
Dunlop, Richard, *Behind Japanese Lines with OSS in Burma* (New York: Rand McNally, 1959).
Dunn, Peter M., *The First Vietnam War* (Hurst, 1985).
Foot, M. R. D., *SOE 1940–46* (BBC, 1984).
Foot, M. R. D. and Langley, J. M., *MI9 Escape and Evasion 1939–1945* (Bodley Head, 1979).
Gilchrist, Sir Andrew, *Bangkok Top Secret* (Hutchinson, 1960).
Guthrie, Duncan, *Jungle Diary* (Macmillan, 1946).
Harrison, Tom, *World Within* (Cresset Press, 1959).
Harris Smith, R., *OSS* (University of California Press, 1972).
Hart-Davis, Duff, *Peter Fleming – A Biography* (Cape, 1980).
Howarth, P., *Undercover* (Routledge and Kegan, 1980).
Hunter, Charles C., *Galahad* (The Naylor Company, Texas, 1963).
Kemp, Peter, *Arms for Oblivion* (Cassell, 1961).
McCrae, Alister and friends, *Tales of Burma* (James Paton of Paisley, 1981).
Merrick, K. A., *Special Duties Operations During World War 2*

(This book is due to be published by Ian Allan in 1987, and I am grateful to the author for his help with researched material and putting me in touch with squadron contemporaries.)

Moon, Thomas N. and Eifler, Carl F., *The Deadliest Colonel* (Vantage Press, 1975).

Morrison, Ian, *Grandfather Longlegs* (Faber and Faber, 1947).

Peacock, Geraldine, *The Life of a Jungle Wallah* (Arthur Stockwell, Ilfracombe, Devon, 1958).

Peers, William R. and Brellis, Dan, *Guerrilla Operations Behind the Burma Road* (Army Publishers, Delhi, 1968).

Ride, Edwin, *BAAG. Hong Kong Resistance 1942–1945* (Oxford University Press, 1981).

Roosevelt, Kermit, *Overseas Targets, OSS War Report*, Vol. 2, Sec. 2.

Slim, Sir William, *Defeat into Victory* (Cassell, 1956).

Spencer Chapman, F., *The Jungle is Neutral* (Chatto and Windus, 1949).

Sweet-Escott, B., *Baker Street Irregular* (Methuen, 1965).

Tan Sri Ibrahim Bin Ismail, *Have you met Mariam?* (Westlight, Johor Bahru, Malaysia, 1984).

Thakin Nu, *Burma Under the Japanese* (Macmillan, London, 1954).

Thorne, Christopher, *Allies of a Kind* (Oxford University Press, 1978).

Trenowden, Ian *Operations Most Secret. SOE: The Malayan Theatre* (Kimber, 1978).

Wheatley, Dennis, *The Deception Planners* (Hutchinson, 1953).

White, T. E. (ed.), *The Stilwell Papers* (Macdonald, 1949).

Ziegler, Philip, *Mountbatten* (Collins, 1985).

REFERENCES

Except for the Mountbatten Archive material (MA) all other reference codes are those of the Public Record Office at Kew. A source has not been given for one or two quotes, nor for an occasional statement which might seem to call for such reassurance, the reason being that they are priveleged.

Page

13   French problems in Kunming: FO 371–46305 typical, but there are literally dozens of files dealing with French–US friction.

41   ISLD network destroyed: MA (Mountbatten Archives)–C112.

46   Objections to arming nationalists: FO 371–46334B, WO 203–53, WO 203–58 all deal with it, and the whole fracas is well summarized in Mountbatten's 'Report 1946 to Combined Chiefs of Staff'.

46   Arms to Siam: FO 371–46560.

46   OSS ask 136 for Siamese site: WO 203–55.

55   Army critical of 136: WO 203–4332, WO 203–5748, WO 203–53.

67   Bowen quote: *Undercover in the Jungle*.

68   Comparative losses: The number of aircrew killed has been totalled from the ORBs of the two squadrons and my notes; the losses of agents has been compiled from the same sources, and from Cruikshank, Peacock, and a private document.

88   Deception reality danger: WO 203–33. The Fleming quote is from a document not yet released from the archives.

88–9   The signal from P Division about my drop: WO 203–4332.

91   Stilwell epithet: *The Stilwell Papers*.

protests. His letter to Mackenzie about this thwarting action is one of the documents not now to be found in the Mountbatten Archives after the FO have passed them for researchers' inspection.

INDEX

359

361